Geological Excursions in Dyfed, South-West Wales

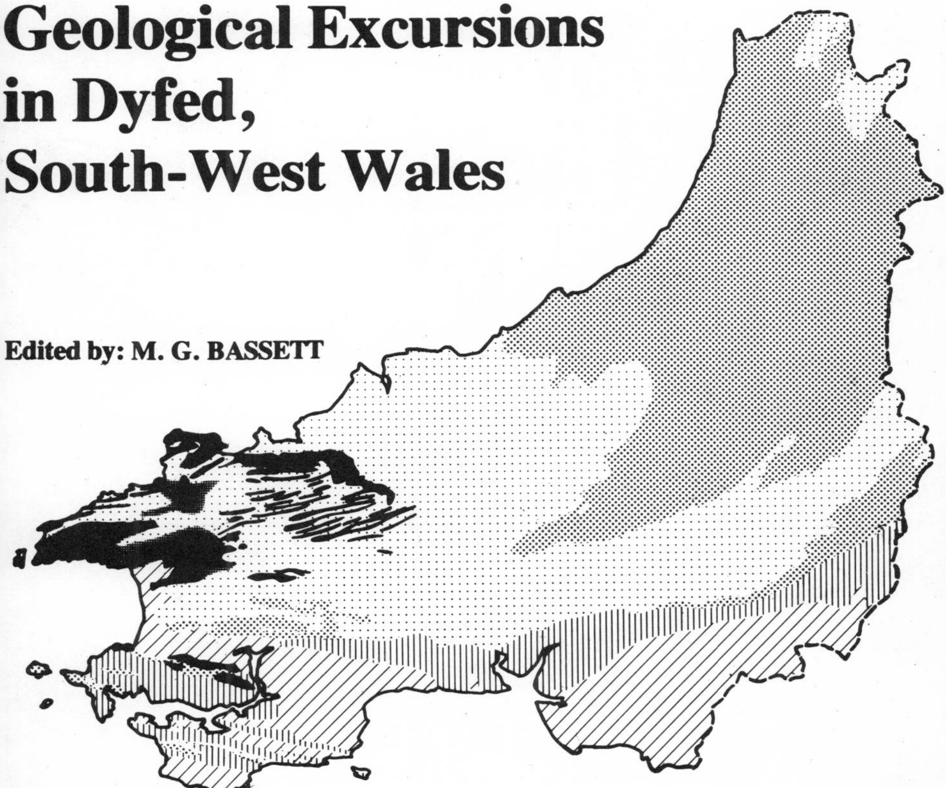

Edited by: M. G. BASSETT

Published for the Geologists' Association, South Wales Group by the National Museum of Wales

Cardiff May 1982

ISBN 0 7200 0249 4

REFERENCES TO THIS VOLUME

It is recommended that reference to the whole or part of this volume be made in one of the following forms, as appropriate:

BASSETT, M. G. (ed.). 1982. *Geological excursions in Dyfed, south-west Wales*. 327 pp., National Museum of Wales, Cardiff.

BOWEN, D. Q. 1982. Pleistocene deposits and fluvioglacial landforms of north Preseli. pp. 289-296 *In* BASSETT. M. G. (ed.). *Geological excursions in Dyfed, south-west Wales*. 327 pp., National Museum of Wales, Cardiff.

Printed by Graphic Print, Taff's Well, Cardiff CF4 7QR

FOREWORD

THE county of Dyfed in south-west Wales was established by the Local Government Act of 1972 as an amalgamation of the three former counties of Pembrokeshire, Cardiganshire, and Carmarthenshire; the new County and District boundaries became effective from April 1974. The long coastline of Dyfed includes numerous sections of outstanding natural beauty, with magnificent outcrops of Precambrian and Palaeozoic rocks ranging up to the Triassic, so that the area has long been a centre of geomorphological and geological attraction. Inland the solid geology is less well exposed, but in recent years it has become known in increasing detail as a result of revision of much of the initial work that took place in the nineteenth and early twentieth centuries. Northern areas of the county in particular contain a wealth and variety of Quaternary deposits and related landforms that together complement the solid geology in making Dyfed as a whole one of the most useful regions in the British Isles for teaching geology at all levels.

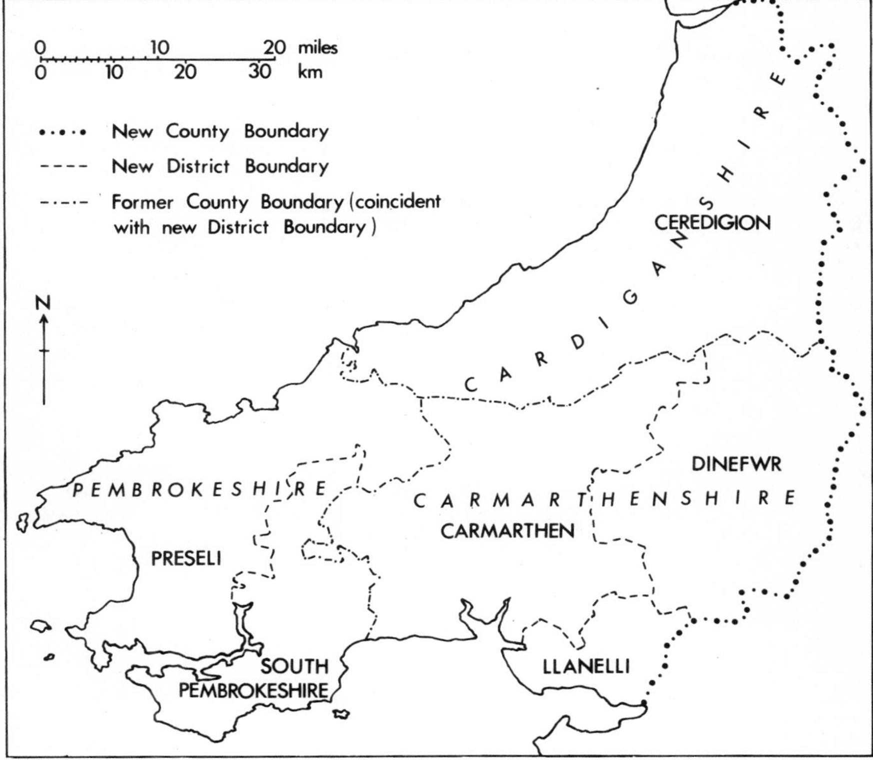

Map of Dyfed showing the relationship of the new County and Districts to the three former counties.

In 1971 the South Wales Group of the Geologists' Association published a volume of twenty-one excursion guides extending throughout South Wales and the Forest of Dean, including ten within what has since become Dyfed. That volume is now out of print and it has become clear that its success was due largely to the popularity of the itineraries in the west; the present volume is a direct response to the continued and concentrated demand for geological guidance in the same area. Six of the original chapters covering Dyfed have been updated, and thirteen new excursions have been added to give a fairly comprehensive stratigraphical and geographical coverage through the county. Of the four previous excursions that are now excluded, a few were thought to be too specialist in nature to be repeated, while itineraries from the others have been incorporated partly into new chapters.

As in the 1971 volume no attempt has been made to provide a general introduction to the geology since the excursions themselves do this more than adequately. The South Wales Regional Guide published by the Institute of Geological Sciences is recommended as background reading for anyone completely new to the area. The lists of maps given at the beginning of each excursion are the familiar sheets produced by the Ordnance Survey; the topographical maps are essential for following the various itineraries, in which localities are pinpointed with a National Grid Reference; the geological maps (published for the IGS) help to give an overview of the regional geology.

The increasing pressure on geological sites for teaching in Dyfed at both university and school level is reflected in statistics produced recently from surveys carried out by the Geology and Physiography Section of the Nature Conservancy Council and by the Association of Teachers of Geology. For example, figures from the former survey indicate that the number of student days spent in the field in western Dyfed has increased by 40% since 1971. This growing pressure places a responsibility on authors of guides such as this to direct parties to sites where no damage can be done, but there is an equal responsibility on visitors themselves to ensure that localities are treated with care. All users of this volume are urged to seek permission from tenants and landowners wherever necessary, and to read the codes of conduct, safety, and behaviour published as an introduction to the excursions. Without proper care the availability of localities as teaching sites for the future will be placed in jeopardy.

Acknowledgements. The South Wales Group of the Geologists' Association is grateful to the National Museum of Wales for its support in publishing this volume. Dr. R. M. Owens and Dr. R. E. Bevins gave advice on the texts, while Mrs. D. G. Evans and Mrs. L. C. Norton assisted with the graphics. Particular thanks are due to Mrs. V. K. Deisler for her secretarial and administrative work, and to both her and Mr. A. J. Thomas for their help in seeing the book through the press.

M. G. BASSETT

CONTENTS

A CODE FOR GEOLOGICAL FIELDWORK

Editorial note. This code was first issued by the parent body of the Geologists' Association, with the support of leading geological organisations in the U.K.

A GEOLOGICAL 'CODE OF CONDUCT' has become essential if opportunities for fieldwork in the future are to be preserved. The rapid increase in field studies in recent years has tended to concentrate attention upon a limited number of localities, so that sheer collecting pressure is destroying the scientific value of irreplaceable sites. At the same time the volume of fieldwork is causing concern to many site owners. Geologists must be seen to use the countryside with responsibility; **to achieve this, the following general points should be observed.**

1. Obey the Country Code, and observe local byelaws. Remember to shut gates and leave no litter.
2. Always seek prior permission before entering private land.
3. Do not interfere with machinery.
4. Do not litter fields or roads with rock fragments which might cause injury to livestock, or be a hazard to pedestrians or vehicles.
5. Avoid undue disturbance to wildlife. Plants and animals may inadvertently be displaced or destroyed by careless actions.
6. On coastal sections, consult the local Coastguard Service whenever possible, to learn of local hazards such as unstable cliffs, or tides which might jeopardise excursions possible at other times.
7. When working in mountainous or remote areas, follow the advice given in the pamphlet 'Mountain Safety', issued by the Central Council for Physical Education, and, in particular, inform someone of your intended route.
8. When exploring underground, be sure you **have the proper equipment,** and the necessary experience. **Never go alone.** Report to someone your departure, location, estimated time underground, and your actual return.
9. Do not take risks on insecure cliffs or rock faces. Take care not to dislodge rock, since other people may be below.
10. Be considerate. By your actions in collecting, do not render an exposure untidy or dangerous for those who follow you.

Collecting and Field Parties

1. Students should be encouraged to observe and record but not to hammer indiscriminately.
2. **Keep collecting to a minimum.** Avoid removing *in situ* fossils, rocks or minerals unless they are genuinely needed for serious study.
3. For teaching, the use of replicas is recommended. The collecting of actual specimens should be restricted to those localities where there is a plentiful supply, or to scree, fallen blocks, and waste tips.
4. Never collect from walls or buildings. Take care not to undermine fences, walls, bridges or other structures.

5. The leader of a field party is asked to ensure that the spirit of this Code is fulfilled, and to remind his party of the need for care and consideration at all times. He should remember that his supervisory role is of prime importance. He must be supported by adequate assistance in the field. This is particularly important on coastal sections, or over difficult terrain, where there might be a tendency for parties to become dispersed.

Health and Safety at Work Act
Since the introduction of this Act, safety measures are more strictly enforced on sites, including quarries. Protective clothing, particularly safety helmets, must be worn by employees, so visitors are expected to observe the same precaution, often as a condition of entry. Suitable helmets are readily available, cheap to purchase, and should be part of the necessary equipment of all geologists. **THEY MUST BE WORN AT ALL TIMES IN QUARRIES.**

Visiting Quarries
1. An individual, or the leader of a party, should have obtained **prior** permission to visit.
2. The leader of a party should have made himself familiar with the **current state** of the quarry. He should have consulted with the Manager as to where visitors may go, and what local hazards should be avoided.
3. On each visit, both arrival and departure must be reported.
4. In the quarry, the wearing of safety hats and stout boots is recommended.
5. Keep clear of vehicles and machinery.
6. Be sure that blast warning procedures are understood.
7. **Beware of rock falls.** Quarry faces may be highly dangerous and liable to collapse without warning.
8. Beware of sludge lagoons.

Research Workers
1. No research worker has the special right to 'dig out' any site.
2. Excavations should be back-filled where necessary to avoid hazard to men and animals and to protect vulnerable outcrops from casual collecting.
3. Do not disfigure rock surfaces with numbers or symbols in brightly coloured paint.
4. Ensure that your research material and notebooks eventually become available for others by depositing them with an appropriate institution.
5. Take care that publication of details does not lead to the destruction of vulnerable exposures. In these cases, do not give the precise location of such sites, unless this is essential to scientific argument. The details of such localities could be deposited in a national data centre for Geology.

Societies, Schools and Universities
1. Foster an interest in geological sites and their wise conservation. Remember that much may be done by collective effort to help clean up

overgrown sites (with permission of the owner, and in consultation with the Nature Conservancy Council).

2. Create working groups for those amateurs who wish to do fieldwork and collect, providing leadership to direct their studies.

3. Make contact with your local County Naturalists' Trust, Field Studies Centre, or Natural History Society, to ensure that there is coordination in attempts to conserve geological sites and retain access to them.

Note for Landowners

Landowners may wish to ensure that visiting geologists are familiar with this Code. In the event of its abuse, they may choose to take the name and address of the offenders and the Institution or Society to which they belong.

Enquiries may be addressed to The Librarian, The Geologists' Association, c/o Geology Department, University College London, Gower Street, London, WC1E 6BT.

ADVICE ON SAFETY AND BEHAVIOUR FOR INDIVIDUALS AND PARTIES CARRYING OUT GEOLOGICAL FIELDWORK

Editorial note. This set of guidelines on safety and behaviour is based on a document directed at students and issued by the Committee of Heads of University Geology Departments in the U.K. The advice contained here is based therefore on many years experience of directing student parties and as such is applicable to all persons carrying out fieldwork.

SAFETY

A. To: *All persons attending geological field courses*
Geological fieldwork is an activity involving some inherent special risks and hazards, e.g. in coast exposures, quarries, mines, river sections, and mountains. Severe or dangerous weather conditions may also be encountered at any season, especially on mountains or the coast.

In accordance with the Health and Safety at Work Act, field leaders are advised that they should follow certain safety precautions and should take every reasonable care concerning the safety of members of their parties. However, *the potential dangers make it imperative that everyone should cooperate by behaving responsibly in order to reduce the risk of accidents.* Each individual is responsible for his or her own safety.

You are specifically asked to:

1. Observe all safety instructions given by party leaders or supervisors. Anyone not conforming to the standards required may be dismissed from the field course.

Stay with the party, except by clear arrangement with the leaders. Assemble where requested (e.g. outside a quarry) in order to receive specific instructions regarding likely hazards.

Observe instructions for reporting after completion of work.

Report any injury or illness.

2. Wear adequate clothing and footwear for the type of weather and terrain likely to be encountered. Shirt, loose-fitting trousers, warm sweater, brightly-coloured anorak with hood, are normally desirable in the U.K. A woollen hat (in addition to the hood of the anorak) is useful in winter or on high ground. Cagoule and waterproof over-trousers are desirable for wet weather. Jeans are generally unsuitable because they do not give sufficient protection when wet and are subjected to a cold wind, but can be all right if waterproof over-trousers are also worn.

Walking boots with rubber mountaineering soles are normally essential. Sports shoes are unsuitable for mountains, quarries and rough country.

Wellingtons are generally best reserved for walking through shallow water, peat bogs and the like.

Leaders may be advised to refuse to allow ill-equipped persons on their field courses, since they have a responsibility to see that individuals observe the provisions regarding personal safety.

3. Wear a safety helmet (preferably with chin strap) when visiting old quarries, cliffs, scree slopes, etc., or wherever there is a risk from falling objects. It is obligatory to do so when visiting working quarries, mines and building sites.

4. Wear safety goggles (or safety glasses with plastic lenses) for protection against flying splinters when hammering rocks or chisels.

Do not use one geological hammer as a chisel and hammer it with another; use only a soft steel chisel.

Avoid hammering near another person, or looking towards another person hammering.

5. Take special care near the edges of cliffs and quarries, or any other steep or sheer faces, particularly in gusting winds.

Ensure that rocks above are safe before venturing below. Quarries with rock faces loosened by explosives are especially dangerous.

Avoid working under an unstable overhang.

Avoid loosening rocks on steep slopes.

Do not work directly above or below another person.

Never roll rocks down slopes or over cliffs for amusement.

Do not run down steep slopes.

Beware of landslides and mudflows occurring on clay cliffs and in clay-pits, or rockfalls from any cliffs.

6. Avoid touching any machinery or equipment in quarries, mines or building sites.

Never pick up explosives, or detonators from rock piles; if found, inform the management immediately.

Comply with safety rules, blast warning procedures, and any instructions given by officials.

Keep a sharp look-out for moving vehicles etc.

Beware of sludge lagoons.

7. Do not climb cliffs, rock faces or crags, unless this has been approved as an essential part of the work.

Take great care when walking or climbing over slippery rocks below high water mark on rocky shores.

More accidents to geologists, including fatalities, occur along rocky shorelines than anywhere else.

8. Beware of traffic when examining road cuttings.

Avoid hammering, and do not leave rock debris on the roadway or verges.

Railway cuttings and motorways are not open to geologists, unless special permission has been obtained from the appropriate authorities.

9. Do not enter old mine workings or cave systems unless it has been approved as an essential part of the work. Only do so then by arrangement, with proper lighting and headgear, and never alone. Ensure that someone on the surface knows your location and expected time of return. Be sure to report after returning.

Leaders of parties should follow the general guidance contained in: *A Code for Geological Fieldwork,* issued by the Geologists' Association (see p. 7), *Mountain Safety — basic precautions,* published by Climber & Rambler; *Guidelines for visits to quarries* — laid down by the British Quarrying and Slag Federation.

B. To: *All persons undertaking geological fieldwork alone, in pairs, or small groups*

ALL the provisions in Section A also apply to independent fieldwork. However, since the nature of the training involves an important element of self reliance and the ability to cope alone, students in this category are necessarily responsible for their own safety in the field, and the following further advice is offered:

1. Discuss likely safety problems or risks, and check equipment, with experienced geologists before departure or commencement of work.

2. Plan work carefully, bearing in mind experience and training, the nature of the terrain and the weather.

Be careful not to overestimate what can be achieved.

3. Learn the mountain safety and caving codes, and in particular the effects of exposure.

Rock-climbing, caving and underwater swimming may be useful in research activities, but are dangerous for the untrained or ill-equipped. They should only be undertaken with the prior approval of people experienced in the particular techniques.

4. Do not go into the field without leaving a note and preferably a map showing expected location and time of return.

Never carelessly break arrangements to report your return to local people.

Camp near habitation if possible.

5. Check weather forecasts. Keep a constant look-out for changes.

Do not hesitate to turn back if the weather deteriorates.

6. Know what to do in an emergency (e.g. accident, illness, bad weather, darkness).

7. Carry at all times a small first-aid kit, some emergency food (chocolate, biscuits, mint cake, glucose tablets), a survival bag (or large plastic bag), a whistle, torch, map, compass and watch.

8. Avoid getting trapped by the tide on inter-tidal banks or below sea cliffs.

Obtain local information about tides and currents. Pay particular attention to tidal range. For sea cliff study, local advice can be obtained from H.M. Coastguards.

Always wear footwear when wading in rivers, lagoons or on the shore.

9. Know the international distress signal: *a,* 6 whistle blasts, torch flashes or waves of a light-coloured cloth; *b,* 1 minute pause; *c,* another 3 blasts (flashes, waves) at 20 second intervals.

10. Always try to obtain permission to enter private property, and follow the recognised procedure for visits to quarries, etc.

Be careful to report after completion of work.

11. Take special precautions when working off-shore; small boats should normally be used only with an experienced boatman or colleague. Always wear a life-jacket. Aqualung equipment should only be used by experienced divers.

12. Ensure that you are conversant with the particular safety and health requirements if you work in a new environment.

GENERAL BEHAVIOUR

All participants in geological field courses, or undertaking independent fieldwork, are expected to observe sensible standards of behaviour, to conduct themselves with consideration for others, particularly in hotels or other accommodation, and not to damage property in any way (e.g. by climbing over walls, leaving gates open, trampling crops).

Please do not disturb the environment more than is absolutely necessary.

Do not collect specimens unless required for serious study.

Do not hammer outcrops casually or indiscriminately.

Do not disturb living plants and animals.

Do not leave litter, including rock chippings.

Observe conservation requirements. Remember that public access is an acute problem in the countryside and especially in areas designated as National Parks.

1
THE PRECAMBRIAN OF SOUTH-WEST DYFED

by J. W. BAKER

Maps *Topographical:*	1 : 50 000	Sheets 157 St. David's and Haverfordwest, 158 Tenby
	1 : 25 000	Sheets SM72, SM81, SM82, SM90, SM91, SN00
Geological:	1 : 50 000	Sheets 226/227 Milford Haven, 228 Haverfordwest
	1 : 25 000	Special Sheet SM72 & Parts of SM62, 73 St David's

THE major Precambrian outcrops in Dyfed occur in two complex belts extending eastwards from the north and south coasts of St Bride's Bay (Fig. 1). Most of these rocks are of igneous origin and so far no fossiliferous beds have been found associated with them. However, the Precambrian age of the northern outcrops is clear from their position beneath the overlying Cambrian conglomerate (see this volume, excursion 2). The field relations of the southern belt indicate only that they are pre-Silurian, but the long standing inference that they are also Precambrian has now been confirmed by radiometric dating (see below).

Recently discovered minor outcrops of Precambrian rocks to the south-west of Carmarthen in eastern Dyfed are described in excursion 14 of this volume.

The main outcrops on the north side of St Bride's Bay are arranged *en echelon* and form the cores of the St David's and Brawdy-Hayscastle horst-like Caledonian anticlines. South of St David's there is evidence that the base of the Cambrian lies unconformably over Precambrian units, whilst in inland areas non-Caledonoid folds also indicate some Precambrian movements (Thomas & Jones 1912; Williams 1934).

The first area to be described in detail was that around St David's (Green 1908), much of which is included in the recent IGS 1:25 000 map of St David's. Here a bedded sequence consisting largely of volcanic detritus is intruded by acid rocks; these were termed Pebidian and Dimetian respectively by Hicks (1877). The volcanic material comprises rhyolitic, trachytic, and andesitic lithic fragments with feldspar crystals in beds of varying coarse-

[pp. 15-25 *In* BASSETT, M. G. (ed.). 1982. Geological excursions in Dyfed, south-west Wales.]

ness. They are usually described as tuffs, but Green (1908) considered that most of this debris was washed off a land surface and deposited as submarine beds; on this interpretation they are really tuffaceous sediments, and indeed they sometimes contain gritty quartz grains. Subordinate members include, on the one hand, the sedimentary Clegyr Conglomerate, and on the other, pyroclastic halleflinta bands and basic lavas.

In the best exposed area south and west of St David's the succession is at least 2000 m thick (the base is not seen). Green's (1908) original Pebidian succession is given below, modified in the light of his later comments (*in* Cox *et al.* 1930) together with data from Prof. A. H. Cox's manuscript maps, which are now in the National Museum of Wales, Cardiff, and from Shackleton (1975).

Ogofgolchfa Group:	felsitic and chloritic 'tuffs'.
Rhosson Group (*c.* 550 m):	basic lavas.
Ramsey Sound Group (*c.*230 m):	soft, rather fine grained and schistose 'tuffs' containing variously sericite, chlorite and feldspar; sometimes porcellanitic.
Caerbwdy Group (*c.* 700 m):	feldspathic and porcellanitic 'tuffs' with a pale blue-green, quartz-chlorite matrix. Halleflinta bands especially in upper part; Clegyr Conglomerate with acid igneous rock pebbles in lower part.
Treginnis Group (*c.* 220 m):	gritty quartz bearing rocks with andesitic (sometimes vesicular), trachytic, and rhyolitic fragments in red or green matrix.
Penrhiw Group (*c.* 300 m):	largely 'tuffs' with feldspathic fragments; these pass up into greenish feldspathic grit with vesicular andesitic fragments, and down into red and green halleflintas.

On the IGS map the two lower groups are united as the Lower Pebidian, but this is divided into essentially the same two parts by a persistent, foliated quartz-felsite sill. Other Dimetian minor acid intrusions occur immediately north of St David's and at St Non's Bay, but the most extensive intrusion is the St David's Granophyre which crops out south-west of the city. Some of the basic dykes are also of Precambrian age.

Part of this Pebidian succession can be traced eastward across the St David's anticline (Williams 1934) and into the Brawdy-Hayscastle anticline (Thomas & Jones 1912). Here, assorted 'tuffs' pass up into lavas of quartz-keratophyre (soda-rhyolite), which contrast with the basic character of the Rhosson Group west of St David's.

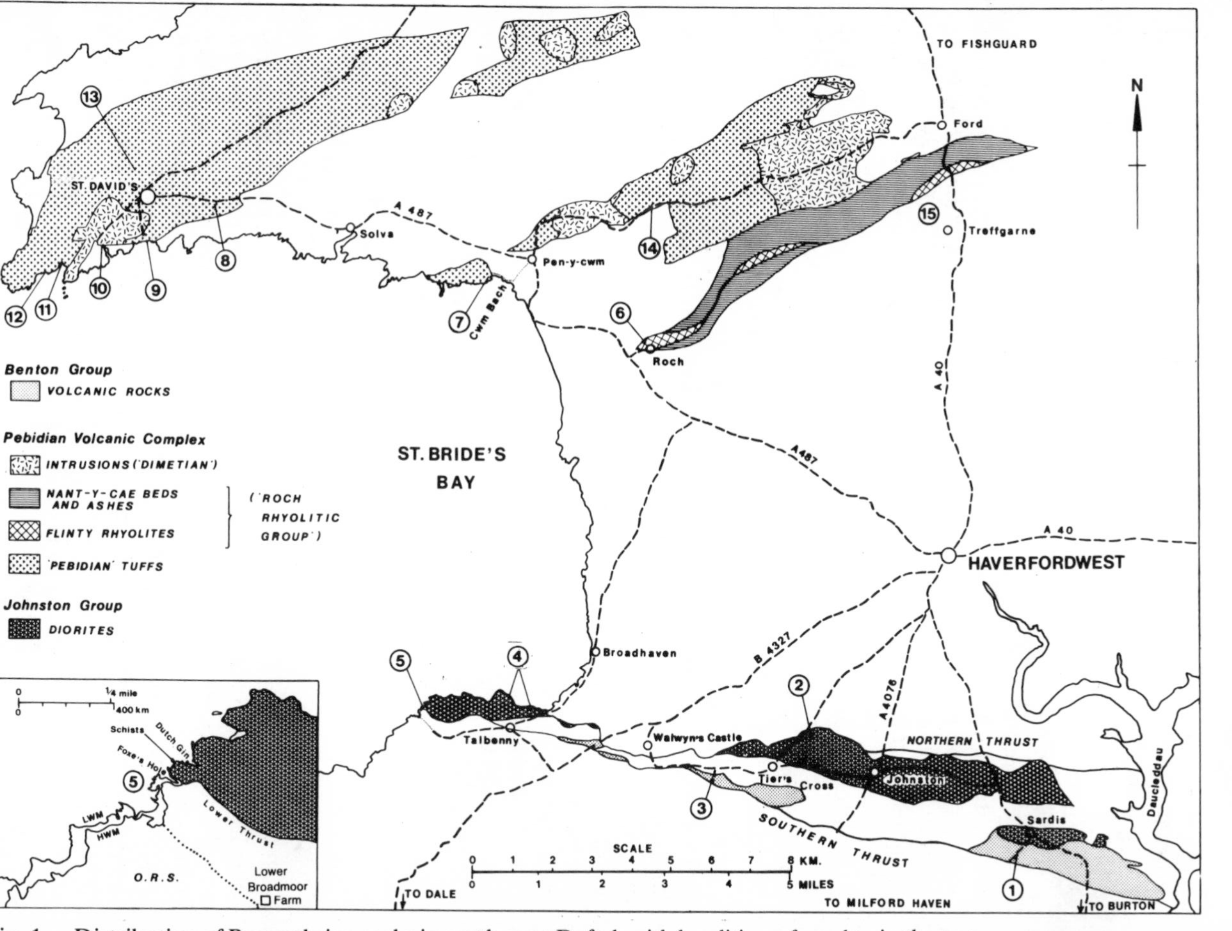

Fig. 1. Distribution of Precambrian rocks in south-west Dyfed, with localities referred to in the text.

A somewhat different group of rhyolites, volcanic breccias, ashes and ashy flags — the Roch Rhyolitic 'Series' (or Group) — occurs in a faulted slice adjoining the south side of the Hayscastle outcrop. Thomas & Cox (1924) showed that there were strong reasons for regarding this Group as Precambrian but not necessarily as Pebidian; nevertheless, they noted some similarity between the higher fine grained beds (Nant-y-Coy Beds) and the Ramsey Sound Group.

In the southern tract igneous rocks of supposed Precambrian age are associated with Upper Llandovery sediments within a complex thrust belt developed near the northern front of the Hercynian fold-belt. The Geological Survey (Strahan *et al.* 1914; Cantrill *et al.* 1916) recognised two groups of igneous rocks, *viz.* the Johnston 'Series' made up mainly of plutonic diorites, and the Benton 'Series', comprising acid volcanics. These are often correlated respectively with the Dimetian and Pebidian of north Pembrokeshire (e.g. George 1970) which implies that the Johnston 'Series' is the younger; however, there is no direct evidence for or against this interpretation, and Baker (1971) deduced the opposite relationship.

The Benton Volcanic Group (Shackleton 1975) resembles the Pebidian volcanics on account of their predominantly acid nature giving sodic rhyolites and trachytes, but they are mainly in the form of lava flows rather than 'tuffs', and often show spherulitic and auto-brecciated structures. The calc-alkaline Johnston diorites (Thorpe 1972) consist of darker quartz-poor to lighter coloured quartz-rich hornblende-diorites, which are extensively veined by pegmatitic granites. It is probable that the diorites formed by reaction or 'hybridisation' between pre-existing gabbros and an acid magma (similar to the pegmatites) as suggested by Wright (1968). They are intruded by quartz dolerite dykes of uncertain age, but probably also Precambrian.

It has been suggested that at the western end of its mainland outcrop, an intrusive junction is exposed between the Johnston diorites and a group of metasedimentary schists, the Dutch Gin Schists (Claxton 1963). However, Baker *et al.* (1968) re-examined this section and concluded that the schists were formed tectonically by thrusting within the diorite mass.

It is clear that the Pebidian comprises a complex of volcanic lavas, pyroclastics, and derived sediments; moreover, the Dimetian intrusions correspond with them petrologically. Baker (1971) suggested therefore that they represent genetically related subvolcanic events, and included both as parts of a single Pebidian Volcanic Complex. It is probable that the Roch Rhyolitic Group is part of this complex, and possible that the Benton Volcanic Group is also related.

The Johnston diorites have counterparts in the Stanner and Hanter Hills area of Radnorshire (Powys), and also in the Malvern Hills where they are demonstrably of Precambrian age. The relation of all these granite-veined diorites to the various Precambrian volcanic and sedimentary rocks of South Wales and the Welsh Borderland has been the subject of much inconclusive debate. Recent radiometric age determinations have not resolved these problems, but they have established that all the events occurred late in the Precambrian. Thus the Johnston diorites give a U-Pb zircon age of 643^{+5}_{-28} m.y., and the St David's Granophyre formed between 650 and 570 m.y. (Patchett & Jocelyn 1979); the latter may be regarded as the age of the whole Pebidian Volcanic Complex. Shackleton (1975) notes that K/Ar ages of 625 and 613 m.y. have been obtained for the Benton Volcanic Group.

ITINERARY

This itinerary is described as a circular tour based on Haverfordwest (Fig. 1). It may, however, be more convenient to visit some localities in association with other itineraries; e.g. localities 4 and 5 lie en route for Marloes Bay (excursions 7 and 8), and localities 7-13 occur near outcrops of Cambrian rocks (excursion 2). For this reason more localities have been included than can be examined in a single day.

Some coastal localities may be visited successively by following the coastal footpath of the Pembrokeshire National Park, in which event additional intervening exposures will be passed; however, great discretion must be exercised before examining these since entry to and exit from many of the tidal baylets cannot be gained safely by scrambling the cliffs.

Many of the minor roads are not suitable for motor coaches.

1. Great Westfield, near Sardis (SM 9667 0820). In general the Benton Volcanic Group is poorly exposed, and mapping of its outcrop depends largely on the evidence of volcanic debris in soils. The type section is near Benton Castle (SN 0018 0687), but the Great Westfield exposure is more conveniently situated as it is close to the through road from Haverfordwest to Burton. Here, in the unmetalled lane and its banks N of the farm, dark coloured rhyolites show flow-brecciation in part, and elsewhere are flow-banded.

2. Bolton Hill Quarry, near Johnston (SM 9170 1140) can be reached from the previous locality along reasonable roads via Johnston and Tier's Cross; **permission** to enter this large active quarry must be obtained from the manager. The rocks being worked are diorites of the Johnston 'Series', intruded by pegmatitic granite veins and younger dolerite dykes. Abundant, freshly broken blocks show very clearly the relationships between the finer grained, homogeneous and most basic diorites, the aplites, and the diverse transitional products of the hybridisation process. A poor foliation can be seen in some of the largest diorite blocks. It is clear that the dolerite dykes — some of which are 2-3 m wide — are unaffected by the hybridisation and therefore post-date it. A number of sub-vertical faults are also prominent.

3. Roman Castle (SM 8907 1057) lies off the road from Tier's Cross to Walwyn's Castle. The northern part of the lane leading to the two farms crosses the outcrop of the Upper Llandovery beds, which are supposed to overlie the Benton Volcanic Group, but there is no clear evidence for this here. The nearest horizon to the Silurian recorded by the Geological Survey (Cantrill *et al* 1916, p. 12) was a spherulitic rhyolite which is no longer exposed. However, purple and green tuffs are exposed in the W bank of the lane, just N of Sydney Lodge farm yard; they are not dissimilar to certain tuffs in the St David's outcrop of the Pebidian.

4. Goultrop Roads, Talbenny. Join the B4327 from Haverfordwest N of Walwyn's Castle and turn N for Talbenny at the first cross roads. A path from the lane 200 m E of the church leads to a **small disused quarry** immediately below the cliff path (SM 8460 1236). Here mainly massive diorites are cut by somewhat foliated aplites, but near the centre of the quarry face the diorites show schistose developments. The quarry cannot be far above the basal thrust plane since Carboniferous rocks occupy most of the cliff below, and it is possible, therefore, that the schistosity is related to the thrusting.

A descent to the shore can be made by following the cliffpath westwards to a stile and there taking the now poorly defined right hand branch. In this area the diorite crops out at shore level, but at the **corner of the cliff,** N of the old lifeboat house (SM 8400 1273) the almost horizontal thrust re-emerges above sea-level. Here the diorite overlies sheared lenticles of Carboniferous Limestone and plant-bearing shales.

5. Dutch Gin (SM 8170 1256) and **Foxes' Hole,** near Talbenny. The cliff path can be reached by turning right at the village towards Lower Broadmoor Farm; follow it northwards across an Old Red Sandstone outcrop to Foxes' Hole. This inlet has been eroded along the thrust plane which brings the Old Red Sandstone northwards over the diorites of the Johnston 'Series'. The brecciation, shearing and schistosity induced along this surface is well displayed on the inclined N side of Foxes' Hole. Typical massive diorite occurs on the headland to the N and is intruded by a dolerite dyke at the cliff top overlooking Dutch Gin. At the W end of this promontory another southerly sloping surface falls sharply seawards. This shows brecciated and schistose patches similar to those at Foxes' Hole (but without any Old Red Sandstone fragments), and, like the latter, has been eroded along a thrust plane which here passes beneath the upper part of the headland. This thrust is subparallel to the upper thrust at Foxes' Hole, but is formed within the massive diorite which occurs above and below it. The schistose rocks are confined to the vicinity of the thrust plane and were produced by movement along it (Baker *et al.* 1968).

6. Roch Castle (SM 8805 2120) is built above a very conspicuous crag which is clearly visible from the A487 Haverfordwest — St David's road near Roch

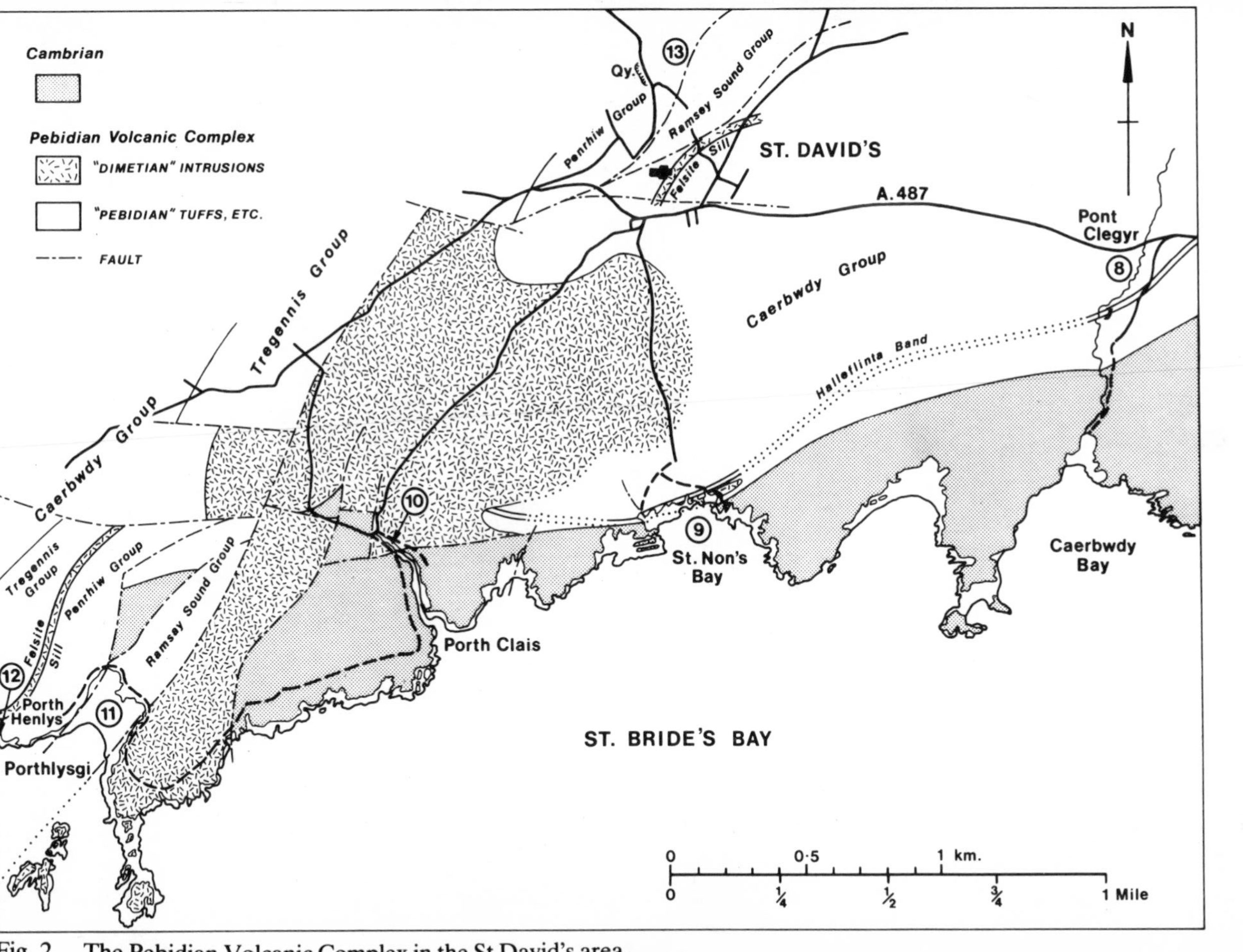

Fig. 2. The Pebidian Volcanic Complex in the St David's area.

Gate. It can be reached from the previous locality via lanes through Broad Haven and Haroldston West. The crag consists of rhyolites belonging to the Roch Rhyolitic Group, but unfortunately it lies within grounds which are **strictly private.**

7. Cwm Bach, at the N end of Newgale Sands, can be reached from the A487 by a track from Pen-y-Cwm which leads to the cliff path. In the NW corner of this bay the Pebidian volcanics of the Hayscastle-Brawdy inlier are faulted against Cambrian rocks, but they are very well seen in numerous crags above the cliffs (SM 8380 2307). Here the structures of the massive rhyolites have been weathered out clearly and show small spherulites, vesicles, and flow banding; this is one of the best localities for examination of the non-tuffaceous facies of the Pebidian.

8. Pont Clegyr (SM 7693 2513) lies on the A487 1.6 km E of St David's (Fig. 2). The lower, coarse-grained members of the Caerbwdy Group are well exposed on both sides of the valley S of the road and include Green's (1908) Clegyr Conglomerate.

In the valley to the S of the road an **old quarry** near the E bank of the stream 250 m below the bridge shows an overlying 30 m thick unit of uniformly fine grained blue-green halleflinta which breaks into translucent splinters. This distinctive unit was mapped for several miles by Green (1908) and in particular occurs at St Non's Bay (locality 9); its distance from the conspicuous Cambrian conglomerate further down this valley should be noted and compared with the corresponding relationship at St Non's.

9. St Non's Bay (Fig. 2). Leave St David's via Goat Street and follow the signposts for St Non's; continue beyond the car park to the cliff path and walk eastwards to reach the **conspicuous cliff top exposures** of the basal Cambrian conglomerates (SM 7532 2425). This outcrop can be traced westwards across the four large sea stacks to the far side of the bay. All the rocks exposed on the N (landward) side belong to the Caerbwdy Group of the Pebidian. In the W cliff of the baylet, immediately below the cliff top exposures of conglomerate, the Precambrian rocks can be seen dipping steeply northwards away from the Cambrian, which they appear to overlie; hence, at this point the sequence must be overturned. Also visible from here in the cliff section is a clearly transgressive sill; this is a Dimetian quartz-porphyry, and can be examined on the cliff top above the NE side of the baylet.

The main bay can be reached by a steep path following the gully cut by the stream from St Non's Well, across the outcrop of the halleflinta seen in the quarry below Pont Clegyr. The closer proximity of this horizon to the Cambrian conglomerate is a measure of the overstep of the latter across the Pebidian.

10. Porth Clais is also sign-posted out of St David's via Goat Street. The old quay (SM 7408 2420) was built in the drowned valley of the River Alan on the outcrop of the most extensive Dimetian intrusion — the St David's granophyre. This highly siliceous leucocratic rock containing orthoclase, perthite and soda-plagioclase, is often referred to as an 'alaskite'. It is well exposed in **hillside crags** on the E side of the quay where greener patches indicate cataclastic deformation. A small dyke, 15-25 cm wide, exposed within the granite near the foot of the cliff path, also shows evidence of deformation; the off-setting of the dyke margins and the S-form of the joints suggest movement in the same sense before and after intrusion.

A major fault occupying a stretch of damp hillside lacking exposures separates the S side of the granite from Cambrian sandstones.

11. Porthlysgi Bay (SM 7310 2360) has no direct road access but can be reached by the cliff path westward from Porth Clais across the Cambrian outcrop. The latter is faulted against the Precambrian near the W end of the last cliff top field, and the headland and islands beyond are built of the resistant St David's granophyre. A large, well-known glacial erratic of a Scottish picrite (marked on older 6 inch maps) has unfortunately rolled over the cliff in recent years.

Another fault zone visible in the eastern corner of Porthlysgi Bay introduces the upper portion of the Ramsey Sound Group. Here this consists principally of sheared leucocratic tuffs and ashes dipping to the NW. The relative softness of these rocks has permitted the erosion of this part of the bay, whereas the small central promontory shows less sheared, multi-coloured tuffs and coarser agglomerates. The volcanics are intruded in this part by a number of small dykes.

Across the valley mouth, the W side of the Bay shows purple and buff tuffs and agglomerates which Green (1908) regarded as the lowest unit of the Pebidian at the base of the Penrhiw Group. In consequence, it must be assumed that a fault line emerges from the valley and passes below the western cliffs, and that the shape of Porthlysgi Bay is fault controlled.

12. Porth Henllys (SM 7363 2360) can be reached by continuing a further 0.5 km W along the cliff path. At the head of this bay a felsite sill intrudes the top of the Penrhiw Group.

13. Penrhiw Quarry, Pont-y-Penyd, St David's (SM 7509 2584). This quarry was opened in the valley N of the Cathedral and can be reached from the centre of St David's by turning first left off Nun Street. Here the Penrhiw Group consists of purple and green, fine to coarse grained tuffs, which have a characteristic grittiness due to conspicuous grains of quartz and feldspar.

[Permission to visit the craggy Rhosson Group lavas near Rhosson Farm (2.5 km W of St David's) may not be readily given].

14. Gignog Quarry (SM 8812 2454), 2 km SW of Hayscastle. This large quarry can be reached from Pen-y-Cwm (locality 7) on the A487 St David's — Haverfordwest road, along country lanes for about 4 km. The site falls within a Cambrian outcrop according to Thomas & Jones (1912), probably because the quarry was not then opened. However, as suggested by Cox on his unpublished field maps it actually forms part of the Precambrian Hayscastle-Brawdy inlier.

Near the entrance, soft, fine grained rocks are possibly bedded ashes, but westwards along the quarry face they become coarser, blue-grey tuffs. The latter are very similar to some parts of the Pebidian in the St David's area; the main contrast is the prominence of small scale bedding in some parts of the sequence. The shallow dip of these beds is disturbed by several faults, certain of which near the W end are reversed.

15. Treffgarne Gorge (SM 9575 2512) and **Maiden Castle.** Continue through Hayscastle Cross to Ford on the A40, and then southwards for 1.5 km to the gorge. The narrow constriction of the valley at this point is due to the outcrop of massive rhyolites, which are well seen on the W side of the road, and up the hillside to the crags of Maiden Castle and Poll Carn (the outcrop is, however, faulted out before reaching the summit of Great Trefgarn Mountain). This lenticular outcrop belongs to the Roch Rhyolitic Group which can be traced discontinuously ESE to Roch (locality 6). Generally, they are rather uniform, dark flinty rhyolites, rarely showing flow-banding, but some silicified rhyolitic tuffs occur in the road section.

North of the gorge the Nant-y-Coy Beds dip northwards off the rhyolites. These bedded rocks comprise a notable thickness of fine grained silicified ashes, and in comparing them with the Ramsey Sound Group, allowance must be made for the effect of shearing on the latter. They can be examined in the track above the S side of Nant-y-Coy farmhouse.

The return to Haverfordwest may be made southwards along the A40.

REFERENCES

BAKER, J. W. 1971. The Proterozoic history of southern Britain. *Proc. Geol. Ass.* **82,** 249-266.

BAKER, J. W., LEMON, G. G., GAYER, R. A. & MARSHMAN, R. R. 1968. The Dutch Gin Schists. *Geol. Mag.* **105,** 493,494.

CANTRILL, T. C., DIXON, E. E. L., THOMAS, H. H. & JONES, O. T. 1916. The geology of the South Wales coalfield, Pt. 12. The country around Milford. *Mem. geol. Surv. U.K.* i-vii, 185 pp., 7 pls.

CLAXTON, C.W. 1963. An occurrence of regionally metamorphosed schists in south-west Pembrokeshire. *Geol. Mag.* **100,** 219-223.

COX, A. H., GREEN, J. F. N., JONES, O. T. & PRINGLE, J. 1930. The geology of the St. David's district, Pembrokeshire. *Proc. Geol. Ass.* **41,** 241-273.

GEORGE, T. N. 1970. *British Regional Geology: South Wales (3rd ed.),* i-xii, 152 pp., 13 pls. N.E.R.C./I.G.S. H.M.S.O., London.

GREEN, J. F. N. 1908. The geological structure of the St. David's area (Pembrokeshire). *Q. Jl geol. Soc. Lond.* **64,** 363-383.

HICKS, H. 1877. On the Pre-Cambrian (Demetian and Pebidian) rocks of St. David's. *Q. Jl geol. Soc. Lond.* **33,** 229-241.

PATCHETT, P. J. & JOCELYN, J. 1979. U-Pb Zircon ages for late Precambrian igneous rocks of South Wales. *J. geol. Soc. Lond.* **136,** 13-19.

SHACKLETON, R. M. 1975. Pre-Cambrian rocks of Wales. *In* HARRIS, A. L. *et al.* (eds.), A correlation of the Pre-Cambrian rocks in the British Isles. *Spec. Rep. geol. Soc. Lond.* **6,** 76-82.

STRAHAN, A., CANTRILL, T. C., DIXON, E. E. L., THOMAS, H. H. & JONES, O. T. 1914. The geology of the South Wales coalfield, Pt. II. The country around Haverfordwest. *Mem. geol. Surv. U.K.* i-viii, 262 pp., 5 pls.

THOMAS, H. H. & COX, A. H. 1924. The volcanic series of Trefgarn, Roch and Ambleston. *Q. Jl geol. Soc. Lond.* **80,** 520-548.

THOMAS, H. H. & JONES, O. T. 1912. The Pre-Cambrian and Cambrian rocks of Brawdy, Hayscastle and Brimaston. *Q. Jl geol. Soc. Lond.* **68,** 374-401.

THORPE, R. S. 1972. Possible subduction origin for two Pre-Cambrian calc-alkaline plutonic complexes from southern Britain. *Bull. geol. Soc. Am.* **83,** 3663.

WILLIAMS, T. G. 1934. The Pre-Cambrian and Lower Palaeozoic rocks of the eastern end of the St. David's Pre-Cambrian area. *Q. Jl geol. Soc. Lond.* **90,** 32-75.

WRIGHT, A. E. 1968. Pre-Cambrian of south-east Eire. *Geol. Mag.* **105,** 75-76.

2
THE CAMBRIAN ROCKS OF THE NEWGALE-ST DAVID'S AREA

by B. P. J. WILLIAMS *and* J. T. G. STEAD

Maps	*Topographical:*	1 : 50 000	Sheet 157 St David's and Haverfordwest
		1 : 25 000	Sheets SM72, SM82, SM92
	Geological:	1 : 25 000	Special Sheet SM72 & Parts of SM62, 73 St David's

FOLLOWING the late Precambrian development of the southern continental margin of the Iapetus Ocean, the Cambrian rocks of South Wales were deposited during a major transgressive event which flooded this margin in early Cambrian times. As such the Cambrian sediments of south-west Dyfed represent mainly shallow water deposits and contain the first evidence of a varied marine fauna.

Lower, Middle and Upper Cambrian rocks are represented in the Newgale — St David's area, which was situated on the southern margin of the subsiding Welsh Basin. The basal Cambrian conglomerates were deposited over an eroded and deeply weathered Precambrian plutonic and volcanic terrain. The Lower Cambrian sequence provides evidence of an upward-deepening profile of intertidal to below wave base (100-200 m depth) sediments (Crimes 1970). The early Middle Cambrian sediments again reflect a shallow marine environment of deposition, whereas the later Middle Cambrian shows less coarse clastic sediment but the quiet water accumulation of black, pyritous mudstones containing a relatively abundant trilobite fauna dominated by *Paradoxides* and *Agnostus*. Towards the end of Middle Cambrian times the sediment input coarsened, heralding the deposition of the Lingula Flags. Deposition of these Upper Cambrian rocks may reflect relatively rapid basin subsidence as evidence is present for shallow water environments (Rushton 1974; Turner 1977).

The distribution of Cambrian rocks throughout the area is associated with the presence of two large, fault-bounded anticlines or horsts of Precambrian volcanic and intrusive rocks in the Hayscastle area and at St David's. These major folds trend ENE-WSW and are flanked to the S by Cambrian rocks dipping steeply S, and to the W and N by Cambrian rocks dipping steeply

[pp. 27-49 *In* BASSETT, M. G. (ed.). 1982. Geological excursions in Dyfed, south-west Wales.]

NW, followed by folded and cleaved Ordovician rocks with a prevalent steep northerly dip.

On the S coast there are sharp, minor, SW- plunging folds in the Cambrian rocks of the Porth-y-Rhaw — Solva area, and inland the broad outcrop of the Solva Group, N of Solva Harbour, again testifies to the intense folding of these rocks. An impressive downward-facing syncline, affecting Lower-Middle Cambrian rocks is evident in Whitesand Bay.

The relationships of the various Cambrian rocks in the area are further complicated by faulting and later intrusions. Strike-slip faulting is dominant in its affect on the Cambrian outcrop of the St David's-Newgale coastline. Movement was essentially of a dextral wrench pattern, and an effect of this faulting, together with bedding strike orientation, is that successively younger Cambrian rocks crop out along the coast between St Non's Bay and Solva Harbour. The folding and faulting are of Caledonian age, later modified by Variscan movements which intensified the folding and reactivated some Caledonian faults.

The present landscape of the area has resulted from the uplift of a Tertiary marine platform that maintains an average level of some 60 m above sea level, while Precambrian and Ordovician igneous intrusions give rise to isolated hills (90-180 m above sea level) and impressive headlands, notably Carn Llidi and St David's Head near Whitesand Bay. Thus, although the coastal sections are spectacular, inland the solid geology is largely obscured by the flat topography and by thin deposits of Glacial Drift and peat. East of Whitesand Bay there is a low lying area masked by blown sand.

The main stratigraphical succession of the area was first established in the latter half of the nineteenth century (Harkness & Hicks 1871; Hicks 1877, 1881; Salter 1863) and later detailed by Green (1908, 1911), Thomas & Jones (1912), and Williams (1934). Little new stratigraphical work on the Cambrian succession was published until relatively recently (Davies & Downie 1964; Stead 1969; Stead & Williams 1971; Rushton 1974). Changes in Cambrian stratigraphical nomenclature, affecting rock units in the area, were introduced by Cowie *et al.* (1972) in their correlation of Cambrian rocks in the British Isles. The Cambrian succession in the Newgale-St David's area is summarised below:

		Thickness (metres)	
	'Lingula Flags'	+600	MERIONETH SERIES (Upper Cambrian)
Menevian Group	Upper Menevian beds	c. 30	ST. DAVID'S SERIES (Middle Cambrian)
	Middle Menevian beds	c. 100	
	Lower Menevian beds	c. 100	
Solva Group	Upper Solva beds	c. 50	
	Middle Solva beds	c. 80	
	Lower Solva beds	c. 50	

Caerfai Group	Caerbwdy Sandstone	up to 150	?COMLEY SERIES (Lower Cambrian)
	Caerfai Bay Shales	15	
	St Non's Sandstone	up to 140	
	Conglomerate	10-50	

Due to the paucity of fossil material from the lower part of the sequence, the presence of the Comley Series in south-west Wales remains unproved (Rushton 1974). The Caerfai Group, which rests unconformably on Precambrian igneous rocks, cannot be correlated with formations elsewhere. The Lower Solva beds embrace the *Paradoxides oelandicus* Zones but the inclusion of the upper part of the Caerbwdy Sandstone within these zones (Cowie *et al.* 1972; Rushton 1974) is conjectural.

Stead (1969) and Stead & Williams (1971) subdivided the Lower and Middle Solva beds into five members and these subdivisions are used in this itinerary as follows:

Middle Solva beds	Purple sandstone member
	Grey sandstone member
Lower Solva beds	Upper pebbly sandstone member
	Sandstone-shale member
	Lower pebbly sandstone member

The outcrops of these subdivisions are shown in several of the text figures, mainly Figs. 3, 4, and 6.

ITINERARY

The locality numbers correspond to those shown in Fig. 1. The letters in brackets indicate the exposures at individual localities and are noted on the relevant figures.

1. From Haverfordwest take the A487 road to the coast at **Newgale** where Cambrian rocks are faulted against Coal Measures sandstones of the Nolton-Newgale coal field. The fault at Newgale does not present a good feature but it must pass between the Coal Measures sandstone quarry (SM 8483 2244) and the Cambrian (Middle Solva) sandstones exposed in the **cutting behind the bungalow** at SM 8471 2245. The position of the fault, between Coal Measures sandstones and Menevian shales, can also be traced **on the roadside** on Newgale hill (Fig. 2).

Proceed across the storm beach (Harrison 1968) to examine the **cliff section** from Newgale to Cwm Mawr, where rocks of the Lower and Middle Solva beds are exposed. At the north end of the section the strata are faulted against Lower Cambrian Caerfai Group sandstones.

(A) In the **N corner of Newgale Sands** (SM 845 224) grey sandstones and

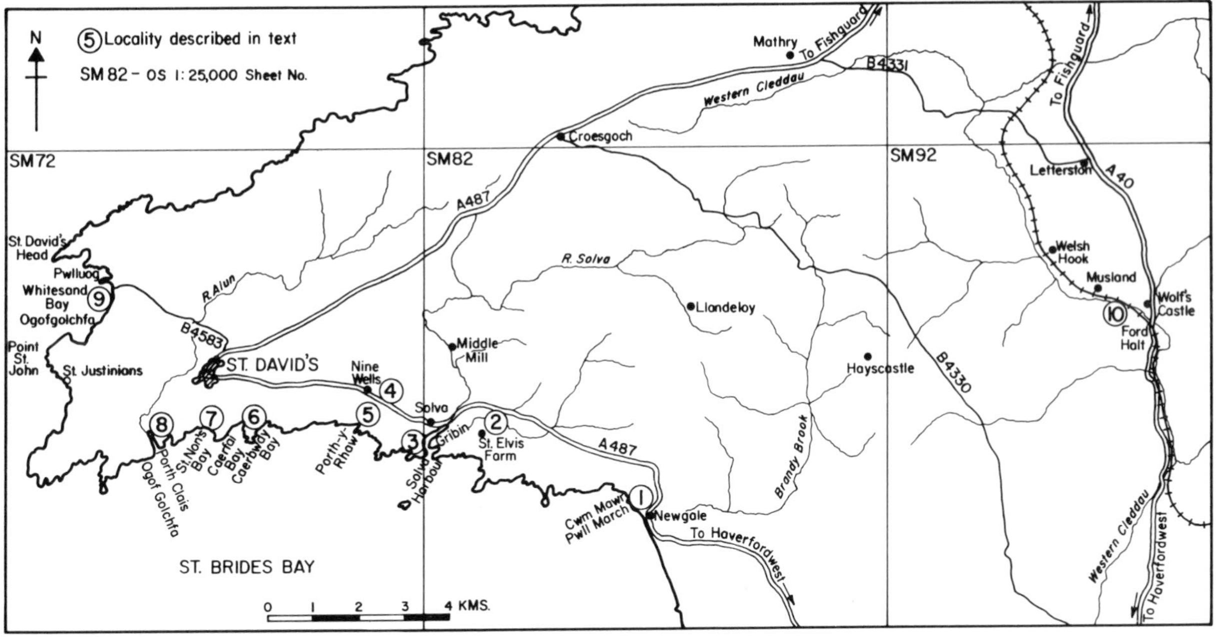

Fig. 1. Sketch map of the Newgale-St David's area, showing position of localities described.

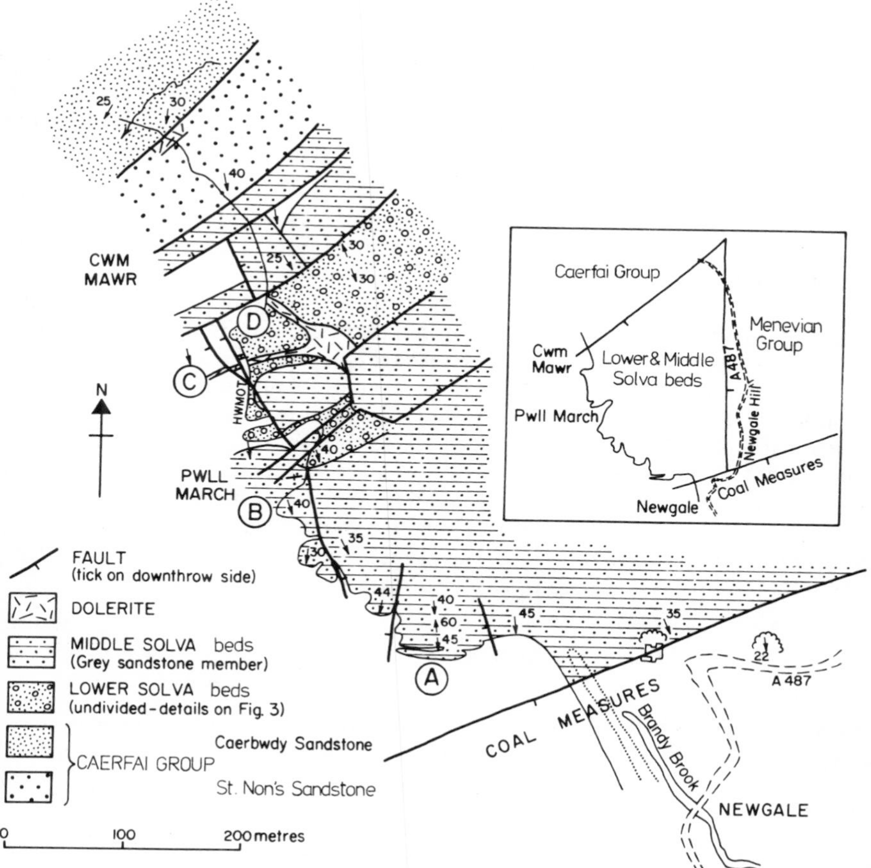

Fig. 2. Geological map of the Newgale-Cwm Mawr area (locality 1). Circled letters indicate outcrops referred to in text.

siltstones, with interbedded conglomerates of the lower part of the Middle Solva beds (grey sandstone member), dip S at 45°. These beds are particularly well exposed in the small caves. The conglomerates contain a variety of igneous, metamorphic and sedimentary clasts. Strong intersecting joint planes and minor faulting are well displayed here. Examination of the bedding-plane surfaces reveals abundant spicules of the sponge *Protospongia major* and various bioturbation features. Sedimentary structures to be seen in this member include scours, with cross bedded fill, graded bedding, parallel lamination, ripple lamination, and small scale load casts. Typically these sandstones are of variable texture, from silty mudstone to medium grained sandstone, Sorting and grading are commonly distinct within the sandy phases. The bulk of the sediment is composed of fine, sub-angular, elongate quartz grains arranged roughly parallel to the bedding especially in the silty laminae. Stringers and laths of biotite and streaks of cabonaceous material define the bedding. Burrows in the silty layers are frequently infilled with fine sand from the overlying layer.

(B) A little to the N an asymmetrical syncline can be seen plunging westward. Proceed around the cliffs towards Pwll March, past lower beds of the grey sandstone member, noting minor faulting as shown by the displacement of the interbedded conglomerate. At **Pwll March** (SM 8443 2261) pulverized grey sandstones are dropped down between two normal faults against the upper pebbly sandstone member (Fig. 3). On the exposed bedding planes W of the fault zone trough cross-bedding, indicating sediment transport from the SE, may be seen in the upper pebbly sandstone member. This member comprises thick beds of moderately sorted, very coarse lithic sandstone, dark green in colour where fresh surfaces are seen, but it weathers rusty brown. Considerable variations in thickness can be detected as individual beds are traced along the cliff section. Many beds are pebbly but few graded units occur. There are no interbedded siltstones in this member. The rocks contain, on average, 16% feldspar and 12% rock fragments, the remainder comprising subrounded quartz clasts.

(C) Near **Cwm Mawr** (Fig. 3) a transgressive dolerite dyke crops out in the cliff and it can also be traced across the foreshore where it is offset by faults (Fig. 2).

(D) On the S side of **Cwm Mawr** bay (SM 8438 2271) the lower pebbly sandstones member comprises alternating coarse, lithic, feldspathic sandstones and dark siltstones. Penecontemporaneous sediment deformation is evident but some corrugated laminae and microfaulting in the siltstones may be related to the major faults in this bay. The fault zone separating the Solva Group from the Caerfai Group is well exposed here, both in the Cliff and on the foreshore (Figs. 2 & 3). The fault breccia includes recognisable blocks of the grey sandstone member. The fault zone has been eroded to produce Cwm Mawr Valley.

2. Return to Newgale village and take the A487 towards Solva, stopping at the turn-off for **St Elvis Farm** (Fig. 1) where there is **a quarry** (SM 8180 2446) in parallel laminated dark siltstones and mudstones. These rocks are strongly cleaved at high angle to the bedding. They probably represent the *Paradoxides davidis* Zone of the mid-Menevian Group.

3. Proceed on the A487 to **Solva Harbour** where a variety of Cambrian rocks are exposed from Lower Solva beds to Lingula Flags (Fig. 4). Major faulting along the inlet is indicated by the truncation of the Ordovician

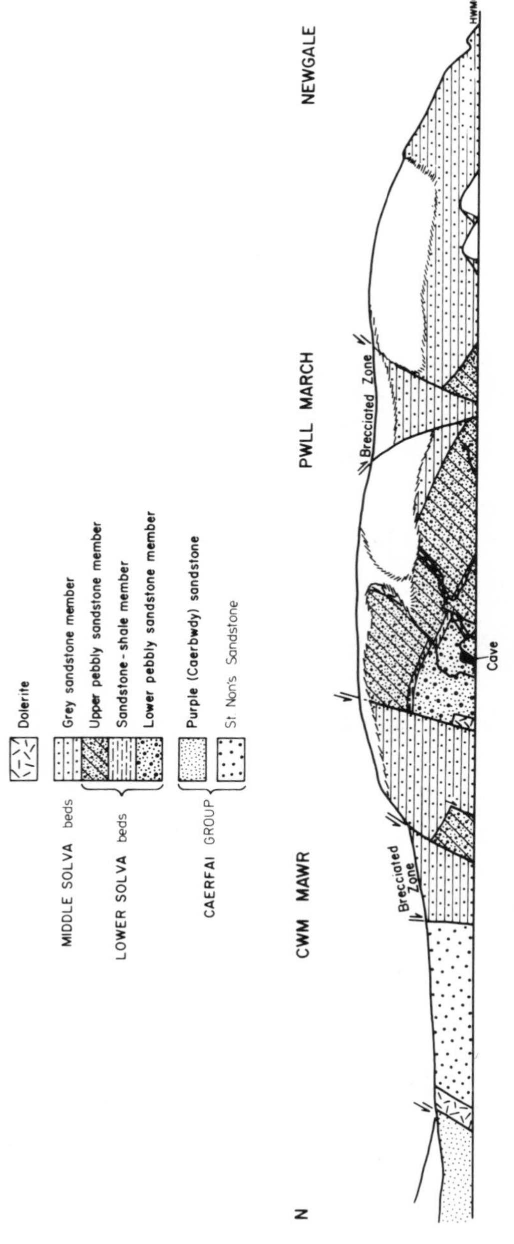

Fig. 3. Sketch section of the geology as seen in the cliff between Newgale and Cwm Mawr and viewed from low water mark (locality 1).

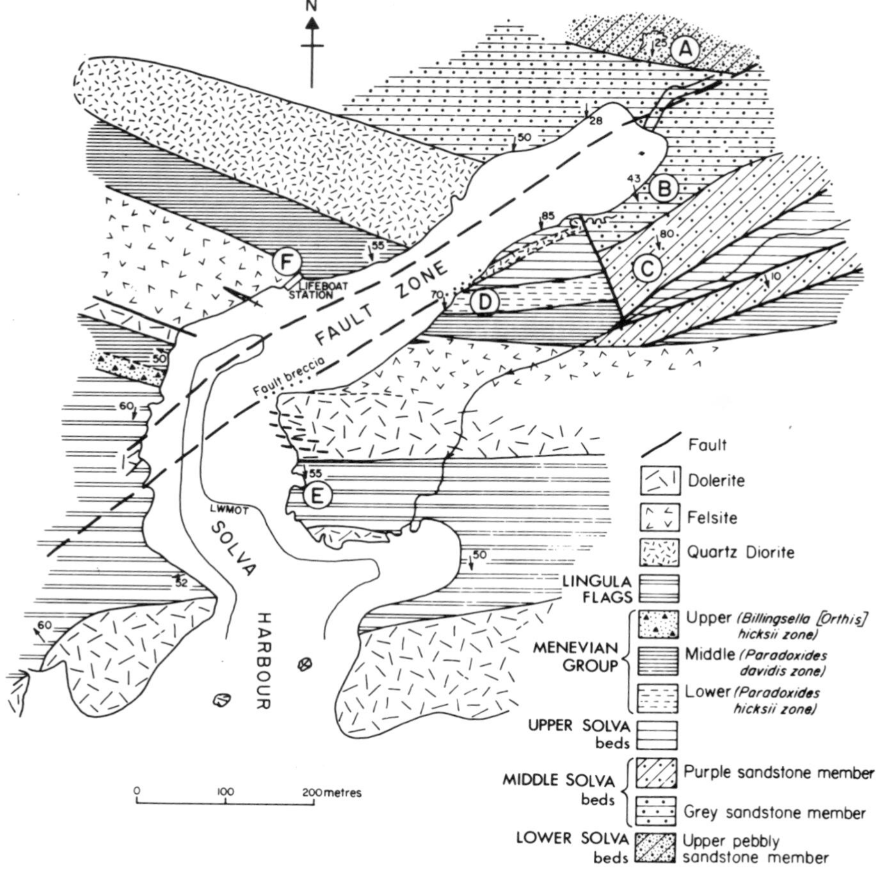

Fig. 4. Geological map of Solva Harbour (locality 3). Circled letters indicate outcrops referred to in the text.

igneous intrusions (SM 8022 2412) and by the displacement of the outcrops of the Lingula Flags (Fig. 4).

(A) In the **old quarry** at SM 8054 2436 the topmost 10 m of the upper pebbly sandstone member of the Lower Solva beds are exposed. The beds are massive feldspathic pebbly sandstones, up to 1.5 m thick, with several thin beds of finer grained sandstone. Minor faulting can be detected here by the displacement of the sandstone beds. This member is followed by the southward dipping grey sandstone member exposed in the road cutting and above high water mark on both sides of the harbour (Fig. 4). As at Newgale the beds exhibit parallel and ripple laminated grey sandstones and siltstones with large burrows, and spicules of *P. major*.

(B) Cross the harbour to the section which extends from the bridge at the head of the inlet to the old lime kilns (SM 8054 2417) and examine the upper part of this sequence. Although essentially similar to the grey sandstone member at Newgale the beds at this locality are more indurated, presumably due to the proximity of the large intrusions. Interbedded conglomerates near the lime kilns are in the same relative position as the conglomerates near the top of the grey sandstone member at Newgale.

(C) The purple sandstones and shales of the upper part of the Middle Solva beds are not exposed in the harbour because they are cut out by faulting. To examine these beds take the left path from the lime kilns to the top of the **Gribin** (SM 8055 2409). Here the dip has steepened to near-vertical, but in the valley to the S the same beds are repeated dipping SE at about 10° (Fig. 4).

(D) Returning to **harbour level** SW of the lime kilns the Middle Solva grey sandstones are faulted against rocks of the Menevian Group, which include grey flags and olive mudstones with *Paradoxides hicksii* and dark siltstones with *P. davidis*. A small igneous intrusion occurs near these Menevian beds (SM 8038 2408).

(E) Immediately to the SW, down the harbour, a large dolerite intrusion occurs between the Menevian and the Upper Cambrian Lingula Flags. The latter display typical features of a distal turbidite sequence with laterally persistent, thin, fine to medium grained sandstones interbedded with siltstones and shales (Crimes 1970, fig. 27). Examples of graded bedding, convolute lamination, ripple lamination, load casts and flute marks are readily found (SM 8013 2386).

(F) Cross to the NW side of the inlet, where the Cambrian sequence is less complete, but the dark mudstones and shales of the *P. davidis* Zone are well exposed near the **Lifeboat Station** (SM 8017 2410), adjacent to a felsitic intrusion of probable Ordovician age (Fig. 4.). The felsite is porphyritic, with a distinct flow texture and small plagioclase laths arranged parallel to the contact with the Menevian sediments. Further down the inlet, cross bedded *'Orthis' hicksii* sandstones underly the Lingula Flags.

4. Return to the main road and proceed along the A487 towards St David's. Stop at a **roadside quarry** about 0.5 km E of **Nine Wells** (Fig. 1). At this locality (SM 7916 2478) olive-green weathering siltstones and mudstones of Lower Menevian age crop out. Specimens of *P. hicksii* and various agnostid trilobites can occasionally be obtained here. There is also a similar exposure **near the pump house** at Nine Wells (SM 7871 2498).

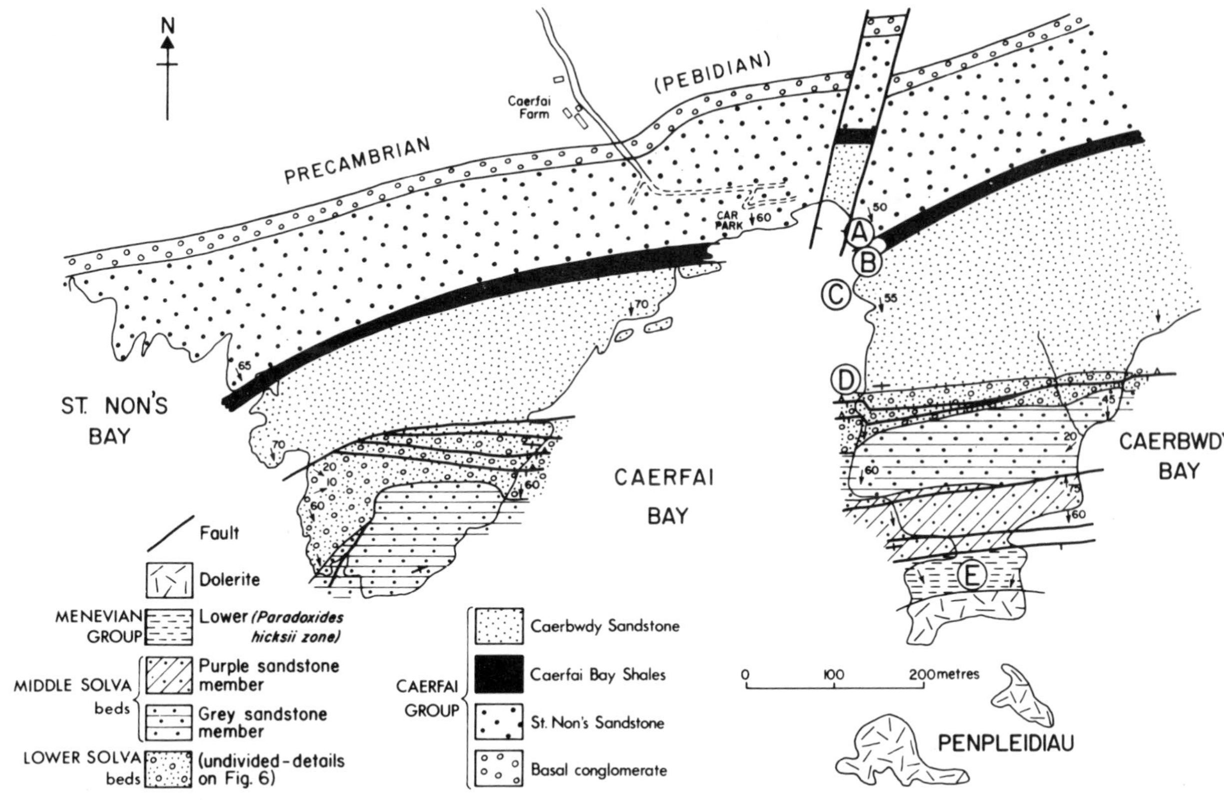

Fig. 5. Geological map of the Caerfai Bay area (locality 6). Circled letters indicate outcrops referred to in the text.

5. Walk down the valley from Nine Wells to **Porth-y-Rhaw** (Fig. 1) noting Lingula Flags and small exposures of coarse sandstones *('Orthis' hicksii* beds) repeated by strike faulting in the valley sides. In **a quarry** near the lower end of the valley (SM 7871 2455) a sill of fine grained quartz dolerite is seen in contact with very fine grained, laminated sandstones and siltstones of probable Menevian age. At the **head of the inlet** Lower Menevian fine sandstones with dark silty laminations are exposed near the old lime kiln (SM 7866 2434). In **the cliffs** on the W side of the inlet folds in more resistant sandstones are well displayed. On **the beach** laminated fine sandstones of the *P. hicksii* Zone pass into dark mudstones and siltstones with fine sand layers and, at low tide, the locality where Salter (1863) first discovered *Paradoxides davidis* can be reached (Cox *et al.* 1930). In the **eastern cliff** near this locality the Middle Menevian *P. davidis* Zone is well exposed. Dark, highly cleaved mudstones with much disseminated pyrite and phosphatic material form beds of vertical attitude. Some 3 m below the base of a small, vertical doleritic intrusion the mudstones yield a rich trilobite fauna including *P. davidis* and *Eodiscus punctatus.* Near the E point of **Porth-y-Rhaw headland** coarse sandstones follow the dark mudstones conformably (SM 7856 2418). These coarse grained beds are traditionally included in the Menevian Group because of the presence of the brachiopod *Billingsella* [*Orthis*] *hicksii.* The Lower and Middle Menevian sediments appear to have been deposited in calm, relatively shallow water under reducing conditions (Crimes 1970; Rushton 1974). The extensive benthonic fauna, together with a low cobalt and nickel content of the mudstones (Price 1963), is again suggestive of relatively shallow marine deposition. The Upper Menevian coarse sandstones probably represent the onset of turbidite deposition, which was to continue into the Lower Lingula Flags of the Maentwrog Stage (Crimes 1970, figs. 2 and 27).

6. Proceed to St David's on the A487, turning left off the main road at SM 7560 2525 and then S to **Caerfai Bay.** This bay is a well known Pembrokeshire locality where rocks of Lower and Middle Cambrian age are exposed (Fig. 5). The bay is eroded in a zone of intersecting strike and dip faults. From the car park at Caerfai (SM 7605 2438) there is an excellent view of the **cliff section** on the E side of the bay where the strike-faulted succession can be seen. Brecciated Caerbwdy Sandstone faulted against the green St Non's Sandstone is exposed in the **path** leading down to the beach. Proceed to examine the succession on the **E side of the bay.** The Caerfai and Lower Solva groups can be reached along the foot of the cliffs but the rest of the Solva and Menevian sequence is not accessible from the beach. The succession is not complete because of disruption by a number of strike faults (Fig. 6).

(A) The St Non's Sandstone crops out at the **head of the bay** (SM 7615 2436). The basal conglomerate of the Caerfai Group is not exposed in the bay, although large boulders of the conglomerate occur on the beach. The St Non's Sandstone is a green, feldspathic, poorly sorted, fine to medium grained sandstone with occasional conglomeratic horizons. The sandstones are generally massively bedded, but in places tabular-planar cross bedding and channelling have been observed (Crimes 1970). Subsidiary siltstones within this sequence may be parallel or ripple-drift laminated. No body fossils have been recorded from this Sandstone although bioturbation is very evident, particularly *Skolithos* burrows.

The green colour is imparted to the St Non's Sandstone by the presence of much interstitial chlorite and epidote, within a detrital framework of quartz, feldspar (15%) and mica (Stead & Williams 1971). The top 5 m of the Sandstone take on a purple-reddish tint, are bioturbated, and pass gradually into the overlying red Caerfai Bay Shales, although the contact at this locality is affected by a high-angle fault. The sedimentary structures and trace fossils indicate a shallow marine origin for the St Non's Sandstone.

(B) The Caerfai Bay Shales (Cowie *et al.* 1972) are red cleaved mudstones which are locally extensively bioturbated. They contain several discrete horizons (individually less than 10 cm thick) of feldspathic crystal tuffs, which are medium to coarse grained and exhibit sharp erosional bases, often load-casted. Internally they may be graded, convoluted or display parallel and cross lamination (Owen *et al.* 1971; Stead & Williams 1971). Bioturbation is ubiquitous and comprises feeding burrows *(Teichichnus)* and undiagnostic worm burrows (Crimes 1970). Turner (1979) has made a detailed mineralogical study of the Shales and has indicated the volcanic origin of the tuffs by the identification of more than 90% euhedral, often zoned feldspars, predominantly plagioclase, and an accessory mineral suite of euhedral zircon, apatite and opaque oxides. The feldspar crystals are usually sericitized, but where fresh comprise andesine and labradorite suggestive of an intermediate to basic volcanic source. These tuffs, which can be traced across the entire outcrop area of the Caerfai Bay Shales from Porth Clais in the west to Cwm Bach, near Newgale, are the only evidence of contemporaneous Cambrian vulcanicity in south-west Dyfed.

Turner (1979) also showed that there is no evidence of detrital pigmentary hematite to impart the red colour to this shallow marine mudstone sequence. Conversely, the Shales contain a diagnostic clay mineral suite which indicates that the red colouration is due entirely to the diagenetic alteration of iron silicates and volcanic ash under oxidizing conditions. The Caerfai Bay Shales are also worthy of note in that this is the lowest horizon from which fossils are recorded in the Cambrian of south-west Dyfed. The fauna includes the inarticulate brachipod *Lingulella* and bradoriid crustacean *Indiania*? (Rushton 1974).

(C) The overlying purple Caerbwdy Sandstone exhibits a gradational contact with the Caerfai Bay Shales, the latter containing thin (2-5 cm), very fine grained sandstones in its topmost part (Turner 1979, fig. 2). These sharp, planar based thin sandstones are usually parallel bedded but cross lamination also occurs, and the units gradually increase in abundance and thickness as the contact with the Caerbwdy Sandstone is approached.

The Caerbwdy Sandstone is a fine to medium grained, poorly sorted

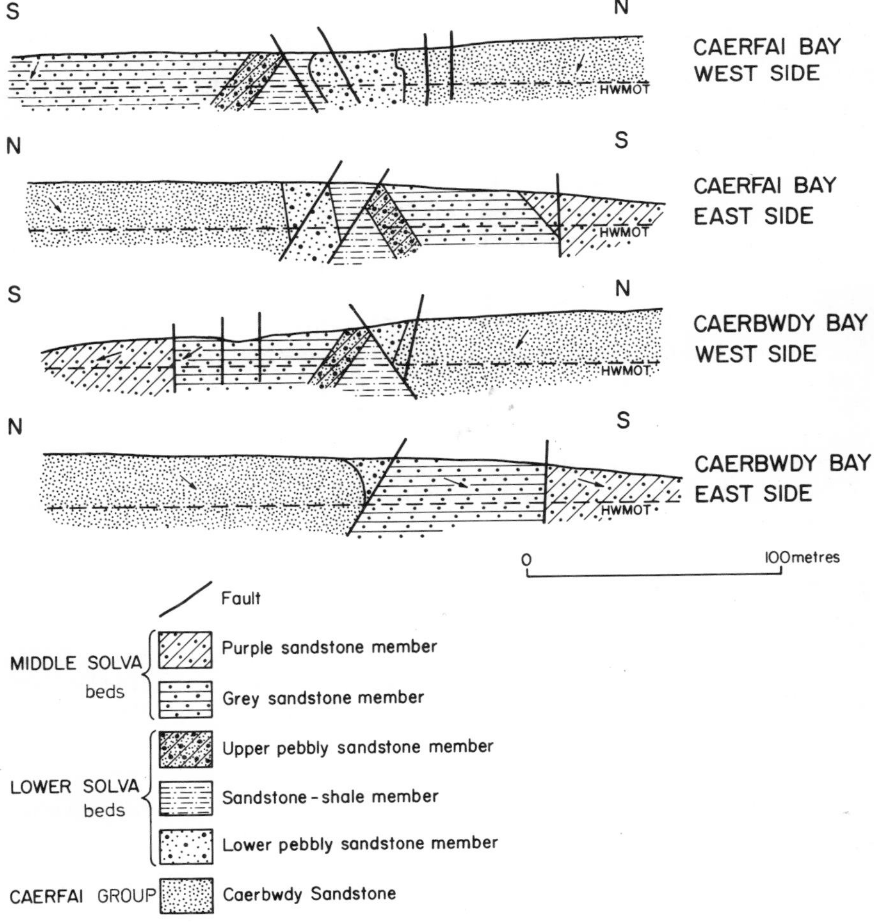

Fig. 6. Sketch sections of parts of the western and eastern headlands of Caerfai and Caerbwdy bays as viewed from the beaches (locality 6).

sandstone, micaceous and feldspathic with a high interstitial clay mineral content. Bioturbation is extremely abundant and this may account for homogenization of the sediment which produced bedding units up to 3 m in thickness. This formation comprises massive units with occasional graded beds and thin subsidiary mudstones. Scattered feldspar crystals in thin layers occur throughout the succession. Near the top of the formation granule-grade clasts of quartz and igneous rock debris can be found in the Sandstone near the contact with Lower Solva beds (Stead & Williams 1971).

Purple and green colours are haphazardly distributed in some beds, which is suggestive of diagenetic origin. The absence of such sedimentary structures in the Caerbwdy Sandstone as large scale tabular cross beds, channels and symmetrical ripple marks (in the non-bioturbated units) has led Crimes (1970) to suggest that the beds were deposited below wave base.

(D) Examine the exposure N of the first strike fault at SM 7617 2420 (Fig. 6). This is the exposure where O. T. Jones found evidence that an unconformity of some magnitude separates the Solva from the Caerfai Group (Jones 1940, p. 406, fig. 1). Recent work by the authors, however, suggests that the junction described by Jones is a fault contact. Higher in the cliff face above the fault there is a gradual transition from purple Caerbwdy Sandstone through purple and green beds to green Lower Solva pebbly sandstone (Fig. 6). At low tide this can be verified on the **W side of the bay** at SM 7578 2411, where the transition is not complicated by faulting. It can be traced in the cliff face and horizontally along a short ledge, but no discordance or notable break in sedimentation is apparent. This sedimentary transition from the Caerfai Group into the Solva Group is described in more detail at **Porth Clais (Locality 8).**

(E) Return to the head of the bay and follow the cliff path along the **promontory on the E side of Caerfai Bay** to examine the Menevian sediments and dolerite sill of the headland (SM 7627 2397). This sill is similar to the intrusion which forms **Penpleidiau** (Fig. 5). From this locality a spectacular fold can be seen in the Caerbwdy Sandstone and Lower Solva beds (Holland 1974, frontispiece) of the headland on the E side of **Caerbwdy Bay** (Fig. 6). These rocks are thrust over Middle Solva grey sandstones which are, in turn, faulted against Middle Solva purple sandstones (SM 768 243).

7. Return to Caerfai Bay car park and proceed W via the cliff path towards **St Non's Bay.** Along the **cliffs on the E side of this bay** the three members of the Lower Solva beds are exposed, gently folded and faulted against the Caerbwdy Sandstone (Fig. 5). These exposures are easily accessible at all stages of the tides. The lower pebbly sandstone member comprises medium bedded, coarse, green sandstones, often pebbly, with occasional purple beds similar to the Caerbwdy Sandstone. Contained rock fragments include granite, dolerite, spilite and quartzite. Examples of cross bedding, which are common here, indicate that the sediment was derived from the ESE. These beds are overlain by the sandstone-shale member which comprises parallel laminated silty mudstone at the bottom, coarsening upwards to fine and medium grained sandstone. Higher still in the sequence coarse sandstones of the upper pebbly sandstone member are exposed as medium to thick bedded, massive units, sometimes wedging out rapidly. In places these beds are intensely quartz veined due to small scale faulting. Overlying these Lower Solva beds, just before the fault in **the gully** at SM 7555 2399, are the lower beds of the Middle Solva grey sandstone member. These sandstones show the same sedimentary features as described at Newgale **(Locality 1A)** and include coarse, pebbly beds with scoured surfaces. South of the fault the rest of the grey sandstone member can be seen but here it is strongly cleaved.

The **cliff path to St Non's monastery** passes down through the Caerfai Group to the basal conglomerate which overlies Pebidian (Precambrian) tuffs. By the lifebuoy the path is steep as it slopes into a narrow cleft giving access to the rocky foreshore of St Non's Bay. Near the cleft are excellent exposures of Pebidian rhyolites and banded silicic tuffs ('halleflintas' of Morgan 1890), locally offset by extension faults. Further E a minor acid intrusion comprising a Dimetian (Precambrian) quartz porphyry dyke is well exposed.

On the **foreshore,** and accessible from mid to low water, is an E-W oriented rib of basal Cambrian conglomerate resting unconformably on purple Pebidian tuffs (SM 7515 2420). The beds here are overturned and dip steeply N. This linear outcrop of the conglomerate extends across the bay and is offset locally, with small displacements, by both dextral and sinistral wrench faults (Morgan 1890). The red-purple colouration of the tuffs at the contact could represent an original weathered surface or the effects of later solutions localized along the general plane of the contact.

The composition of the basal Cambrian conglomerate can be studied at this locality. The clasts are commonly well rounded and of pebble grade, but examples of cobble and boulder grade material can be found. The clasts are composed of vein quartz, liver coloured quartzite, schistose quartzite, acid tuff, and red argillites set mainly in a sandstone matrix. Less common are clasts of schistose greywacke, green schist, jasper, and granophyre. The acid tuffs, red argillites and granophyres can be matched with underlying Precambrian rock types, but the more exotic clasts, e.g. jasper and schistose rock fragments, were probably derived from older strata not now exposed (Crimes 1970). The conglomerate is framework supported and at this locality a preferred orientation of the clasts, in part of tectonic origin, is apparent. The sedimentary structures in the finer, upper part of the conglomerate are best seen at Ogofgolchfa, Whitesand Bay, and are described at that locality **(9).**

8. Return to St David's and take the road for St Justinian's, branching left at SM 7502 2529 to **Porth Clais.** In this small inlet Lower Cambrian rocks are exposed, downfaulted against the Precambrian by E-W trending normal faults and displaced by N-S dextral wrench faults (Fig. 7). Near the **site of the gasometer** (only the circular concrete base now remains at the N end of the car park) the trench (SM 7395 2427) cut by Green (1908, 1911), to prove that the Cambrian basal conglomerate rests without tectonic disturbance on the Dimetian granophyre, is still open. There is difficulty in determining precisely the granophyre-conglomerate junction because of extreme weathering of the exposure. The trench is now partly overgrown and is of more historical than geological interest (Owen *et al.* 1971, p. 21). **Permission** should be sought from the owner of this land before visiting the exposure.

The Dimetian alaskite-granophyre is best seen by the path immediately **adjacent to the ford** (SM 7413 2419). The granophyre is highly quartzose and extensively brecciated and fractured. A thin basic dyke cuts the granophyre at this locality.

Next examine the rocks **in the harbour** where green sandstones are faulted against purple sandstones and red shales, all dipping N (Fig. 7). **Near the quay** another fault throws down purple sandstones against the green sandstones and here the dip of the Caerbwdy Sandstone is to the S.

The **headland** beyond the fort is also in Caerbwdy Sandstone, which displays magnificent bedding planes dipping at high angles to the S (SM 7435 2388). From here, looking E, there is an excellent view of **Trwyncynddeiriog** (SM 7468 2395), where Lower Solva green sandstones can be seen overlying the Caerbwdy Sandstone and dipping steeply S.

Return to the ford at the head of the inlet and take the cliff path on the W side of Porth Clais. From this path the repetitions of the Lower Cambrian formations can be viewed in the eastern headland of the harbour. Proceed along the path to a point (SM 743 238) where a descent can be made to the **rock platform,** above high water mark, and where the transition from the Caerfai Group into the Solva Group is magnificently displayed.

The authors have logged a 17 m section across the contact between the Caerbwdy Sandstone and the lower pebbly sandstone member of the Lower Solva beds at this locality. The sequence is a transitional one with no major breaks in sedimentation. The section is sandstone dominated, with much rounded detritus, and with occasional granule grade conglomerates, thin mudstones and tuffaceous layers. Ash bands and horizons of scattered feldspar crystals are more prominent near the base of the section in the Caerbwdy Sandstone. Bioturbation phenomena *(Skolithos)* are also more abundant in this part of the measured section.

The sandstones grade in colour from purple to green across the contact but

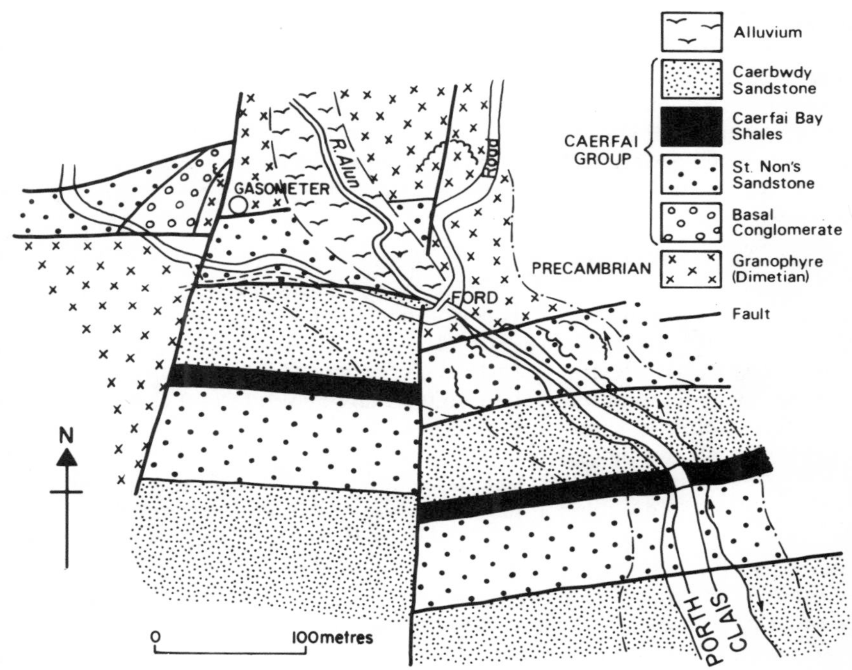

Fig. 7. Geological map of Porth Clais (locality 8) (after Green 1908).

maintain compositional similarities, commonly 60% quartz, 10% feldspar, and 20% rock fragments. The rock fragments include granite, gneiss, metaquartzite, phyllite, siltstone and basic volcanic debris. Other material present in thin section includes mica, zircon, hematite and chlorite. The sandstones are fine to medium grained, massive and graded, parallel or cross bedded. Scoured bases are present on some sandstone units, and sandstone upper surfaces may be planar or commonly exhibit large symmetrical, and occasionally asymmetrical, ripple marks. The association of sedimentary structures and biogenic phenomena all suggest shallow marine deposition and continuity in sedimentation across this contact. The Lower Solva beds have yielded a variety of fossils of *Paradoxides oelandicus* Zone age (Rushton 1974).

Return to the main cliff path and proceed to the cliff top at **Ogof Golchfa** (SM 7407 2367), a steep sided fault gully, where an excellent exposure of a dolerite intrusion into vertical Middle Solva beds crops out across the rock platform.

9. Return to St David's and follow the B4583 to **Whitesand Bay.** Boulders of igneous rock found in abundance on the beach at this locality have been derived from a glacial till which is exposed, above high water mark, in the **N corner of the bay** (SM 7323 2735). The Cambrian geology of Whitesand Bay is extremely enigmatic both from lithostratigraphical and tectonic aspects (compare maps of Cox *et al.* 1930; Owen *et al.* 1971; Stead & Williams 1971; and IGS Special Sheet SM 72). Fig. 8 is reproduced from Stead & Williams (1971) while new detailed mapping of the bay is being completed by the authors.

(A) At **Trwynhwrddyn** (SM 7318 2733) the Upper Cambrian (?Ffestiniog Stage) Lingula Flags crop out. The sequence youngs and dips steeply N but the thickness is uncertain as the rocks are involved in several, tight isoclinal folds. Crimes (1970) recognized shallow water sediments in the Upper Cambrian Ffestiniog Beds and Turner (1977) has described two main lithofacies developments in the Lingula Flags at Whitesand Bay to which he ascribed a shallow water intertidal or subtidal environment. One lithofacies is a rhythmite characterised by very thin to thin bedded alternations of fine grained sandstones with black shales or mudstones. The facies is rippled and forms wavy or lenticular bedding interpreted as the deposits of tidal mud flats (Turner 1977). The second lithofacies comprises medium to thick bedded quartzitic sandstones which are commonly cross bedded, flat bedded, or contain convolute lamination. Turner (1977) interprets this facies as a deposit of subtidal sand shoals or channels on the seaward side of the tidal flats which formed the rhythmites. *Lingulella davisii* (M^C^Coy) is common on some bedding planes, again supporting the interpretation of a nearshore shallow marine environment for the Lingula Flags. Near the top of the sequence a mud pellet conglomerate is present which may mark an unconformity. At **Pwlluog** (SM 7327 2737) the controversial contact between the black mudstones of the Arenig Series and Lingula Flags is exposed (Jones 1940; Owen *et al.* 1971).

(B) No exposures are visible in the bay near the stream, but the sand burrows are probably underlain by the very thin bedded, fine grained sandstones and mudstones of Menevian aspect exposed S of the car park. The latter are tightly folded, dipping steeply towards the N and S alternately (Fig. 8). These beds are terminated by a fault near the **steps leading to the lifebelt** (SM 7334 2688), where there is dolerite intrusion.

(C) Green, fine grained sandstones crop out S of the fault zone and towards Ogofgolchfa. Small doleritic intrusions occur locally in this sequence. The sandstones are massive or flat bedded with thin, laminated, dark mudstone bands. Occasional ripple lamination is evident, as are a variety of bioturbation phenomena (SM 7313 2643). These sandstones may be of Lower Cambrian age, comparable in their facies characteristics with similar rocks at Porth Selau but dissimilar to the St Non's Sandstone of

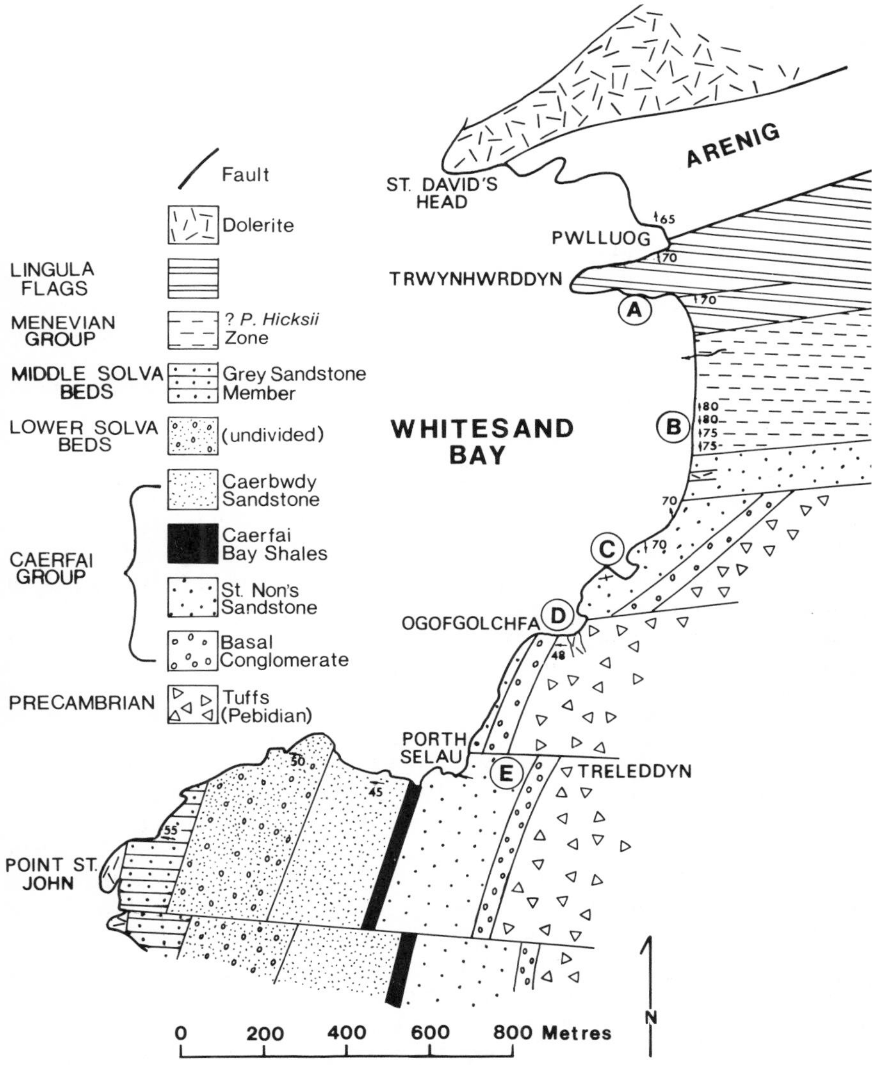

Fig. 8. Geological sketch map of Whitesand Bay (locality 9). Circled letters indicate outcrops referred to in the text.

Caerfai Bay. However, the IGS (Special Sheet SM 72) have ascribed a Middle Cambrian (Solva) age to these rocks. The most striking feature of this part of the section is the bedding/cleavage relationship which, when mapped in detail, defines the presence of a large, downward-facing syncline plunging at a moderate to high angle to the SW. Work is currently in progress on the structure and lithostratigraphy of this part of Whitesand Bay which will, hopefully, resolve some of the problems.

(D) At **Ogofgolchfa** (SM 7303 2643) the basal conglomerate of the Caerfai Group is well exposed, dipping at about 50° WNW off Pebidian tuffs and agglomerates. The contact is locally faulted but the unconformable junction between the tuffs and the conglomerate can be seen here. The conglomerate contains well rounded pebble and cobble grade clasts of similar composition to those at St Non's **(Locality 7).** The clasts are set in a red-purple sandstone matrix and locally exhibit imbrication. Bed thickness and clast size tend to diminish upwards through the formation as sandstones become dominant. The higher beds on the headland exhibit large scale cross bedding, scoured surfaces, ripple marks and *Skolithos* burrows (Crimes 1970) consistent with deposition in an intertidal environment.

A few metres E of the unconformity in Ogofgolchfa the Pebidian volcanics are intruded by a massive, dark-green dolerite which is again seen, in fault-bounded contact with the tuffs, high in the cliff in the E corner of the inlet.

In the N corner of the inlet (SM 7307 2646) a sliver of basal Cambrian conglomerate, up to 1 m thick, crops out between Pebidian tuffs and the overlying green sandstones. The latter show a concentration of oriented quartz veins.

(E) If tidal conditions are unsuitable for examining the beach section, all the rocks described above, including the basal conglomerate, can be seen along the **cliff path** leading from Whitesand Bay car park (SM 7338 2712) to Treleddyn. At **Treleddyn** (SM 7316 2594), where the footpath leads down to the bay at Porthselau, the basal conglomerate has been displaced by faulting (Fig. 8) and the fault junction can be delineated. Green sandstones, overlain by red shales and Caerbwdy Sandstone are visible from the path. If the path is followed onto the **headland** the conformable junction between the Caerfai and Lower Solva Groups may be examined in the cliff section (SM 7243 2613). The coarse, feldspathic, cross bedded sandstones of the Lower Solva beds are faulted and tightly folded. These rocks are similar to those described at St Non's Bay but, on average, they are a little less coarse at this locality. The thinner bedded grey sandstones and siltstones of the Middle Solva beds follow on the headland. They are intruded by a dolerite dyke which has been displaced by faulting near **Point St John** (SM 7194 2577).

10. Finally, take the A487 from St David's towards Fishguard. Turn left onto the B4331 near Mathry and proceed to the junction of this road with the main Fishguard-Haverfordwest road (A40) at Letterston. Follow the A40 S for about 3 km to Wolf's Castle in order to examine the Ford Beds exposed in

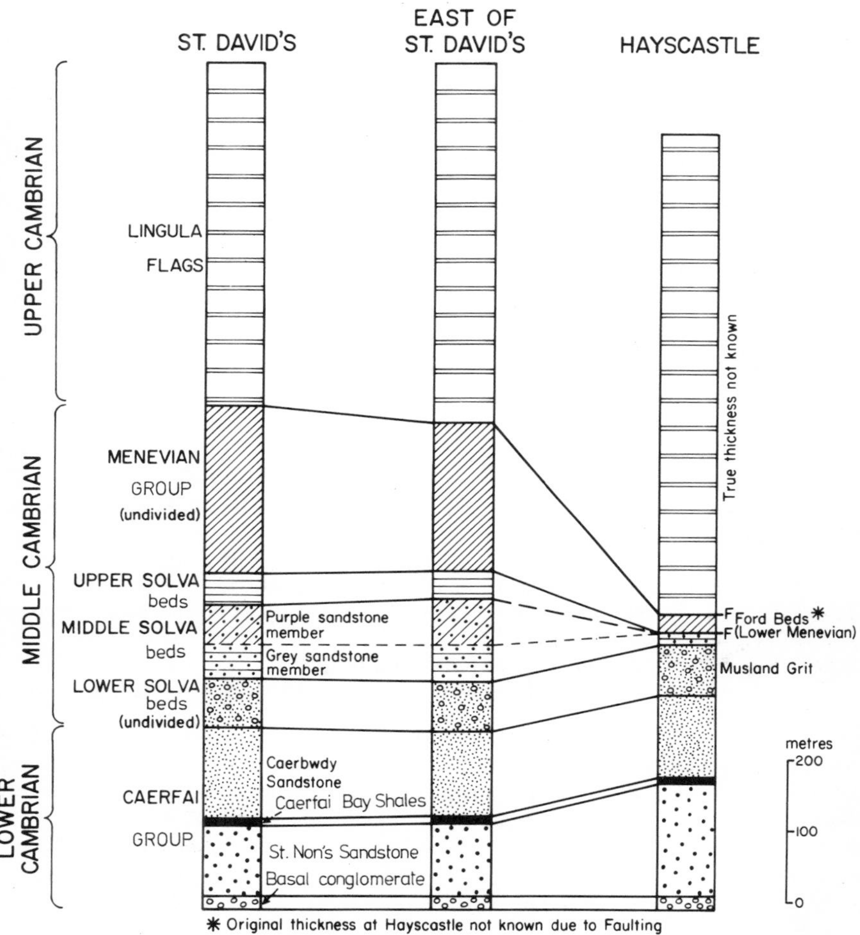

Fig. 9. Comparative stratigraphical columns showing the correlation of Cambrian rocks between St David's and Hayscastle.

the **railway cutting near Ford Halt** from SM 9585 2593 to SM 9555 2643. The Ford Beds comprise thinly bedded, fine grained sandstones and shales partly of Menevian age (Nicholas 1933). A fauna characteristic of the *Paradoxides hicksii* Zone has been obtained from the exposure behind the old railway shed at SM 9575 2618. The most northerly exposure of the Ford Beds is seen near the bridge NW of the first cutting, where they dip N at 65°. Walk N towards **Musland,** alongside the railway track to the cutting at SM 9534 2658, where the Musland Grit dips ENE at 30°. The Grit is a medium bedded, coarse, feldspathic sandstone with conglomerate beds. It is followed conformably by thin bedded grey sandstones and siltstones with dark mudstone bands. These beds differ from the Ford Beds, from which they are separated by major faulting near the dolerite dyke at SM 9528 2667. It was previously assumed that the Ford Beds rested conformably on the Musland Grit (Thomas & Jones 1912; Cox *et al.* 1930). Work by Stead (1969) suggested that the Musland Grit is probably of Lower Solva age and that the overlying grey sandstones represent the lower part of the Middle Solva since they so closely resemble those sequences in the St David's area.

Further N from Musland, near **Welsh Hook** (SM 9354 2786), the Caerfai Group is followed by coarse, green, feldspathic sandstones which are also of Lower Solva aspect. Thus although parts of the sequences are cut out by faulting, the Cambrian succession in the Hayscastle area is directly comparable with the succession in the classic localities of St David's (Fig. 9).

REFERENCES

COWIE, J. W., RUSHTON, A. W. A. & STUBBLEFIELD, C. J. 1972. A correlation of Cambrian rocks in the British Isles. *Spec. Rep. geol. Soc. Lond.* No. 2, 42pp.

COX, A. H., GREEN, J. F. N., JONES, O. T. & PRINGLE, J. 1930. The geology of the St. David's district, Pembrokeshire. *Proc. Geol. Ass.* **41,** 241-273.

CRIMES, T. P. 1970. A facies analysis of the Cambrian of Wales. *Palaeogeogr. Palaeoclimat. Palaeoecol.* **7,** 113-170.

DAVIES, H. G. & DOWNIE, C. 1964. Age of the Newgale Beds. *Nature, Lond.* **203,** 71,72.

GREEN, J. F. N. 1908. The geological structure of the St. David's area. *Q. Jl geol. Soc. Lond.* **64,** 363-383.

GREEN, J. F. N. 1911. The geology of the district around St. David's, Pembrokeshire. *Proc. Geol. Ass.* **22,** 121-141.

HARKNESS, R. & HICKS, H. 1871. On the ancient rocks of the St. David's promontory, South Wales, and their fossil contents. *Q. Jl geol. Soc. Lond.* **27,** 384-404.

HARRISON, C. 1968. Origin of the Newgale shingle embankment, St. Bride's Bay, Pembrokeshire. *Nature, Lond.* **217,** 155,156.

HICKS, H. 1877. On the pre-Cambrian (Dimetian and Pebidian) rocks of St. David's. *Q. Jl geol. Soc. Lond.* **33,** 229-241.

HICKS, H. 1881. The classification of the Eozoic and Lower Paleozoic rocks of the British Isles. *Pop. Sci. Rev.* n.s. **5,** 289.

HOLLAND, C. H. (ed.) 1974. *Lower Palaeozoic rocks of the world. Volume 2. Cambrian of the British Isles, Norden, and Spitzbergen.* 300 pp. Wiley, London.

JONES, O. T. 1940. Some Lower Palaeozoic contacts in Pembrokeshire. *Geol. Mag.* **77,** 405-409.

MORGAN, C. L. 1890. The Pebidian volcanic series of St. David's. *Q. Jl geol. Soc. Lond.* **46,** 241-269.

NICHOLAS, T. C. 1933. The age of the Ford Beds of Pembrokeshire. *Geol. Mag.* **70,** 383,384.

OWEN, T. R., BLOXAM, T. W., JONES, D. G., WALMSLEY, V. G. & WILLIAMS, B. P. J. 1971. Summer (1968) field meeting in Pembrokeshire, South Wales. *Proc. Geol. Ass.* **82,**

17-60.

PRICE, N. B. 1963. *The Geochemistry of the Menevian rocks of Wales.* Unpublished Ph.D. thesis, University of Wales, 233 pp.

RUSHTON, A. W. A. 1974. The Cambrian of Wales and England pp. 43-121. *In* HOLLAND, C. H. (ed.), *Lower Palaeozoic rocks of the world. Volume 2. Cambrian of the British Isles, Norden and Spitzbergen.* 300 pp. Wiley, London.

SALTER, J. W. 1863. On the discovery of *Paradoxides* in Britain. *Q. Jl geol. Soc. Lond.* **19,** 274-277.

STEAD, J. T. G. 1969. *The sedimentology and structure of the Newgale Beds and their correlation with some other Lower Palaeozoic rocks in Pembrokeshire.* Unpublished M.Sc. thesis, University of Wales, 207 pp.

STEAD, J. T. G. & WILLIAMS, B. P. J. 1971. The Cambrian rocks of north Pembrokeshire. pp. 180-198 *In* BASSETT, D. A. & BASSETT, M.G. (eds.), *Geological excursions in South Wales and the Forest of Dean.* 267 pp. Geol.Ass., South Wales Group, Cardiff.

THOMAS, H. H. & JONES, O. T. 1912. The Precambrian and Cambrian rocks of Brawdy, Hayscastle and Brimaston. *Q. Jl geol. Soc. Lond.* **68,** 374-401.

TURNER, P. 1977. Notes on the depositional environment of the *Lingula* Flags in Dyfed, South Wales. *Proc. Yorks Geol. Soc.* **41,** 199-202.

TURNER, P. 1979. Diagenetic origin of Cambrian marine red beds: Caerfai Bay Shales, Dyfed, Wales. *Sedim. Geol.* **24,** 269-281.

WILLIAMS, T. G. 1934. The Precambrian and Lower Palaeozoic rocks of the eastern end of the St. David's Precambrian area, Pembrokeshire. *Q. Jl geol. Soc. Lond.* **90,** 32-75.

3
ABEREIDDI BAY AND THE ADJACENT COAST

by C. P. HUGHES, C. J. JENKINS, *and* R. B. RICKARDS

Maps	*Topographical:*	1 : 50 000 Sheet 157 St David's and Haverfordwest
		1 : 25 000 Sheets SM72, SM73, SM82, SM83
	Geological:	1 : 25 000 Special Sheet SM72 & Parts of SM62, 73 St David's

THE Abereiddi [Abereiddy] area on the N side of the St David's peninsula (Fig. 1) is best known geologically for its inclusion of the stratotype area of the Llanvirn Series within the Ordovician System (Hicks 1875, 1881; Whittington & Williams 1964; Williams *et al.* 1972). However, there are also other interesting sections to be seen at Abereiddi Bay and along the adjacent coast. Indeed, one of the finest sections in the St David's peninsula, ranging from the Upper Cambrian to Upper Ordovician, is exposed along the coast from Abereiddi Bay to Pen Porth-egr, some 1.5 km to the N, illustrating the nature and variety of the region's sedimentary succession, the faunas, and the tectonics. The area is ideal for teaching purposes at a variety of levels from amateur to advanced undergraduate. The region lies on the N limb of the St David's Anticline, an upright fold of Caledonian age plunging to the W and with a NE to SW axial trend in common with other Caledonian folds. The local structure, only recently fully elucidated (Waltham 1971; Black *et al.* 1971; Rickards 1973; Jenkins 1979), consists of a syncline with an overturned N limb. The axis of this, the Llanrian Syncline, runs through Abereiddi Bay and thus the sequence to the N is regionally inverted (Fig. 1). It is the erosion of the soft Llandeilo-Caradoc shales in the core of the fold that has resulted in the formation of Abereiddi Bay with its characteristic black sand. Not only this bay, but the form of the entire coastline reflects very closely the nature of the rocks themselves. Most of the stratigraphical nomenclature used in previous publications on the region has been informal. The terminology adopted here is that of Jenkins (1979), and a comparison of this and previous stratigraphical nomenclature is shown in Fig. 2.

Access to all the exposures referred to in the itinerary is from the Pembrokeshire Coast Path, and all such exposures are marked on the maps as 1A to 4B. Parties travelling by private car or minibus may park in the small

[pp. 51-63 *In* BASSETT, M. G. (ed.). 1982. Geological excursions in Dyfed, south-west Wales.]

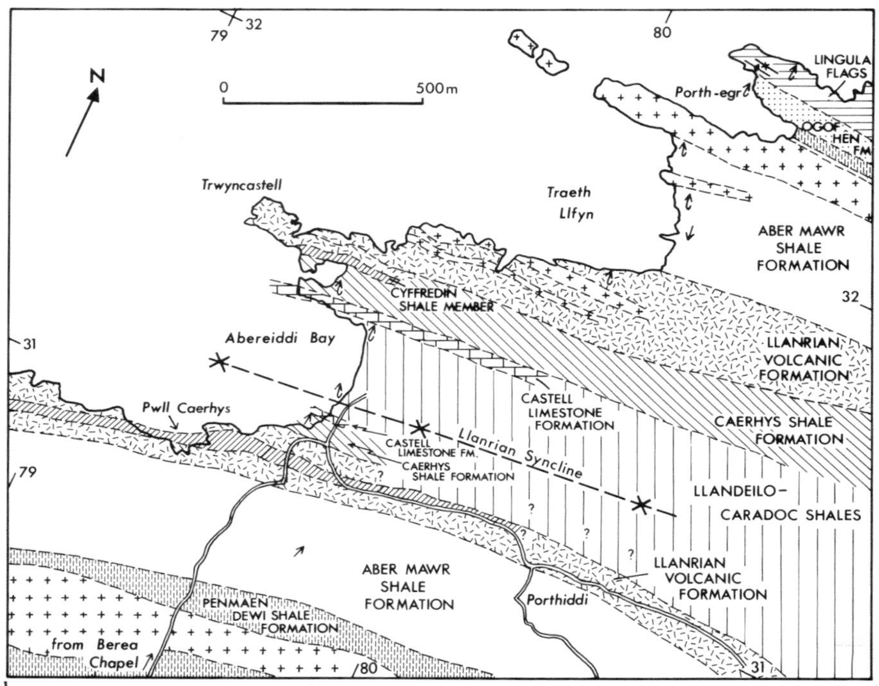

Fig. 1. Simplified geological map of the Abereiddi area.

car park at Abereiddi Bay; those with larger coaches should leave the coach at Berea Chapel (SM 795 299) and walk down the minor road past Caerhys Farm (SM 795 303) to Abereiddi Bay. Although historically the inland exposures in the vicinity of Llanvirn-y-frân Farm (SM 800 305) have played an important rôle, these are now somewhat overgrown and not readily accessible. Visitors are urged not to visit these but to confine their studies to the coastal exposures which are very much better. **Hammering and collecting are not permitted** from the Caerhys Shales occurring at the lane junction at the S side of Abereiddi Bay.

The itinerary is arranged starting in the N at Pen Porth-egr, working up the stratigraphical column, finishing at Abereiddi. However, depending on time and tide, arrangements can be modified to suit individual needs. Many of the exposures described are only accessible at and below half-tide, and it should be remembered that tidal ranges along this coast can be in excess of 8 metres.

Earlier graptolite zonation	Graptolite zones (Jenkins 1979)	Series (no designated stages)	Formations (Jenkins 1979)	Members (Jenkins 1979)	Horizon of guide localities	past lithostratigraphy mostly after Cox 1916 and/or Cox et al. 1930
gracilis	? gracilis ? gracilis		Llandeilo – Caradoc shales		4A 3F	Dicranograptus shale
gracilis	inclitus	Llandeilo	Castell Limestone		3E	Castell Limestone
teretiusculus	inclitus	Llandeilo	Caerhys Shale		3D 4B	(unnamed shales) Black et al. 1972 murchisoni shales
murchisoni	priscus	Llanvirn "upper"	Llanrian Volcanic	Abereiddi Tuff	3C	Llanrian Group (with murchisoni ash)
murchisoni	? coelatus	Llanvirn "upper"	Llanrian Volcanic	Cyffredin shale	3B	Llanrian Group (with murchisoni ash)
bifidus	confertus subzone	Llanvirn "lower"	Llanrian Volcanic	"Lower Rhyolitic Tuff"	3A 2D	Llanrian Group (with murchisoni ash)
bifidus	dentatus	Llanvirn "lower"	Aber Mawr Shale		2C 2B 2A	Bifidus shales
extensus	? hirundo–gibberulus ↓ ?	Arenig	? Penmaen Dewi Shale		1C	Tetragraptus shales
		Arenig	Ogof Hên		1B	Abercastle, Porth Gain Beds
		Merioneth (upper Cambrian)	Lingula Flags		1A	Lingula Flags

Fig. 2. Stratigraphical units occurring in the Abereiddi area.

ITINERARY

1. Porth-egr. From Abereiddi Bay car park follow the coast footpath N to Pen Porth-egr (SM 803 325). Here the Lingula Flags of the Upper Cambrian Merioneth Series crop out. These are the oldest beds exposed in the vicinity of Abereiddi (Figs. 1, 3), consisting essentially of cross-bedded quartzites with interbedded shales. **On the N headland** (locality **1A,** SM 8017 3249) minor folds are well exposed and show clear axial planar cleavage. The overlying Ordovician Ogof Hên Formation shows three facies. The basal conglomerate, some 30 cm thick, is exposed along the **N side of Pen Porth-egr** (**1B,** SM 8021 3248). It is overlain by a sandy silt and shale unit which is followed by grey-green, coarse sands containing phosphatic oncolites. At the top of the formation, as developed at Pen Porth-egr, the sandy silt and shale facies returns before the onset of deposition of the soft, black Penmaen Dewi Shale Formation, which form the centre of Porth-egr. The Ogof Hên Formation has yielded a rich shelly fauna on Ramsey Island (Bates 1968, 1969), but at Pen Porth-egr fossils are not common, although orthid brachiopods are present along the S shore of this bay.

The Penmaen Dewi Shale Formation (type section 8.5 km to the SW) in the **centre of Porth-egr** equates with what has been called '*Tetragraptus* Shales' in the past. The sandy shales of the Ogof Hên Formation here grade upwards into silty, grey-black shales (**1C,** SM 8038 3242). Within the lower part of the Penmaen Dewi shales exposed on the N side of Porth-egr, there are coarser beds consisting of reworked shale and Ogof Hên Formation

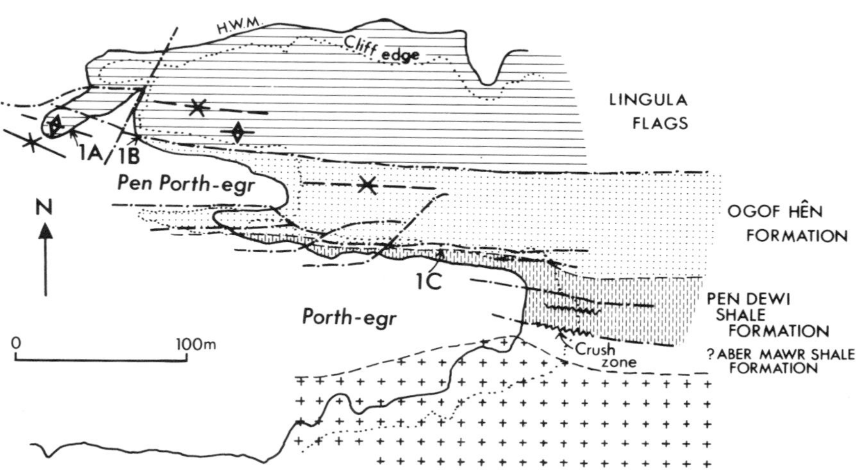

Fig. 3. Geological map of Pen Porth-egr and Porth-egr.

clastics. Also present are dark calcareous nodules and thin tuffs. The nodules are up to 60 cm in width, but are not known to yield fossils. A poorly preserved graptolite *(Didymograptus sparsus)* and inarticulate brachiopod fauna, indicating an Arenig age, is known from the NE corner of the bay (SM

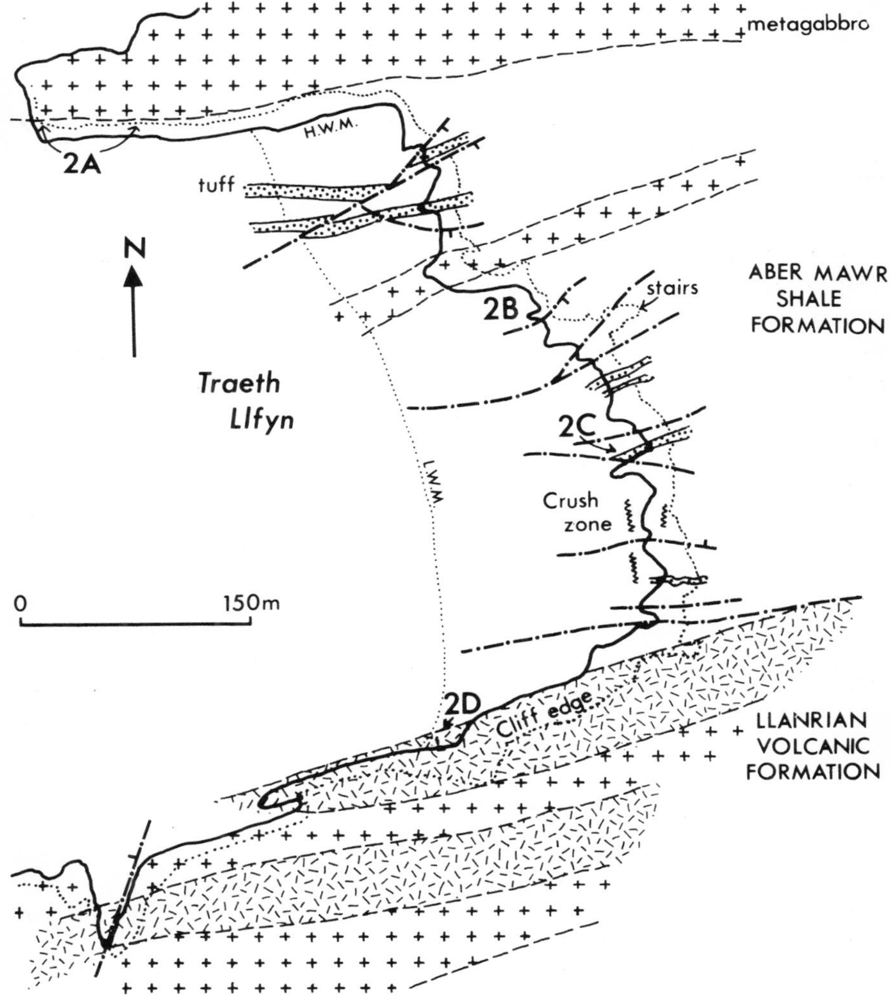

Fig. 4. Geological map of Traeth Llfyn.

8040 3240). A number of faults cut the N side of Porth-egr (Fig. 3), some of which show massive quartz veining.

Towards the **S of the bay** a major fault, trending slightly S of E cuts out the upper part of the Penmaen Dewi shales and throws shales that are interpreted on both lithological and structural grounds as belonging to the Aber Mawr Shale Formation of Llanvirn age against the Arenig shales. However, the Llanvirn age of these beds has yet to be proved palaeontologically. Fossils are unlikely to be easy to find as the shales have been baked by the gabbroic intrusion immediately to the S. This intrusion, which forms the **promontory delimiting the S side of Porth-egr,** is a metagabbro similar to others in the region (Roach 1969) and contains clino- and orthopyroxenes, sphene, albite, quartz, chlorite, calcite, and epidote.

2. **Traeth Llfyn.** The next bay to the S, Traeth Llfyn, lies essentially within the outcrop of the Aber Mawr shales (Fig. 4). At the **N end of the** bay the upper, undisturbed surface of the metagabbro is exposed with the overlying baked shales (**2A,** SM 7991 3222). The Aber Mawr shales are a monotonous, thick sequence, the appearance of which is strongly affected by the style and development of cleavage. A number of horizons have yielded fossils, particularly to the **N of the stairs** into the bay (**2B,** SM 802 321), including the graptolites *Didymograptus artus, Didymograptus nicholsoni, Glyptograptus dentatus,* and the trilobites ?*Bergamia* sp. and *Placoparia* cf. *barrandei.* The monotonous nature of the sequence is relieved by the occurrence of a number of tuff horizons. These occur in two types. The first as thin, singly occurring fine tuffs, generally between 10 and 20 cm thick, with a sharp base but an upper gradational boundary into black shales. These beds lack any evidence of erosional contacts or intraclasts and are presumed to be air-fall deposits. A number of examples occur in the **S part of the bay** (Fig. 4). The second type of occurrence takes the form of several tuff beds, each generally graded and with the whole fining upwards. Shale intraclasts and trilobites and hyolithids often mark the base of these units, and erosional surfaces may be seen within them. Interbeds of black shales occur especially towards the top of the units. These thicker tuff units are interpreted as being deposited by density currents. Examples of these are seen in the two northernmost tuffs in the bay, cropping out about 50 and 100 m from the **N corner of the bay.** To the S of the stairs a prominent tuff occurs (**2C,** SM 8025 3198), referred to by Cox (1916) as the 'cellular' ash. The unusual nodular appearance of this is due to the interaction of an oblique cleavage and the alteration of the tuff by carbonisation.

The **S end of the bay** is formed by the Llanrian Volcanic Formation, which varies greatly in thickness and facies. Here it is about 220 m thick, but to the S of Abereiddi Bay it is much thinner. The base of the Llanrian Volcanic

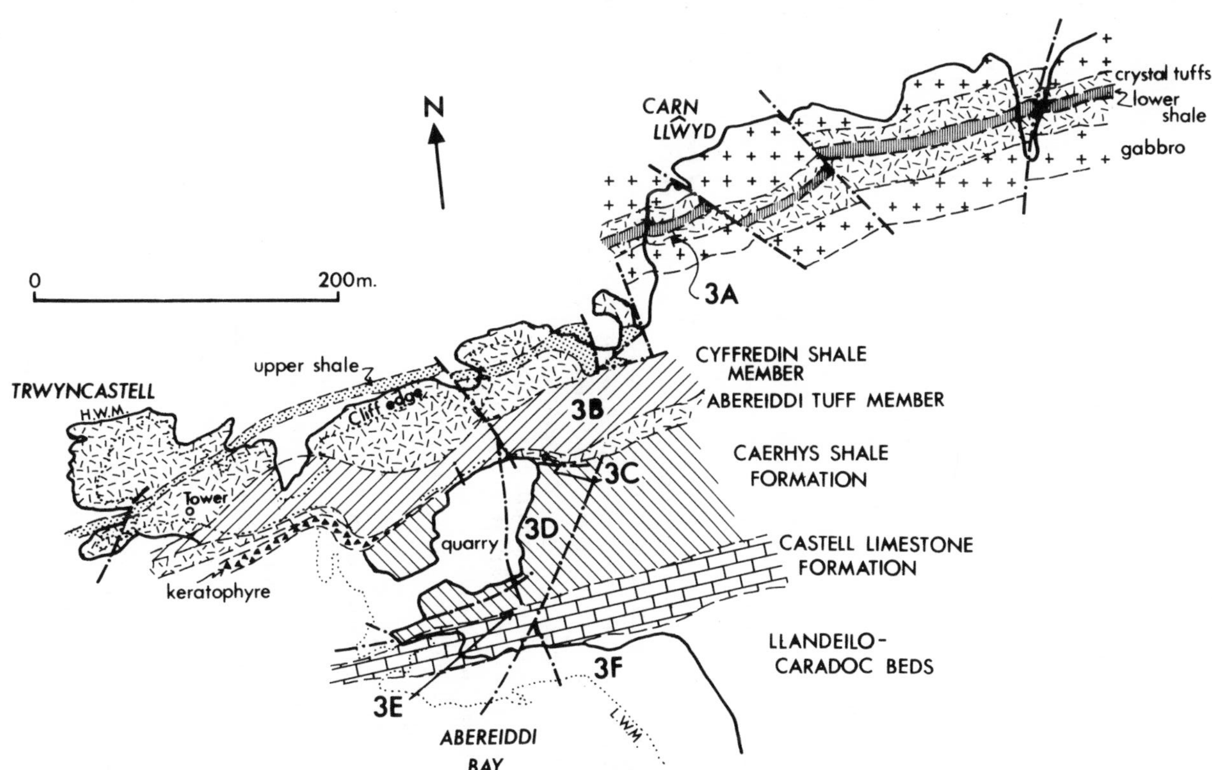

Fig. 5. Geological map of the N side of Abereiddi Bay and Carn Llŵyd.

Formation is well seen just above low water mark in the S of Traeth Llfyn (**2D,** SM 8012 3180) where crystal and vitric tuffs of the Lower Rhyolitic Tuffs lie abruptly on the Aber Mawr shales. This rhyolitic unit is about 170 m thick and thus forms the main part of the Llanrian Volcanic Formation as developed N of Abereiddi.

3. Abereiddi Bay, N side (Figs. 1, 5). Beds from the middle part of the Llanrian Volcanic Formation crop out between the two gabbros in the vicinity of **Carn Llŵyd (3A,** SM 7966 3164). Occurring here is a highly distinctive 2 m thick, massively bedded, black shale unit with matrix-supported angular volcanic debris, which is well seen **in the cliff path.** The upper beds of the Lower Rhyolitic unit underlie the **tower on Trwyncastell.** Here there is another shale horizon (noted by Black *et al.* 1971) with thin interbedded tuffs. None of the shales within the Lower Rhyolitic unit have yielded fossils.

In the cutting above the **NW corner of Porth Gain Quarry (3B,** SM 7955 3056), approached from the cliff path to the NW of the quarry, shales of the Cyffredin Shale Member of the Llanrian Volcanic Formation overlie the Lower Rhyolitic Tuffs. Contrary to the report by Black *et al.* (1971), the shale contains a fauna of *Didymograptus murchisoni, Diplograptus* sp. *Cryptograptus latus, Lasiograptus* sp. nov., and the trilobites *Geragnostus* and *Cnemidopyge* cf. *nuda,* now interpreted as upper Llanvirn in age. The shales are tuffaceous, especially near their base. At the W end of the **S wall of the cutting** occur fine grey vitric-lithic crystal tuffs with a vesicular keratophyre intrusive, which stratigraphically overlie the Cyffredin Shale Member. These tuffs are correlated with the Abereiddi Tuff Member to the S of the bay. The upper part of the Abereiddi Tuff Member may be inspected on the **raised bench** in the main Porth Gain Quarry and includes tuffs with accretionary lapilli, indicating that some of these tuffs were air-borne (**3C,** SM 7954 3150).

The overlying shales of the Caerhys Shale Formation yield a rich fauna which may be collected easily from the scree (**3D,** SM 7956 3148) and includes *Didymograptus murchisoni, Diplograptus priscus, Cryptograptus latus,* and *Lasiograptus* sp. nov. Hammering of the quarry face should be discouraged because of its unstable condition. The Caerhys Shales are tuffaceous near their base, becoming more silty towards the top, finally grading into siltstones before passing into the overlying Castell Limestone. Some 9 m above the base of the Caerhys Shales, a prominent graded tuff horizon occurs which is probably an air-fall deposit. Another such tuff occurs about 3 m below the base of the Castell Limestone. These two horizons may correlate with the two bentonitic bands on the S side of the bay (see below, locality 4).

The boundary between the upper Llanvirn *Didymograptus murchisoni* Zone and the overlying lower Llandeilo *Glyptograptus teretiusculus* Zone is within the Caerhys Shale Formation and is not marked by any significant lithological change. However, pendent didymograptids are absent from the upper part of the formation, which yields instead a fauna of gastropods, inarticulate brachiopods, bivalves, and trilobites including *Protolloydolithus* sp., *Geragnostus* sp., *Ogygiocarella* cf. *angustissima,* and *Platycalymene* cf. *tasgarensis simulata,* which suggest a lower Llandeilo age. Bedding-cleavage relationships can be well demonstrated in this quarry, but the relatively high angle mitigates against the collection of undistorted fossils.

Near the base of the Castell Limestone where the path narrows at the **entrance to the quarry** (**3E,** SM 7952 3142), a fauna can be obtained including trinucleid trilobites, *Dicellograptus* cf. *sextus, Pseudoclimacograptus riddellensis, Orthograptus* cf. *acutus,* and *Isograptus* sp. In the silty beds near the top of the Castell Limestone, cropping out at the top of the S-facing **low cliff** S of the old quarry buildings, trinucleid fragments are abundant. Though

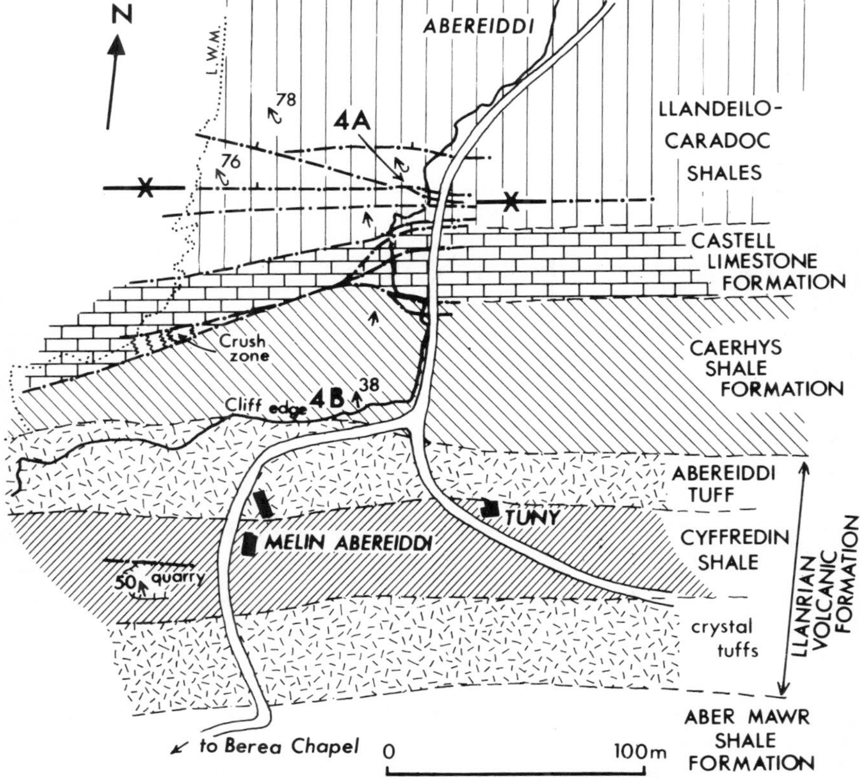

Fig. 6. Geological map of the S side of Abereiddi Bay and Melin Abereiddi.

generally poorly preserved, both *Trinucleus fimbriatus* and *Telaeomarrolithus* cf. *intermedius* have been recorded. **N.B. Locality 3E can be dangerous in conditions of blustery wind.**

Although the presence of *Dicellograptus* near the base of the Castell Limestone may indicate the presence of the *Nemagraptus gracilis* Zone, the first proof of the Zone is found in the shales immediately overlying the Castell Limestone exposed in the prominent cleft in the cliff outcrop just seaward of the wall in the **N end of the bay** (**3F**, SM 7963 3038). From these shales a fauna has been recovered including *Nemagraptus* sp., *Diplograptus foliaceous,* and *Trinucleus* cf. *fimbriatus.*

4. Abereiddi Bay, S side (Figs. 1, 6). The central part of Abereiddi Bay is occupied by shales of Llandeilo-Caradoc age. In the S corner of the bay a generally similar sequence to that of the N side is found, though here it is essentially the right way up. There are, however, some notable differences. The most northerly of the outcrops in the S part of the bay consist of black silty shales and shales with pyritous bands, which from the bedding-cleavage relationship are seen to be still inverted (Rickards 1973) (**4A,** SM 7970 3116). However, on passing southwards, but still within this shale unit, the bedding-cleavage relationship reverses on crossing the axis of the Llanrian Syncline. The whole of this sequence is cut by closely spaced faults (Fig. 6) commonly forming gullies in the wave cut platform and with well exposed fault breccias. Rare trinucleid trilobites and graptolites are present within these shales, which are now believed to correlate with the Llandeilo-Caradoc shales above the Castell Limestone on the N side of the bay. Previous interpretations of the S side of the bay have not recognised the Castell Limestone to be present. Recent work by one of us (CJJ) has shown that a 9 m thickness of calcareous and decalcified beds including 2 m of micritic limestone is present in the cliff just **S of the small cave** (SM 7970 3112), stratigraphically immediately beneath the Llandeilo-Caradoc shales. These beds yield a fauna of *Trinucleus, Telaeomarrolithus* and bryozoa, mostly fragmented, but specimens are difficult to collect and in somewhat dangerous circumstances. The 9 m of strata are taken as representing the Castell Limestone, though considerably thinned and of a slightly different facies from that present on the N side of the bay.

The underlying Caerhys Shale Formation yields a similar fauna to that found in Porth Gain Qarry, with a lower Llandeilo fauna near the top and an upper Llanvirn fauna nearer the base. Collecting from the cliff here is both difficult and dangerous and it is recommended that the fauna of this part of the Caerhys Shale is demonstrated from the scree material in Porth Gain Quarry. The outcrops of Caerhys Shale in the **southernmost corner of the bay** (**4B,** SM 7965 3104) are famous for their abundant large specimens of *Didymograptus murchisoni.* The large size of these specimens, compared to

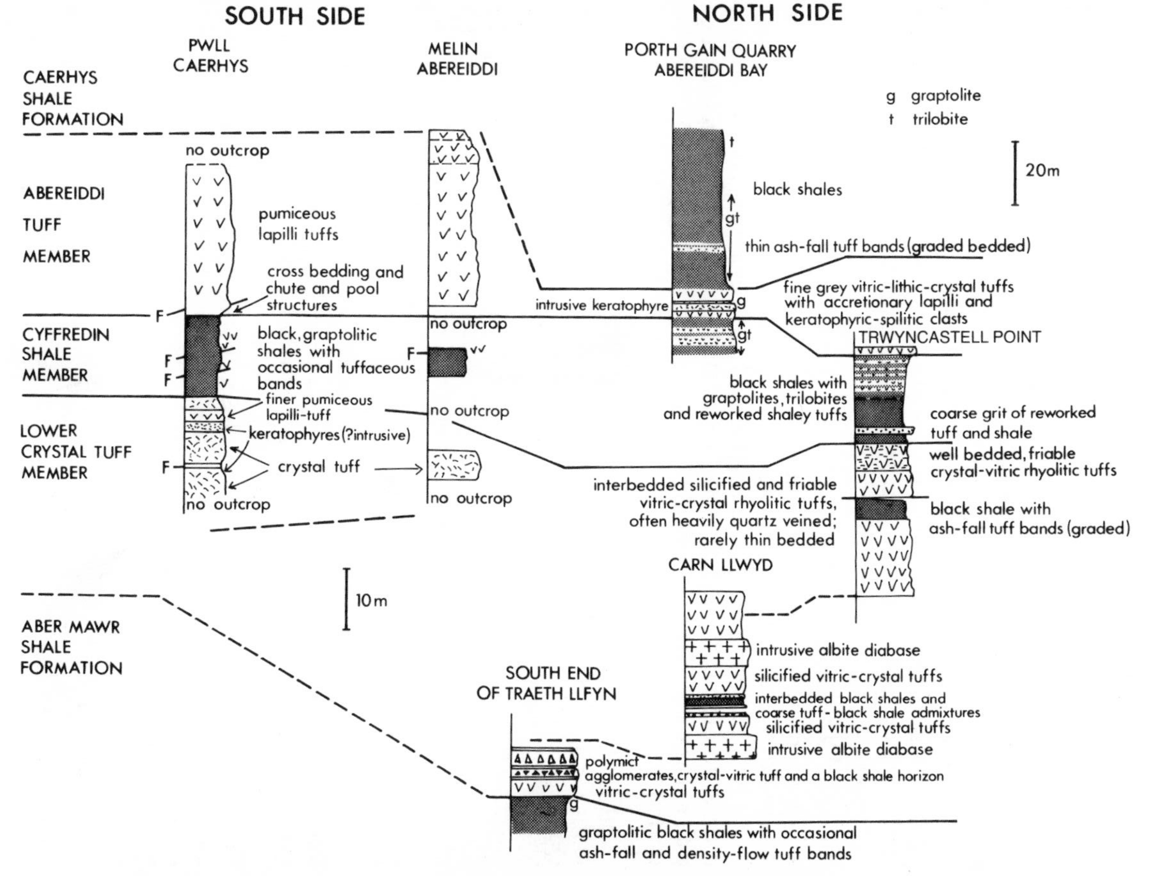

Fig. 7. Comparison of the Llanrian Volcanic Formation N and S of Abereiddi Bay.

those occurring in equivalent beds on the N side of the bay is attributed partly to tectonic deformation. The lowest 1-2 m of the Caerhys Shales, which can only be reached with ease at low water, contain a number of 1-2 cm thick redeposited tuff bands intercalated with grey-black shales. There are also more massive beds up to 20 cm thick, composed of a mixture of shale and lapilli. Two thin bentonite beds occur in this section at about 3 m above the base (i.e. in the *D. murchisoni* bearing portion; Fig. 6) and 2 m below the Castell Limestone. They are 3-4 cm thick and pale, grey-green creamy in colour. Pyritous nodules are common in the lowest 5 m and often contain pyritised specimens of *D. murchisoni*. These lower tuffaceous beds are succeeded by approximately 16 m of shales, giving way to a more silty upper interval of about 6 m. The last occurrence of *D. murchisoni* is a little below the top of the uniform shales.

The Llanrian Volcanic Formation exposed in the cliffs along the S side of Abereiddi Bay exhibit some marked differences from the sequence exposed to the N. The uppermost unit, the Abereiddi Tuff Member (Fig. 6), is here a coarse, pumiceous lapilli tuff some 28 m thick. It is well exposed **between high water mark and Melin Abereiddi** (Fig. 6), and is the '*Murchisoni* Ash' of Cox (1916). The lapilli, which occur throughout, are generally 1-2 mm in size.

Immediately beneath this unit is the Cyffredin Shale Member, seen earlier in the cutting NW of Porth Gain Quarry. It is well exposed in **Melin Abereiddi Quarry** and is also visible from the coast path at Pwll Caerhys (Fig. 1; SM 792 308) to the W. Tuffaceous beds occur within this member, and one, in Melin Abereiddi Quarry, has been wrongly interpreted in the past as forming the base of the overlying tuff unit (Bassett *et al.* 1974). The shales yield a graptolite-trilobite fauna similar to that from the cutting above Porth Gain Quarry which indicates a lowest upper Llanvirn age, and not an uppermost lower Llanvirn age as has been stated (Bassett *et al.* 1974).

The lowest unit of the Llanrian Volcanic Formation in the S consists of about 12 m of crystal tuff composed of phenocrysitc quartz and feldspar crystals set sparsely in a fine crystal and vitric matrix. This unit is well seen from the cliff path at Pwll Caerhys (SM 7930 3083). Therefore, although the three-fold division of the Llanrian Volcanic Formation is developed both N and S of Abereiddi Bay, the nature and thickness of the units vary considerably. It should also be noted that the correlation proposed here between the N and S outcrops (Fig. 7) differs from earlier interpretations (Black *et al.* 1971; Bassett *et al.* 1974).

The ground from just S of Melin Abereiddi to Berea Chapel is underlain mainly by Aber Mawr shales and Penmaen Dewi shales.

REFERENCES

BASSETT, D.A., INGHAM, J. K. & WRIGHT, A. D. (eds.). 1974. *Field excursion guide to type and classical sections in Britain.* The Palaeontological Association, Ordovician System symposium, Birmingham 1974, 66pp.

BATES, D. E. B. 1968. On *"Dendrocrinus" cambrensis* Hicks, the earliest known crinoid. *Palaeontology,* **11,** 406-409.

BATES, D. E. B. 1969. Some early Arenig brachiopods and trilobites from Wales. *Bull. Br. Mus. nat. Hist.* (Geol.) **18,** 1-28.

BLACK, W. W., BULMAN, O. M. B., HEY, R. W. & HUGHES, C. P. 1971. Ordovician stratigraphy of Abereiddy Bay, Pembrokeshire. *Geol. Mag.* **108,** 546-548.

COX, A. H. 1916. The geology of the district between Abereiddy and Abercastle (Pembrokeshire). *Q. Jl geol. Soc. Lond.* **71** [for 1915] 273-342.

COX, A. G., GREEN, J. F. N., JONES, O. T. & PRINGLE, J. 1930. The geology of the St David's district, Pembrokeshire. *Proc. Geol. Ass.* **41,** 241-273.

HICKS, H. 1875. On the succession of the ancient rocks in the vicinity of St David's, Pembrokeshire, with special reference to those of the Arenig and Llandeilo groups and their fossil contents. *Q. Jl geol. Soc. Lond.* **31,** 167-195.

HICKS, H. 1881. The classification of the Eozoic and Lower Palaeozoic rocks of the British Isles. *Pop. Sci. Rev.* n.s. **5,** 289-309.

JENKINS, C. J. 1979. *Stratigraphy and graptolite biostratigraphy of the Llanvirn Series' type area, St. David's, Dyfed, Wales.* Unpublished Ph. D. thesis, University of Cambridge.

RICKARDS, R. B. 1973. The structure at Abereiddy Bay, Pembrokeshire. *Geol. Mag.* **110.** 185-187.

ROACH, R. A. 1969. The composite nature of the St. David's Head and Carn Llidi intrusions of north Pembrokeshire. *In* WOOD, A. (ed.). *The Pre-Cambrian and Lower Palaeozoic rocks of Wales.* University of Wales Press, 409-433.

WALTHAM, A. C. 1971. A note on the structure and succession at Abereiddy Bay, Pembrokeshire. *Geol. Mag.* **108,** 49.

WHITTINGTON, H. B. & WILLIAMS, A. 1964. The Ordovician Period. *In* HARLAND, W. B., SMITH, A. G. & WILCOCK, B. (eds.). *The Phanerozoic Time Scale. Q. Jl geol. Soc. Lond.* **120S.** 241-254.

WILLIAMS, A. *et al.* 1972. A correlation of Ordovician rocks in the British Isles. *Geol. Soc. Lond. Spec. Report* **3.** 74pp.

4
ORDOVICIAN IGNEOUS ACTIVITY IN SOUTH-WEST DYFED

by R. E. BEVINS *and* R. A. ROACH

Maps	*Topographical:*	1 : 50 000 Sheet 157 Fishguard
		1 : 25 000 Sheets SM72, SM83, SM93
	Geological:	1 : 25 000 Special Sheet SM72 & Parts of SM62, 73 St David's

IN SOUTH-WEST Dyfed, between Ramsey Island in the west and the Prescelly [Preseli] Hills in the east, there are extensive outcrops of Ordovician lavas and volcaniclastic rocks, associated with a suite of igneous intrusions. These rocks have been described by various workers, the most important literature being Reed (1895), Elsden (1905, 1908), Cox (1915, 1930), Cox *et al.* (1930 *a, b*), Pringle (1930), Evans (1945), Thomas & Thomas (1956), and Roach (1969). More recently, a review of Ordovician igneous activity in this area has been presented by Bevins & Roach (1980), in which they recorded two important volcanic centres, one in the west, centred on Ramsey Island, and the other to the east, in the Fishguard area. Other volcaniclastic horizons, such as those at Abereiddy [Abereiddi] Bay, and at Abercastle (see Cox 1915) are accumulations of tuffaceous material, apparently derived from these or similar volcanic centres. In addition, Bevins (1979) and Bevins & Roach (1980) demonstrated that the majority of the intrusions of this region are contemporaneous high level equivalents of the volcanics.

The aim of the three itineraries presented here (Fig. 1) is to examine the variety of rock types produced during this igneous episode, to demonstrate their mutual relationships, and to speculate on their origins. Itineraries 1 and 2 demonstrate the various products of a subaqueous volcanic centre in the Fishguard area, while itinerary 3 describes the various rock types of the magmatically differentiated St. David's Head and Carnllidi intrusions. The three itineraries correspond approximately to three separate field days, although detailed study of any part of them might necessitate an extra day.

ITINERARY 1 — PWLLDERI TO OGOF MELYN

The starting point for this itinerary (Fig. 2) is a small car park above Pwllderi (SM 8936 3862). This car park and the approach road are suitable only for

[pp. 65-80 *In* BASSETT, M. G. (ed.). 1982. Geological excursions in Dyfed, south-west Wales.]

cars and minibuses, and coaches should be left at the large lay-by at Tref-Asser Cross (SM 8968 3765), about 1 km S of Pwllderi. Coaches should approach Tref-Asser from the A487 at SM 9037 3332 via St. Nicholas. The localities described are exposed along the coast between Pwllderi and Ogof Melyn, a short distance S of Strumble Head. Car parking facilities are also available at Strumble Head, but it should be noted that the road to Strumble Head is not suitable for coaches past Tresinwen Farm (SM 9015 4067).

An outline of the local stratigraphy for the areas described in itineraries 1 and 2 is given below, based on the terminology of Bevins & Roach (1980), with that of Thomas & Thomas (1956) included for comparison.

1. Pwllderi is eroded in soft mudstones of Arenig Tetragraptus Shales, which crop out in the **quarry** at the car park (SM 8936 3862). These sediments, which show a well developed slaty cleavage, have yielded occasional

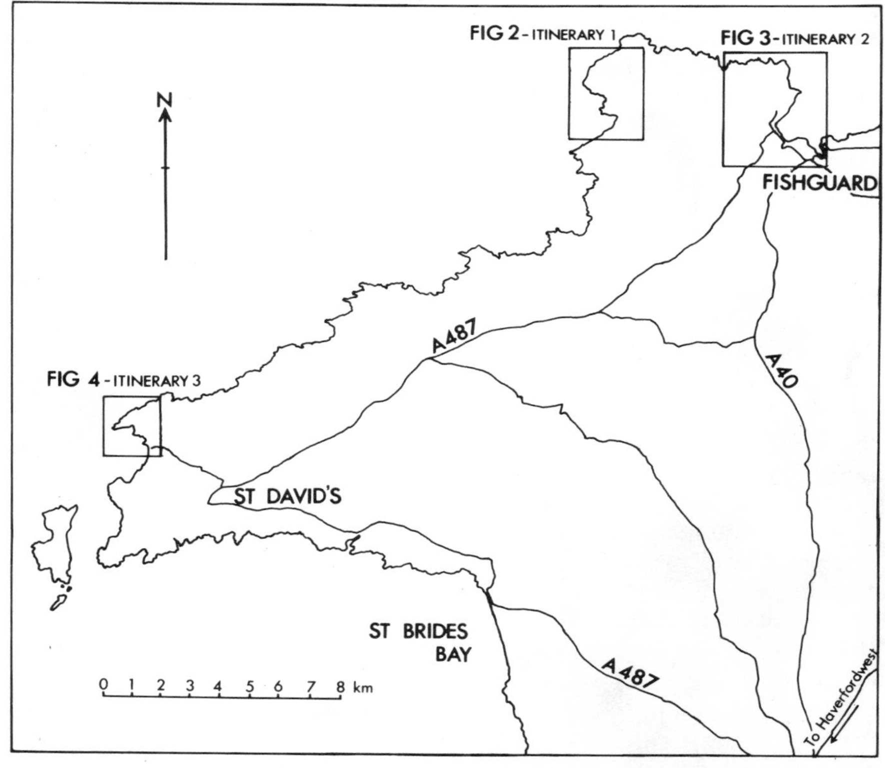

Fig. 1. Sketch map indicating the location of the areas described in the three itineraries.

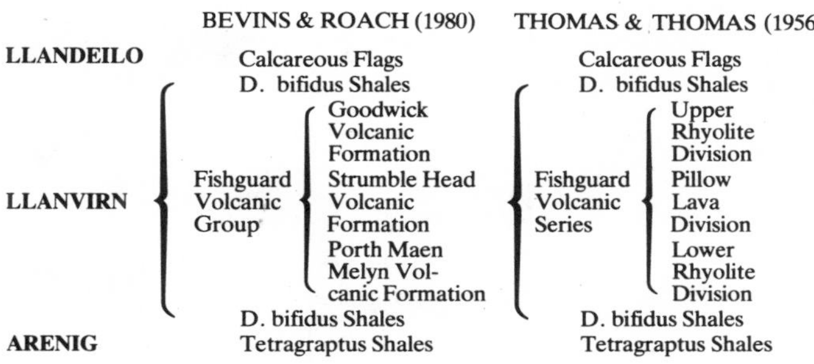

	BEVINS & ROACH (1980)		THOMAS & THOMAS (1956)	
LLANDEILO	Calcareous Flags		Calcareous Flags	
LLANVIRN	D. bifidus Shales		D. bifidus Shales	
	Fishguard Volcanic Group	Goodwick Volcanic Formation	Fishguard Volcanic Series	Upper Rhyolite Division
		Strumble Head Volcanic Formation		Pillow Lava Division
		Porth Maen Melyn Volcanic Formation		Lower Rhyolite Division
	D. bifidus Shales		D. bifidus Shales	
ARENIG	Tetragraptus Shales		Tetragraptus Shales	

extensiform graptolites (Cox 1930).

2. Dinas Mawr. Follow the road northwards on foot to the Youth Hostel, and then descend to Dinas Mawr (SM 8880 3867) by the coastal path. This headland is composed of an intrusion of fine grained, grey microtonalite which shows a crude columnar jointing. Thin sections show the rock to be composed predominantly of plagioclase feldspar with only minor mafics. It forms a sill-like body, and a sharp intrusive contact against steeply dipping dark, cleaved mudstones is exposed on the E side of Aber Twn (SM 8891 3869).

3. Following the path northwards, the **bay immediately N of Dinas Mawr** is eroded into weakly resistant, cleaved mudstones (possibly Tetragraptus Shales), while the succeeding headland is composed of dolerite, exposed in the vicinity of SM 8882 3880. Further cleaved mudstones occur in exposures adjacent to the path.

4. Pass on northwards to the major inlet of **Porth Maen-Melyn.** In the path which descends to the beach, at SM 8886 3929, strongly cleaved mudstones crop out. Where the path is enclosed within a cutting, well developed sub-horizontal kink bands are excellently exposed. Since no fossils have been found in these mudstones, it is not known whether they are of Arenig or Llanvirn age.

5. Return to the coastal path and follow it northwards up slope, passing a prominent crag of rhyolite. Immediately after the path crosses a low wall, examine exposures to the **W of the path** (SM 8882 3935). These are breccias belonging to the Porth Maen Melyn Volcanic Formation, composed predominantly of angular clasts of rhyolitic lava set within a crystal-rich matrix. Although rare, dolerite and mudstone clasts are also present. As all the important features of these rocks may be observed on weathered surfaces, hammering of these outcrops is not necessary. Upwards, the breccias pass rapidly into volcaniclastic sandstones and siltstones. These various units are considered to represent a debris flow deposit, derived from the unstable flanks of a nearby subaqueous rhyolitic dome.

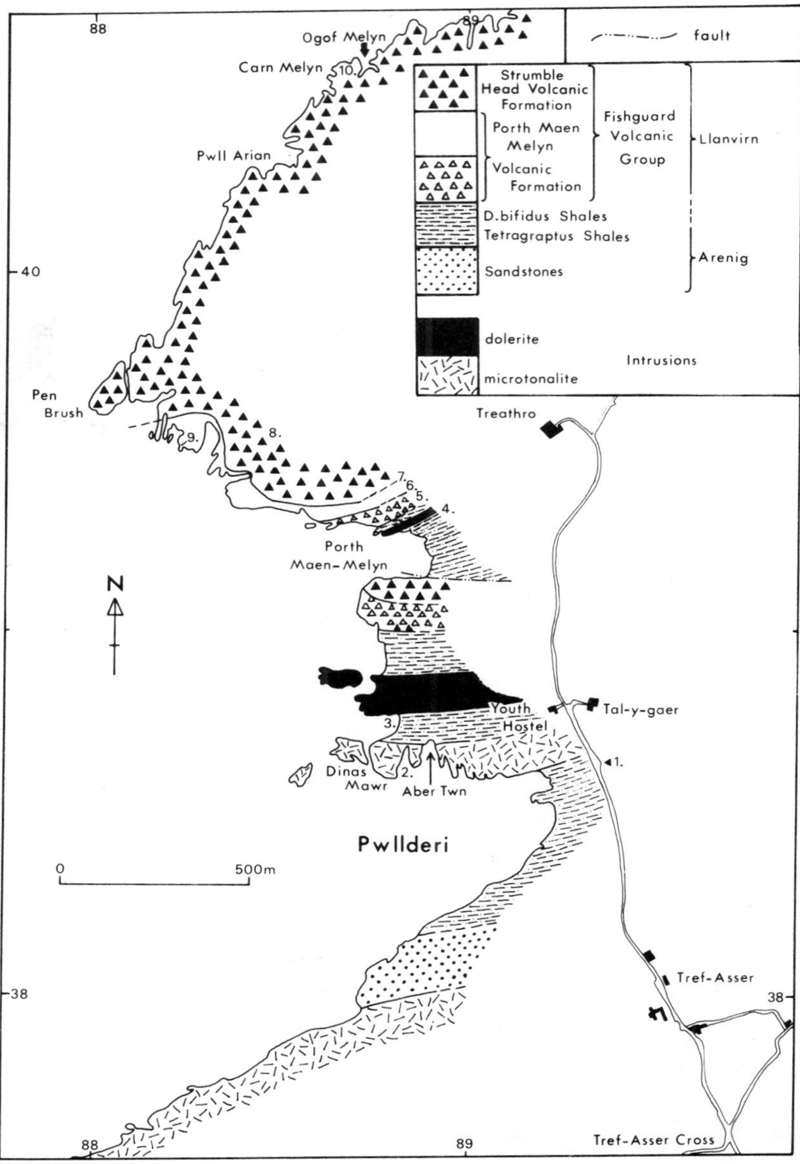

Fig. 2. Geological sketch map of the Pwllderi to Ogof Melyn area.

6. A short distance up slope, at SM 8876 3936, the volcaniclastic siltstones are overlain by grey to green, fine grained, siliceous lavas which crop out adjacent to the coastal path. These lavas are dacitic to rhyodacitic in composition (Bevins & Roach 1979), and show a well developed perlitic texture, as well as flow banding. The topmost part of the flow is autobrecciated, with angular lava blocks up to 15 cm in diameter contained in a lava matrix.

7. By the **bend in the wall** (SM 8872 3938) the lowermost unit of the Strumble Head Volcanic Formation is exposed. It is a thin hyaloclastite horizon, composed predominantly of altered basic glass fragments (now chlorite), but also contains blocks of dacitic lava, derived from the autobrecciated part of the underlying flow. This horizon is overlain by basic pillow lavas, which are best observed in **adjacent crags** reached by descending seawards some 10 m. Here, all the features characteristic of pillow lavas may be examined (e.g. glassy vesiculated margins, drape features, radial joint patterns). Epidote-quartz veins are also abundant. The lavas are fine grained and aphyric, but thin sections show that they are composed predominantly of albitised feldspar and clinopyroxene. In addition, epidote and pumpellyite are present, reflecting the effects of low grade Caledonian metamorphism (Bevins 1978).

8. Locality 8 (SM 8847 3947) is reached by leaving the coastal path and traversing north-westwards along the cliff top, walking over further exposures of pillowed lava. At this locality pillow breccias crop out, in which fragments of basic lava are contained within a partly silicified glass-rich matrix.

9. To reach locality 9, return to the coastal path, and then by the bend in the wall at SM 8841 3960 take the left hand track. Some 40 m to the W this track steeply descends the cliffs, and care is needed. Leave this track on reaching a prominent, grassy slope descending towards the sea; the exposures are on the well developed **wave cut platform** at SM 8825 3950. The outcrop is predominantly of dacitic lava of the Porth Maen Melyn Volcanic Formation, but at the western end of the exposure is a doleritic intrusion. The contact between the dolerite and the dacite is highly irregular and this relationship suggests that the dolerite and dacite were penecontemporaneous. Follow the track back up the cliff to join the coastal path at the bend in the wall (SM 8841 3960).

10. Continue along the coastal path, which now runs approximately NE. Further exposures of pillow lava occur in this section, particularly around Pwll Arian (SM 8850 4035), where pillow breccias, thinly bedded silicic tuffites, and mudstones also crop out. On the headland immediately W of **Ogof Melyn** (SM 8867 4056), a 15 m thick unit of pillow breccia is exposed in the sea cliffs. It lacks internal stratification, and contains whole pillows and broken pillow fragments, in a partly silicified matrix in which glass shards may be distinguished in thin section. Within the breccia there appears to be a slight coarsening upwards. In the overlying basic pillow lavas irregular tube-like bodies occur in the NE-facing crags. Such features have been observed in recent submarine flows, and have been taken as evidence that pillows do not form discrete sacs, but are more likely part of a complex budding flow system. Looking E across Ogof Melyn, a thin columnar jointed doleritic sheet intruding basic pillow lavas is exposed. This is one of a number of

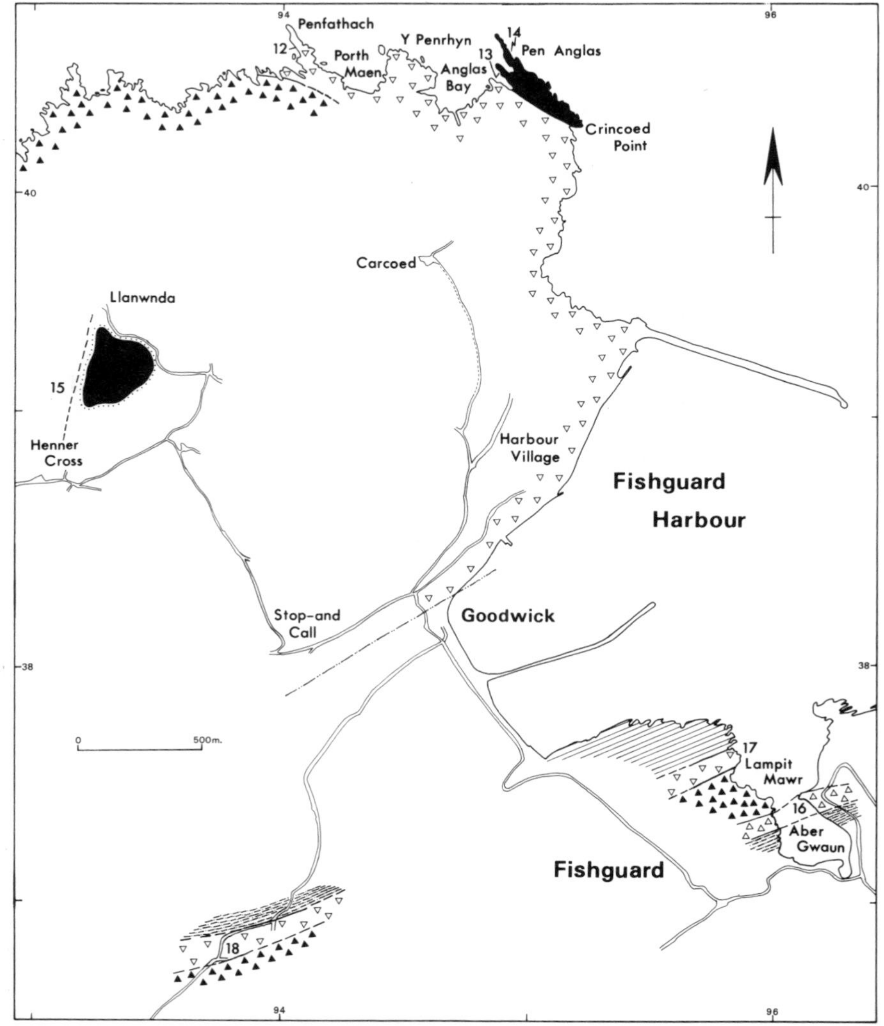

intrusions exposed in the coastal section northwards towards Strumble Head which are thought to have intruded into the lava pile at a high level during its development. Return S by the coastal path to the car park at Pwllderi, or continue N to the car park at Strumble Head (at SM 8950 4120). In the vicinity of Strumble Head further good exposures of pillow lavas occur.

ITINERARY 2 — GOODWICK AND FISHGUARD AREAS
This itinerary covers localities 11-18 (Fig. 3). Drive to Goodwick and take the steep road up New Hill, towards Harbour Village, and park in the car park at SM 9475 3890, which is reached by the small lane on the left side of the road, at the top of the hill. Leave the car park following the track which leads NW, away from the houses. Take the first track to the right and follow this almost to Carcoed, then take the path to the right towards Crincoed Point. At the end of this path bear NW, to the headland of Y Penrhyn (SM 945 405).

11. Y Penrhyn. Here, rhyolitic lavas and rhyolitic breccias belonging to the Goodwick Volcanic Formation crop out in the cliffs and in cliff top exposures. Good flow banding and flow folding are present on both a small and large scale. An example of a large scale flow fold can be examined by descending the cliffs on the S side of the **small inlet** at SM 9440 4052. Once again the important features of the acidic rocks can be examined on weathered surfaces and hammering is therefore not essential. The breccias,

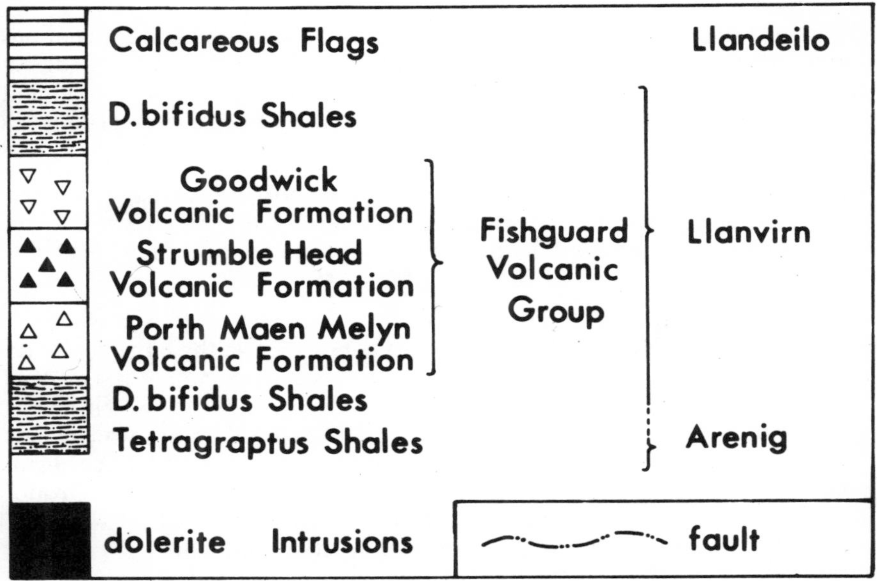

Fig. 3. (opposite, with key above). Geological sketch map of the Fishguard to Llanwnda area.

which are well exposed on the **E end of Y Penrhyn** (e.g. at SM 9456 4046) are composed entirely of rhyolitic clasts, in a rhyolitic matrix, and are considered to represent autobrecciated rhyolitic lava accumulations which developed on the flanks of short, thick rhyolitic lava flows or domes. These are known as 'crumble breccias'.

12. Similar rhyolites to those of Y Penrhyn are exposed on **Penfathach** (SM 9406 4053), the next headland to the W. Here columnar jointing is locally developed, in addition to a good perlitic texture, reflecting the fact that these lavas were originally glassy (i.e. obsidians). Phenocrysts are relatively scarce; the common white spots are chiefly recrystallization spherulites. The volcanic rocks of the Fishguard Volcanic Group are relatively competent when compared with the surrounding sedimentary sequences. As a result, during the Caledonian Orogeny strain appears to have been taken up along discrete zones within the volcanic rocks, resulting in inhomogeneous deformation. An example of this is exposed on Penfathach, where approximately E-W trending zones of sheared, grey rhyolite indicate areas of high strain.

13. Traverse eastwards, around Anglas Bay, walking over further exposures of lavas and volcaniclastic rocks belonging to the Goodwick Volcanic Formation, to the NW-trending **headland immediately W of Pen Anglas** (SM 9486 4046). This headland, like Pen Anglas, is largely dolerite. However, on the steep but accessible SW-facing cliffs is a thin silicic tuffite which contains lobes and isolated pillow-like bodies of dolerite. These relationships indicate that the sediments were wet and unconsolidated at the time of emplacement of the doleritic intrusion, and is further evidence of contemporaneous intrusive and extrusive activity.

14. Proceed to **Pen Anglas** (SM 9490 4053). The NE-facing cliffs below the pillar display excellent sections through columns of the prominent cooling joints within a doleritic intrusion. Return S by the coastal path, which leads back to Harbour Village and the car park.

15. Drive down the hill, and then take the steep hill out of Goodwick via Stop-and-Call, to **Henner Cross** (SM 9310 3875). Park in the large lay-by on the right of the road, adjacent to the radio masts approximately 100 m W of Henner Cross. Locality 15 is in the Llanwnda Gabbro, which forms Carnwnda (SM 9335 3918) and is reached by following the track which leads N from Henner Cross, past Henner School. The intrusion, which again appears to have been contemporaneous with the Fishguard Volcanic Group, shows a number of facies, resulting from varying proportions of (variably albitized) plagioclase feldspar, iron-titanium oxide, and clinopyroxene. In addition to these phases, a number of other minerals, including pumpellyite, prehnite, and epidote, are present. These developed during low grade prehnite-pumpellyite facies Caledonian metamorphism. Return to the vehicle by the same path, and drive to Fishguard. Then take the A487 eastwards out of Fishguard, to Lower Town (SM 9630 3720).

16-18. At localities 16 to 18 it is possible to examine deposits of sub-aqueous ash flows. Access is easiest to locality 16, which is reached by following the road along the **E side of Abergwaun** to the quay at SM 9611 3744. Coaches are best parked in Lower Town. In the crags above the quay are feldspar-rich tuffs containing scattered mudstone clasts. Thin sections reveal a matrix rich in glass shards and rarer pumice. The tuff is considered to represent the deposit of a submarine ash flow, which picked up mudstone clasts during flow over the sea-floor. Locality 17 is on the **W side of Abergwaun** but can only be reached at low tide by walking along the shore. Access to the beach is possible at SM 9595 3744, where a path from the town terminates in steps. In the section exposed at SM 9584 3760, to the N of Lampit Mawr, the thin basal zone of an ash flow is seen to be rich in lithic blocks, particularly of mudstone, whilst upwards these disappear but pumice blocks increase in both size and proportion. Petrographic examination shows the matrix to be shard- and pumice-rich. The third locality (18) is a **new roadside exposure** on the A487 to the **N of Manorwen,** at SM 9375 3682. Here ash flow tuffs crop out; these are laterally equivalent to those of locality 17, and sampling is relatively easy. The rock contains scattered mudstone clasts, in a shardic and pumiceous matrix, although the latter components cannot be distinguished with the naked eye.

The origin of the tuffs exposed at localities 17 and 18 is considered to be similar to that suggested for the tuff unit at locality 16, and the tuffs are somewhat similar in nature to subaqueous ash-flow tuffs described from the Tokiwa Formation, Japan, by Fiske & Matsuda (1964).

ITINERARY 3 — St DAVID'S HEAD AND CARNLLIDI INTRUSIONS

From St David's take the A487 and then the B4583 to Whitesand Bay. A short stop near the junction of these two roads en route for Whitesand Bay allows a panoramic view of the high level basic to intermediate intrusions which characterise the coast in this region. These intrusions, which occur as thick sheets, here within the Arenig Tetragraptus Shales, are aligned broadly NE-SW, parallel to the regional Caledonoid trend. Differential erosion has led to the development of a series of ridges, rising to peaks such as Carnllidi, Carnedd-lleithr, Carn Treliwyd, and Penbiri, which rise above the 50-70 m Pliocene/Pleistocene platform.

The aim of this itinerary is to examine the various types of gabbro within the St David's Head and Carnllidi intrusions. Roach (1969) suggested that these intrusions were two separate bodies, but they have now been re-interpreted as probably belonging to the same intrusion, emplaced into Tetragraptus Shales and subsequently folded about a NE-SW trending synclinal axis. Within the intrusions a number of zones can be distinguished, which correspond to layers approximately parallel to the margins. The sequence is slightly different, however, for the two intrusions as shown in the representative sections below:

ST. DAVID'S HEAD		CARNLLIDI	
	Top of intrusion		
SE	*Max. thickness*	*NW*	*Max. thickness*
Quartz gabbro and quartz dolerite	107 m	Quartz gabbro and quartz dolerite	70 m
Pegmatitic quartz gabbro	47 m	Quartz leucogabbro	49 m
Granophyric gabbro Fluxion quartz-magnetite gabbro	76 m	Pegmatitic quartz gabbro and thin underlying granophyric gabbro	20 m
Fluxion quartz gabbro	60 m	Fluxion quartz gabbro	43 m
Quartz leucogabbro	47 m	Quartz leucogabbro	85 m
		Fluxion olivine gabbro	214 m
Quartz gabbro and quartz dolerite	50 m	Quartz gabbro and quartz dolerite	92 m
NW		*SE*	
	Bottom of intrusion		

The marginal quartz gabbro is considered to represent undifferentiated magma, while the various other gabbros are thought to have been largely generated by *in situ* magmatic differentiation.

The traverse across the Carnllidi and St David's Head intrusions begins at the car park at the N end of Whitesand Bay (SM 7340 2720), which is overlooked by Carnllidi, the highest peak of the St David's Peninsula. Localities described in this itinerary are shown on Fig. 4.

1. Pwlluog. Walk N from the car park, along the beach, to the promontory of Trwynhwrddyn. Here, at SM 7318 2734 (locality **1a**) Cambrian Lingula Flags are overlain by sandy beds of early Arenig age, but the nature of the junction is problematical (Jones 1940; Evans 1948). Continue northwards, into the bay of Pwlluog, which is eroded into relatively weak, strongly cleaved Arenig sediments (Tetragraptus Shales) and volcaniclastic rocks. The sequence exposed in Pwlluog, is thought to young northwards. Some 15 m N of the prominent fault at the S end of the bay, at SM 7326 2739 (locality **1b**), dark mudstones occur, which have yielded fossils on certain bedding planes. R. M. Owens and R. A. Fortey (pers. comm.) have recorded common dendroid graptolites (*Callograptus*) and lingulid brachiopods, along with occasional agnostid, cyclopygid, and trinucleid trilobites and orthid brachiopods. Continue N across the bay, passing over monotonous dark cleaved mudstones with occasional thin intermediate intrusive sheets. Volcaniclastic sandstone beds up to 50 cm thick are prominent between localities **1b** and **1c**. They commonly show grading and contain scattered mudstone clasts. Just before the prominent stack in the centre of the bay, which is composed of a

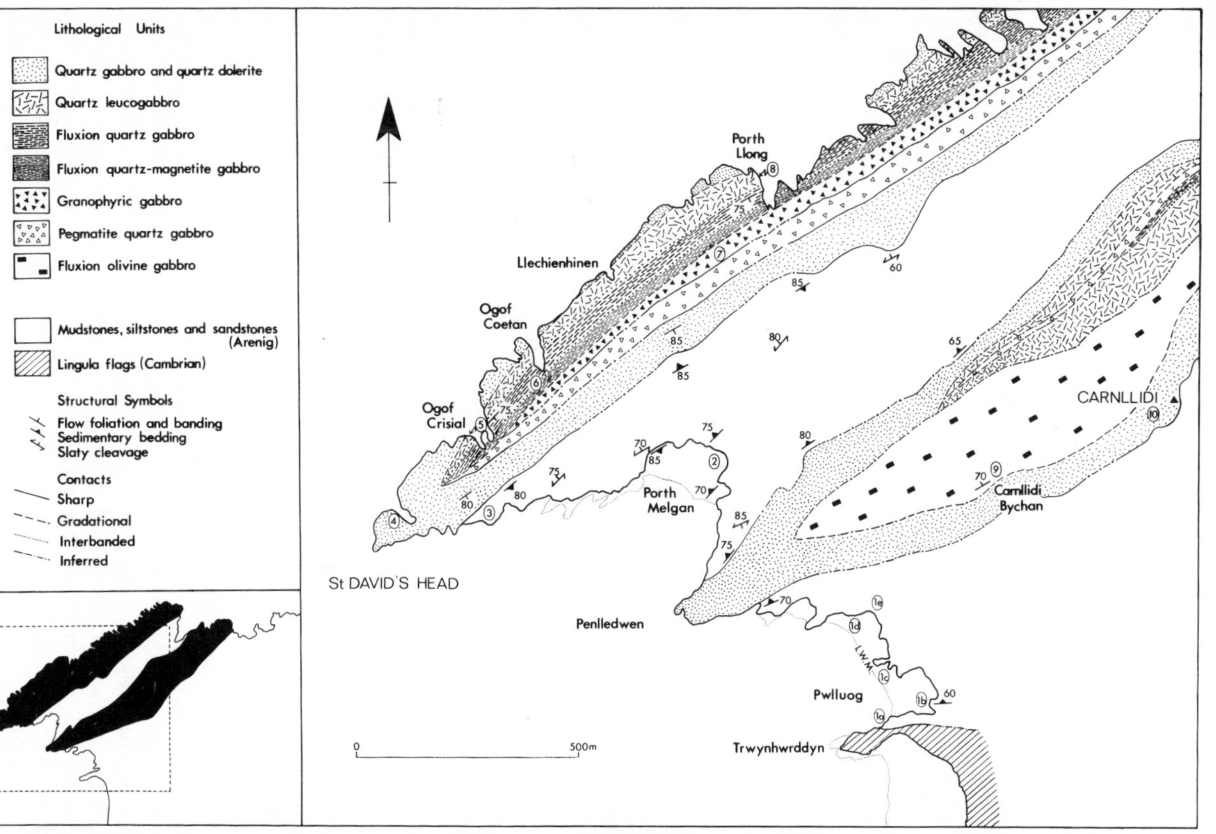

Fig. 4. Geological sketch map of the St David's Head — Carnllidi Intrusion (adapted from Roach 1969).

thick, slightly graded silicic tuff, a prominent bedding plane which faces the stack (at SM 7320 2749, locality **1c**) shows dendroid *(Callograptus)* and extensiform didymograptid graptolites. It is urged that this bedding plane is **not hammered** and the graptolites are left *in situ*. N of the stack, further thin intrusions of intermediate composition invade the sediments, as seen for example at SM 7318 2755, where the resistant nature of the intrusion results in it standing above the general level of the beach. At the N end of the bay at SM 7309 2758 (locality **1d**) sediments have yielded abundant specimens of the trinucleid trilobite *Bergamia gibbsii,* while other trilobites such as *Ampyx salteri, Microparia grandis* and *Shumardia sp.* also occur in smaller numbers (Owens and Fortey pers. comm.). Return S along the beach to Trwynhwrddyn and then take the coastal path to the N along the cliff top above Pwlluog. At SM 7315 2761 (locality **1e**), just below the coastal path on the seaward side, an exposure in a small bluff (along strike from the previous exposure) yields an abundant trilobite fauna. *B. gibbsii* is once again abundant, while *B.? sedgwicki, M. grandis, A. salteri,* and *Gog scutatrix* also occur. Occasional orthid brachioods have been found.

Continue N along the footpath and descend into Porthmelgan (SM 7280 2790) crossing en route the western end of the Carnllidi Intrusion.

2. Porthmelgan. This lies at the SW end of a broad valley excavated within cleaved mudstones with minor siltstones, of probable late Arenig age. These beds separate the St David's Head and Carnllidi intrusions. Careful inspection of the bedding/cleavage relationships in the cliffs near H.W.M. on the SE (SM 7281 2786) and NE (SM 7270 2794) sides of the bay suggests the presence of a syncline, the axial trace of which trends NE towards Gesail Fawr.

3. Cwter Sewyn. From Porth Melgan follow the footpath leading W towards St David's Head. Leave the path (at SM 7237 2791) just before crossing the prehistoric embankment and traverse obliquely downslope towards the southern margin of the St David's Head Intrusion, exposed above Cwter Sewyn (SM 7230 2785). Here the sediments were contact metamorphosed into hornfelses prior to the Caledonian deformation and show only a poorly developed fracture cleavage. These hornfelses possess a lithological lamination and exhibit occasional relict sedimentary structures, such as cross lamination and convolute lamination. Because of the subsequent low grade prehnite-pumpellyite facies Caledonian regional metamorphism, the original mineralogy of these hornfelses has suffered retrogressive alteration. However, thin section study suggests that the inner part of the contact aurole of this and other gabbroic and dioritic intrusions of the area were originally characterised by biotite and cordierite, or sometimes biotite and andalusite assemblages. The distinctive purple lenses in these hornfelses are rich in manganiferous garnets.

The marginal chilled facies of the intrusion is a plagioclase phenocrystic quartz dolerite with occasional quartz ocelli (see Fig. 4), and is broadly conformable with the lamination in the hornfelses. Within approximately 15 m of the contact the dolerite passes into a quartz gabbro.

4. St David's Head. Traverse carefully W to St David's Head where the quartz gabbro, which forms the outer envelope to the differentiated sheet, crops out on either side of the **deep inlet of Ogof Penmaen** (SM 7215 2783). The quartz gabbro, as with the other varieties of gabbro within the St David's Head and Carnllidi intrusions, contains both orthopyroxene and clinopyroxene, the former generally altered (but with a bright sub-metallic lustre in hand specimen). Full details of the petrography of this and other varieties of gabbro within these bodies have been reported by Roach (1969). A view NE across Ogof Penmaen from the W end of St David's Head (SM 7212 2780) towards the large rock face above the inlet reveals numerous thin (up to 5 cm across) mafic-felsic segregation bands lying approximately parallel to the strike of the intrusion. Some of these bands have been traced for a distance of over 100m along their strike and over 30m down dip. Bifurcation of the banding may occur and locally they pass into small areas of pegmatitic gabbro. Often the felsic part dominates the mafic (Roach 1969, fig. 95).

5. Ogof Crisial. Carefully traverse N along the wide rock ledge, several metres above H.W.M., along the E side of Ogof Penmaen and head E, gradually gaining height until Ogof Crisial is reached (SM 7232 2801). Descend the S side of this inlet to a point about half way down the cliffs. Here the quartz gabbro marking the N side of the intrusion grades southwards into the quartz leucogabbro (Fig. 4) and this in turn is interbanded with the fluxion quartz gabbro. The irregular interbanding of these two varieties of gabbro is clearly visible on the N side of the inlet (Fig. 5B). This boundary dips steeply S and strikes parallel to the length of the intrusion. The fluxion fabric is defined in particular by the preferred planar orientation of tablet shaped plagioclase crystals.

6. Ogof Coetan. Proceed NE to the SE side of Ogof Coetan (SM 7249 2815) where a zone of dark rusty-brown weathering fluxion quartz-magnetite gabbro (generally with more than 12% modal Ti-Fe ore) occurs S of the fluxion quartz gabbro. The 2 m wide contact zone between these two varieties of fluxion gabbro shows considerable interbanding. As at Ogof Crisial the banding dips steeply S and strikes parallel to the intrusion.

7. Proceed NE, keeping to the high ground within either fluxion quartz gabbro or fluxion quartz-magnetite gabbro. Occasional examples of aplite veins and quartz-rich pods and veins (containing calc-silicate minerals such as epidote and prehnite) may be observed. Join a footpath near the **head of Llechcenhinen,** where further outcrops of the fluxion quartz-magnetite gabbro can be examined, and proceed to the **high crags** (locality **7,** SM 7278 2830) to the SSE of the site of the old coastguard tower.

At this locality the fluxion quartz-magnetite gabbro grades to the SE into granophyric gabbro (the stilpnomelane-quartz gabbro of Roach 1969). Concurrent with this compositional change there is a gradual loss of the fluxion fabric. The granophyric gabbro in its most perfect development has a purplish-brown colour due in part to the presence of stilpnomelane (forming up to 13% of the mode), which is one of the products of the prehnite-pumpellyite facies regional metamorphism.

Further to the SE the granophyric gabbro grades over a distance of a few metres into a coarse or very coarse pegmatitic quartz gabbro, which contains prismatic pyroxene crystals up to 12 cm long. A distinctive feature of this rock type is the segregation of the mafic and felsic minerals to produce irregular patches of coarse melagabbro and leucogabbro. Occasionally the segregated patches coalesce to form poorly defined light and dark bands

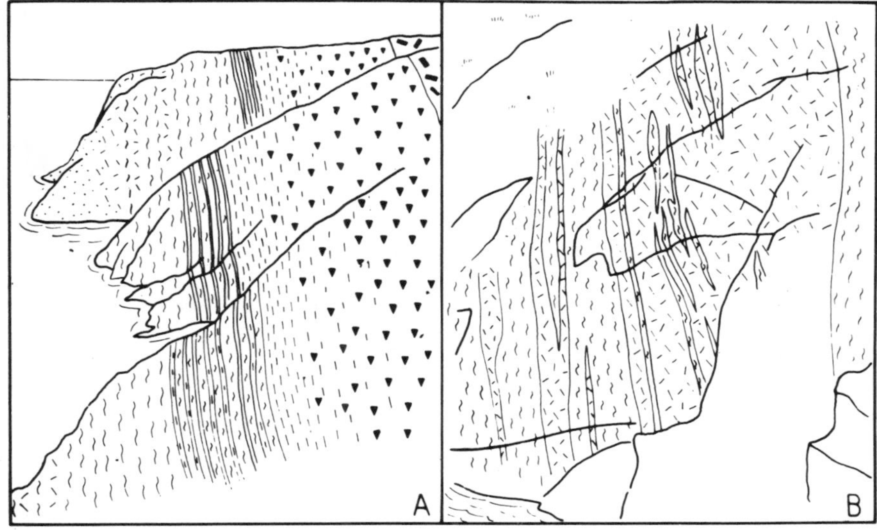

Fig. 5. Banding within the St David's Head Intrusion. (A) Interbanding of fluxion quartz gabbro (curved dashes) and fluxion quartz-magnetite gabbro (dashes), as seen looking NE from the W side of Porth Llong. Other zones depicted are those of pegmatite quartz gabbro (solid blocks), granophyric gabbro (solid triangles), quartz leucogabbro (randomly orientated dashes), and quartz gabbro (dots). Height of cliffs approximately 50 m. The cliffs in the background are approximately 400 m. from the observer. (B) Less regular interbanding of fluxion quartz gabbro and quartz leucogabbro (randomly orientated dashes) as seen in vertical cliff face approximately 15 m high on the E side of Ogof Crisial (from Roach 1969).

which trend parallel to the length of the intrusion. The pegmatitic fabric grades over less than a metre into the quartz gabbro, forming the SE side of the intrusion.

8. Porth Llong. Traverse NE towards the cliff top above the W side of Porth Llong (SM 7292 2846), where there is a good view of the continuation of the St David's Head Intrusion for a distance of over 1.5 km (Fig. 5A). If conditions are favourable, note in particular the apparent regular alternation of bands of dark weathering fluxion quartz-magnetite gabbro and the lighter weathering fluxion quartz gabbro.

9. Carnllidi Bychan. Proceed SE and rejoin the path which leads from the old coastguard station towards Porthmelgan. Leave the main path at SM 7313 2815 to follow a subsidiary path which leads uphill to the S, around the W side of Carn-hen (SM 7320 2796), which lies within the envelope of quartz gabbro on the northern margin of the Carnllidi Intrusion.

Leave the path at SM 7338 2786 before reaching the top of the rise and traverse in an easterly direction towards the **N slopes of Carnllidi Bychan.** The outcrops in this area (SM 7360 2795) are within slightly plagioclase-phenocrystic fluxion olivine gabbro. The fluxion fabric is not as strongly developed as in the fluxion quartz gabbro of the St David's Head Intrusion at locality 5. In contrast to the other varieties of gabbro examined, this rock contains little or no quartz, has a higher pyroxene content and contains up to 5% modal olivine (usually altered to serpentine). In addition to the fluxion olivine gabbro the N slopes of Carnllidi Bychan and Carnllidi also reveal thin bands and lenses of (a) more mafic lenses, (b) medium grained leucocratic fluxion gabbro, and (c) coarse grained leucogabbro.

10. Carnllidi. Weather permitting, traverse up the ridge leading to the summit of Carnllidi (SM 7380 2800). On a clear day there are excellent views E along the coast, with Strumble Head and the Prescelly Hills in the distance. In the foreground can be seen the various outcrops belonging to the Penrhyn Halen and Carnedd-lleithr intrusions, composed of rocks transitional in character between quartz gabbro and diorite. In the middle distance lies the prominent mass of Penbiri, composed of two-pyroxene-hornblende-quartz microdiorite. In the opposite direction (W) there are good views over the St David's Peninsula and across Ramsey Sound to Ramsey Island. Immediately to the N the whole length of the St David's Head Intrusion may be seen, while Carnllidi itself is composed of quartz-gabbro of the southern margin of the intrusion. If the weather is poor and visibility is limited, however, then the S side of Carnllidi Bychan (SM 7355 2782) is a suitable alternative locality for examining the southern marginal quartz gabbro, while the outcrops just E of the path at SM 7343 2785 are suitable for the examination of the fluxion olivine gabbro.

Return to the path and follow it SE to a lane which passes through Porth Mawr Farm (SM 7370 2753) descending downhill to the main road leading back to the car park.

REFERENCES

BEVINS, R. E. 1978. Pumpellyite-bearing basic igneous rocks from the Lower Ordovician of North Pembrokeshire. *Mineralog. Mag.* **42,** 81-83.

BEVINS, R. E. 1979. *The geology of the Strumble Head - Fishguard region, Dyfed, Wales.* Unpublished Ph.D. Thesis, University of Keele, 256 pp.

BEVINS, R. E. & ROACH, R. A. 1979. Pillow lava and isolated-pillow breccia of rhyodacitic composition from the Fishguard Volcanic Group, Lower Ordovician, S. W. Wales, United Kingdom. *J. Geol.* **87,** 193-201.

BEVINS, R. E. & ROACH, R. A. 1980. Early Ordovician volcanism in Dyfed, SW Wales. *In* HARRIS, A. L., HOLLAND, C. H. & LEAKE, B. E. (eds.), The Caledonides of the British Isles — reviewed. *Spec. Publs. geol. Soc. Lond.* **8,** 603-609.

COX, A. H. 1915. The geology of the district between Abereiddy and Abercastle. *Q. Jl geol. Soc. Lond.* **71,** 273-340.

COX, A. H. 1930. Preliminary note on the geological structure of Pen Caer and Strumble Head, Pembrokeshire. *Proc. Geol. Ass.* **41,** 274-289.

COX, A. H., GREEN, J. F. N., JONES, O. T. & PRINGLE, J. 1930*a*. The geology of the St. David's district, Pembrokeshire. *Proc. Geol. Ass.* **41,** 241-273.

COX, A. H., GREEN, J. F. N., JONES, O. T. & PRINGLE, J. 1930*b*. The St. David's district. Report of the summer field meeting, 1930. *Proc. Geol. Ass.* **41,** 412-438.

ELSDEN, J. V. 1905. On the igneous rocks occurring between St. David's Head and Strumble Head (Pembrokeshire). *Q. Jl geol. Soc. Lond.* **61,** 579-607.

ELSDEN, J. V. 1908. The St. David's Head 'Rock Series', Pembrokeshire. *Q. Jl geol. Soc. Lond.* **64,** 273-296.

EVANS, W. D. 1945. The geology of the Prescelly Hills, north Pembrokeshire. *Q. Jl geol. Soc. Lond.* **101,** 89-107.

EVANS, W. D. 1948. The Cambrian-Ordovician junction, Whitesand Bay, Pembrokeshire. *Geol. Mag.* **85,** 110-113.

FISKE, R. S. & MATSUDA, J. 1964. Submarine equivalent of ash flows in the Tokiwa Formation, Japan. *Am. J. Sci.* **262,** 76-106.

JONES, O. T. 1940. Some Lower Palaeozoic contacts in Pembrokeshire. *Geol. Mag.* **77,** 405-409.

PRINGLE, J. 1930. The geology of Ramsey Island (Pembrokeshire). *Proc. Geol. Ass.* **41,** 1-31.

REED, F. R. C. 1895. The geology of the country around Fishguard, Pembrokeshire. *Q. Jl geol. Soc. Lond.* **51,** 149-195.

ROACH, R. A. 1969. The composite nature of the St. David's Head and Carn Llidi intrusions of North Pembrokeshire. pp. 409-433 *In* WOOD, A. (ed.), *The Pre-Cambrian and Lower Palaeozoic rocks of Wales.* x + 462 pp. Univ. Wales Press, Cardiff.

THOMAS, G. E. & THOMAS, T. M. 1956. The volcanic rocks of the area between Fishguard and Strumble Head, Pembrokeshire. *Q. Jl geol. Soc. Lond.* **112,** 291-314.

5
THE ABERYSTWYTH GRITS

by DENIS BATES

Maps *Topographical:* 1 : 50 000 Sheets 135 Aberystwyth, 145 Cardigan, 146 Lampeter and Llandovery
1 : 25 000 Sheets SN35, SN36, SN46, SN58, SN68

THE Aberystwyth Grits (Silurian) are justly regarded as one of the best examples of a turbidite sequence in Great Britain, following their description and interpretation by Wood & Smith (1959). They are magnificently exposed in a series of coastal cliffs along Cardigan Bay, extending for some 40 km from New Quay in the S to Harp Rock, S of Borth (Fig 1). Both sedimentary and tectonic structures can be easily studied throughout the coastal sections.

The Formation, with an estimated thickness of 1200 - 1500 m, crops out in a crescentic belt (Fig. 1), with older rocks to the N, E and S. Graptolites recovered mainly from fine grained shales between the 'grits' indicate that the Upper Llandovery *Monograptus turriculatus* and *M. crispus* zones are present, but correlation in more detail within the outcrop area is not possible, since distinctive marker beds can only be traced for distances of up to a few hundred metres. Structural considerations would suggest that the beds exposed at New Quay and S of Borth are nearer to the base of the Formation than those in the central part of the outcrop, at Aberarth.

Whatever the uncertainties in correlation along the strike, the coastal section from S to N can be treated as a demonstration of the transition from proximal to distal turbidite characters. The beds at New Quay are typical proximal turbidites, coarse grained and full of intraclasts, often composite, and with irregular and sometimes appreciably downcutting bases. North of Aberarth these beds are replaced by finer units with more even bases, while in the Borth region the majority of the turbidites are very thin and fine grained. Current indicators, principally flute and groove casts, are very consistent and also show S to N current directions (Fig. 1).

The strata north of Harp Rock belong to the Borth Mudstones, a formation taken by Cave (1976) to underlie the Aberystwyth Grits. They are, however, a unit of distal turbidites, comprising only d and e units, and can be

[pp. 81-90 *In* BASSETT, M. G. (ed.). 1982. Geological excursions in Dyfed, south-west Wales.]

imagined as being distal to more southerly outcrops of the Aberystwyth Grits.

The tectonic structure of this region has been worked out principally by Price (1962). The major folds are a swarm of en echelon periclinal anticlines

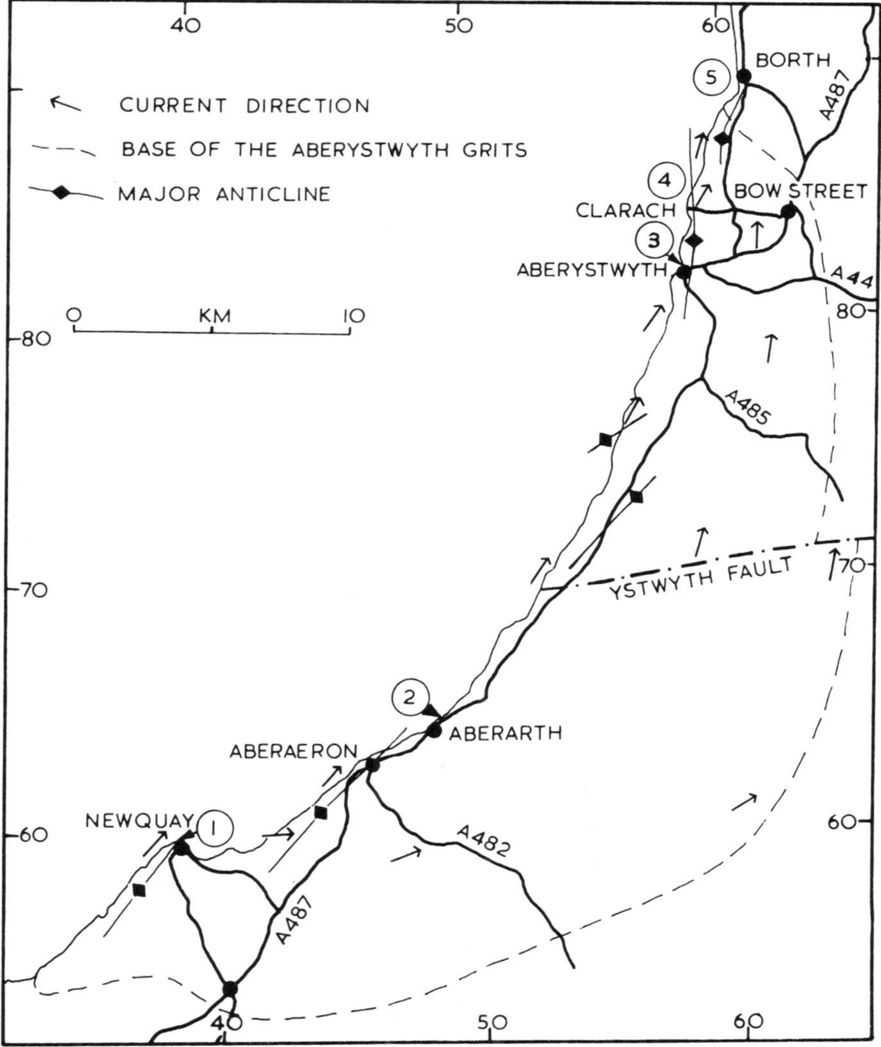

Fig. 1. Sketch map of the Newquay-Borth area showing the position of localities described in the text.

with a dominant southerly plunge in the N and northerly plunge in the S, where axial planes run parallel to the coastline. The W limbs of these folds are steeper, and are complicated by minor folding, while the E limbs have a lower and relatively even dip. Accordingly, the cliffs formed by these limbs are respectively either irregular and dipping at the maximum angle of repose, or vertical. Faults also abound, as thrusting accompanying the folding, and later normal and wrench faulting.

Recently, Davies & Cave (1976) interpreted much of the folding, and some of the faulting, as soft-sediment deformation consequent on down slope sliding (to the W) of thick packets of turbidites, soon after deposition. This process is also thought to have given rise to the slaty cleavage found in the finer beds.

The geomorphology of the coast also repays study. Many of the cliffs have recently been exhumed from behind glacial deposits, and thus antedate at least the last glaciation. Two main boulder clays occur, a Welsh Boulder Clay, grey in colour and with local erratics, and an Irish Sea Boulder Clay, light red in colour, calcareous, with far travelled boulders. The last glacial event was a period of permafrosting of previous deposits and intense solifluction (see also excursion 19, this volume).

ITINERARY

This itinerary is intended as a traverse along the coast from S to N, from proximal to distal turbidites. However, if time is limited the outcrops in the Aberystwyth - Clarach region (localities 3 or 4) will suffice to demonstrate the major tectonic and sedimentary features of the area. Tidal range is quite considerable in Cardigan Bay, hence **tide tables should be consulted,** especially for the sections at New Quay, Aberarth, *between* Aberystwyth and Clarach, and at Clarach and Borth.

1. New Quay. (SN 3868 6044, Fig. 2). Parking, for both coaches and cars, is available at the top of the town. Coaches can drive down to the harbour, but cannot park there; a car park is available near here but may be crowded in the summer. Cars and minibuses can drive down to the harbour, and turn W by a small road along the cliff top which ends in a turning place by an old quarry and a seafood factory.

Descend to **the beach** by a steep scramble down a dip slope just W of the factory building. The latter is built on thick units which are disposed in an anticline, while the section immediately ahead (locality **1A**) is cut in thinner beds, which are strongly folded and faulted. About 100 m from the start of the section, the cliff turns SW round a small promontory opposite a large stack. Pass through between the stack and the main cliff and then turn left as soon as possible.

In this **dip section (1B)** there is a remarkable sedimentary sill below the

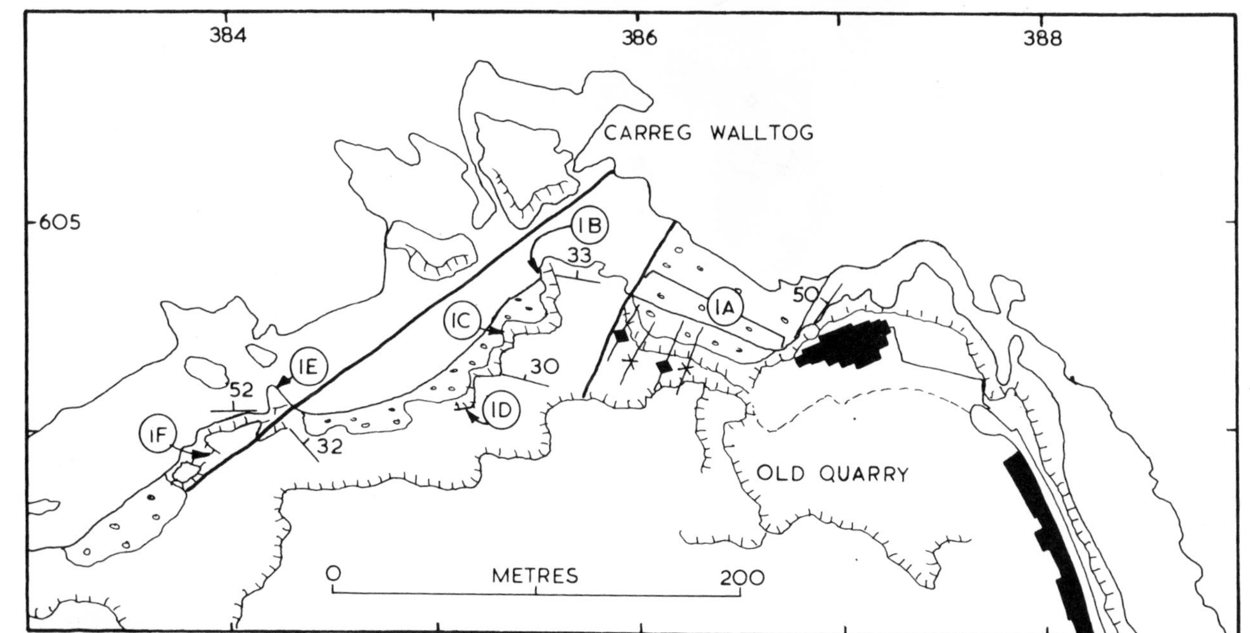

Fig. 2. Newquay Head (locality 1).

uppermost turbidite (which is multiple), with a number of vertical dykes injected up from it through mudstone into this turbidite. At beach level this sill can be seen to have its origin in the upper part of this turbidite, while in the up-dip direction it gradually dies out. This sequence of thick units is underlain by 3 m of mudstones with sandstone beds 1-10 cm thick. These are well laminated and show prominent current ripples.

Pass along the dip slope adjacent to this band, with clear ripple marks, to the **next dip section (1C)** some 25 m from the last. Some of the turbidites show well developed slump features, and carry large intraclasts of thin turbidites and shales.

A few metres further on is an **oblique dip section (1D) roughly parallel to the main cliff trend.** Large sub-angular blocks appear in the beach, and in the cliff face there is a thick mudstone just above beach level. This mudstone thins rapidly to the SW and observation will show that it occupies a curved hollow in a thick greywacke. This is interpreted as a slide-scar on the sea floor, later almost entirely filled by mud.

Look to the SW, along the beach. A **jagged promontory (1E)** shows beds dipping seawards. Pass through a narrow cleft between this promontory and the main cliff, and on the left examine a plunging anticline with a faulted axis. There is a massive bed at beach level in the left limb, and upward projections extend into the rather thick mudstone above. The thinner projections are contorted, the thicker expanded, presumably by compaction of the mudstone. These features are interpreted as sedimentary dykes, injected upwards, possibly by earthquake shocks. They are well exposed again, above the same bed, on the right side of the fold where the mudstone with dykes forms a prominent, steeply seaward dipping bedding plane.

At the SW end of this bedding plane turn SE to examine the **dip section** underneath it **(1F)**. In one bed in this section is a spectacular intraclast, about 30 cm in diameter, containing a cone-in-cone concretion, truncated by the clast surface. It suggests that these concretions may have formed very soon after deposition of the enclosing sediment.

2. Aberarth (SN 480 642 to 498 654, Fig. 1.). This is a good section in which to study turbidites with intermediate characters, and also to see glacial and geomorphological phenomena. Coach parties should leave the vehicle on the main A487 road by the bridge in the centre of Aberarth (SN 4795 6378) and walk to the beach by the minor road and footpath NE of the stream. Minibuses and cars can park on this minor road. Turn right (N) along the beach and walk for some 75 m to **the first cliffs.** These are composed of boulder clay alternating with layers of sand and gravel, soliflucted at the top of the cliff.

The solid rock cliffs to the N form a strike section with an inland dip, cut by

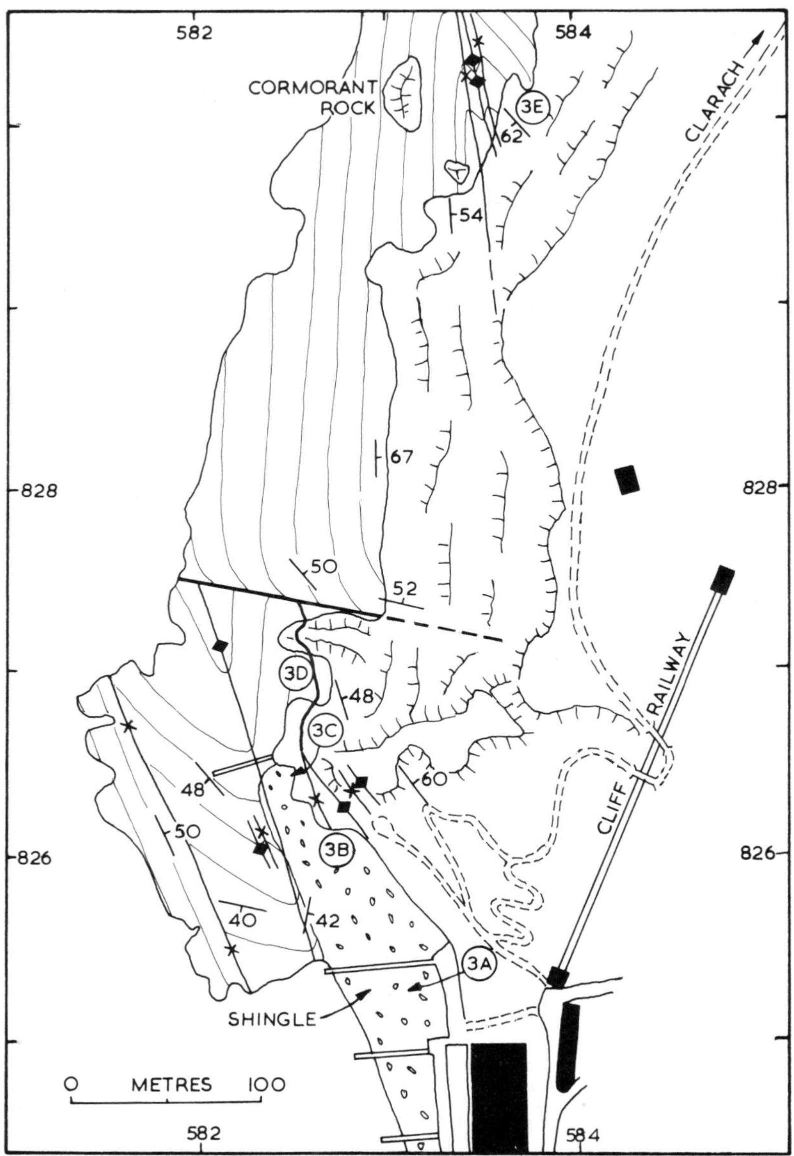

Fig. 3. The coastal platform and cliffs between the Promenade and Cormorant Rock, Aberystwyth (locality 3).

small dip faults. It is remarkable for the presence in some of the thicker units of intraclasts, varying from small flakes a centimetre in length, to rafts more than a metre long. In addition, many of the turbidites show slurrying, with the foundering of laminated portions, down into presumably less dense material. The sedimentary structure described as 'prolapsed bedding' by Wood & Smith (1959, p. 172) occurs at several horizons. Bottom structures can be seen in the higher beds, in the cliff, at eye level and above, and are very well displayed in a **shallow cave** further N along the section.

The first cliffs are cut in beds about 30-50 cm thick, dipping inland at about 40°, displaying a wealth of sedimentary features. About 36 m N from the start of the section is a fault trending at 075°; N of this a 1 m thick turbidite with prolapsed bedding appears in the cliff, containing folded and contorted rafts of thinly bedded strata in a slurried matrix; it can be followed for about 100 m.

This sequence of fairly thick units forms the cliffs to the N for some 360 m from the beginning of the solid rock section. They are then faulted against a finer sequence, in which most turbidites are less than 10 cm thick, for the next 700 m of the section. These are succeeded in turn (geographically and stratigraphically) by a unit of exceptionally thick beds, which descends the cliff gradually **to sea level.** This unit, containing one multiple bed 5 m thick, can be recognised from a distance because the exposures look as if the bedding is vertical and parallel to the cliff face. This bed has a number of spectacular horse shoe shaped flute casts, seen both in outcrop and in a large fallen block. The bed below it, 10 m N of the fallen block, shows a suite of climbing ripples, and a number of erosion surfaces within it. It can be followed along the **foot of the cliff** for 130 m to a **blunt promontory** formed by the 5 m bed reaching sea level. Immediately N of this is a **shallow cave,** with good bottom structures. Towards its N side is a sinistral ruck, which causes a sharp deflection of the groove casts on several of the bedding planes.

3. Aberystwyth to Clarach (SN 583 825 to 586 835, Fig. 3). This section is arguably the finest in the Aberystwyth Grits, and can be taken as the type section of the Formation. Access to the S end is gained from the N end of the promenade at Aberystwyth. A coach will have difficulty turning here, and should turn off the promenade 200 m to the S by the former Queens Hotel. If time permits, a traverse may be made along the shore to Clarach, either rejoining transport at Clarach north beach (locality 4), or returning to Aberystwyth by the cliff top path. The shore section is extremely tide-dependent, and it is only too easy to be caught by the rising tide, which cuts off access to both ends of the section. If this happens **do not try to scale the cliffs** since they are extremely dangerous.

The pebble beach at the north end of Aberystwyth promenade (SN 5830 8255, locality **3A**) is notable for its wide variety of exotic pebbles, derived from the Irish Sea Boulder Clay. These include igneous rocks from North Wales (rhyolite, porphyry) and Scotland (Ailsa Craig micro-granite), and sedimentary rocks from beneath the Irish Sea (Cretaceous flint, Carboniferous and Jurassic limestones). It has recently (1978) been artificially fed with debris from the vicinity of the cliff railway, and local pebbles predominate.

Bedding in the cliffs above and S of a **prominent breakwater** dips to the E, but this dip is interrupted by a fold pair in the lower cliff (at present (1979) obscured by the dumping of spoil on the beach). This fold pair **(3B)** is gradually replaced along the strike to the N by a thrust, dipping E, which can be examined in the **cove to the N (3D.).**

Many of the sedimentary structures in the turbidites here can be examined in the base of the cliff S of the breakwater, even when the tide is relatively high. Individual turbidites are relatively thinner than further S, slurried beds and intraclasts are rare, but bottom structures are varied, and convolute bedding, parallel lamination and ripple-drift bedding are common. Bottom structures, with a very consistent orientation, are clearly exposed in the roof of a small cave **S of the breakwater (3C).**

If the tide permits, climb the breakwater by the ladder and enter the **first cove to the N** (SN 5826 8270, **3D**). Here all the beds dip inland, and the thrust referred to above strikes N-S across the cove; the cave through the N spur of this cove is excavated along it. Bottom structures are again well displayed here, while one bed, in the cave mouth, has yielded a number of specimens of the brachiopod *Eocoelia.*

Rounding the N spur of this cove the cliffs recede farther to the E, and the N side of the spur is formed by an E-W tear fault, with a sinistral movement of 75 m. The cliff runs due N for the next 180 m, the beds still with an easterly dip. The cliff line then swings E round a headland, and in the **next 60 m of cliff** is a complex synclinal hinge zone **(3E)**. The zone is faulted, while adjacent to it are the enigmatic 'tectonic ripples' described by Wood (1958) and Davies & Cave (1976).

From this point it is 600 m to the beach at Clarach, and a further 500 m to the car and coach park at Clarach north beach (SN 5865 8405). The succession is gradually descended going N, the beds dipping seaward.

4. Clarach to Wallog (SN 586 841 to 590 857, Fig. 1). Drive to Clarach north beach (SN 5865 8405) by turning W off the A487 Aberystwyth - Machynlleth road either at the top of the hill leaving Aberystwyth, or in the centre of the village of Bow Street. Both coaches and cars can be parked adjacent to the beach.

Exposures start 100 m N of the car park, both in the **wave cut platform and the cliffs,** and a wealth of features can be studied in the next 150m of slope as far N as the large headland at SN 5855 8435. Sedimentary structures abound, as at Aberystwyth, but there are three prominent slumped beds, seen both high on the cliffs and in the shore platform. Structurally this section is a good deal more complicated than at Aberystwyth. The **first 100 m of platform** are cut in a sequence of 'haphazard' folding (Davies & Cave 1976). Individual folds vary greatly in profile, plunge and trend, die out and are replaced en echelon by others. Slaty cleavage is sporadically developed, but it shows differing relationships to individual folds; pre-cleavage, syn-cleavage, and post-cleavage folds are all present. Since the folds appear to form a single suite it is possible that the cleavage formation was patchy, both in space and time, during the formation of the folds. Davies & Cave (1976) interpreted this entire suite of folds, and the cleavage formation, as of soft sediment origin. NW-SE and E-W faults are present, eroded into gullies across the shore platform.

Similar beds and structures are exposed along the next 1.5 km to Wallog (SN 5905 8575). However, except at low spring tides it is not possible to go round the headland at SN 5855 8435. Wallog is more conveniently reached by the cliff top path, studying the cliff form en route. At Wallog, particularly at low to mid tides, the landward end of Sarn Cynfelyn can be studied. This is the most southerly of a trio of modified moraines in Cardigan Bay (Garrard & Dobson 1973).

5. **Borth** (Fig. 1). The Borth Mudstone Formation, immediately underlying the Aberystwyth Grits, crops out in the cliffs and shore platform just S of the road junction in Borth (SN 6073 8887). Cars and coaches can be parked alongside the beach just S and N of the junction.

Cliff exposures start immediately by the steps at the end of the promenade; a traverse for some 300m will suffice to demonstrate both the sedimentary and tectonic features. The dominant rock type is slate, with 1-2 cm siltstone horizons at intervals of 10-30 cm which are either plane-laminated or show small scale foreset bedding. Within this traverse at least four anticlines and intervening synclines are crossed. Dips on the limbs are uniform; beds either strike towards 010° and are vertical to overturned, younging to the W, or strike towards 030° and dip at moderate angles to the SE. Cleavage is strongly developed in the vertical limbs, but is not seen in the other limbs since it is parallel to the bedding. Several gullies are marked by transverse faults and prominent quartz veining. The faults trend at about 050° and dip to the SE.

REFERENCES

CAVE, R. 1976. Field investigations in the United Kingdom. *Annual Rep. Inst. geol. Sci.* **1975,** 24-25.

DAVIES, W. & CAVE, R. 1976. Folding and cleavage determined during sedimentation. *Sedim. Geol.* **15,** 89-133.

GARRARD, R. A. & DOBSON, M. R. 1973. The nature and maximum extent of glacial sediments off the west coast of Wales. *Mar. Geol.* **16,** 31-44.
PRICE, N. J. 1962. The tectonics of the Aberystwyth Grits. *Geol. Mag.* **99,** 542-557.
WOOD, A. 1958. Whitsun field meeting at Aberystwyth. *Proc. Geol. Ass.* **69,** 28-31.
WOOD, A. & SMITH, A. J. 1959. The sedimentation and sedimentary history of the Aberystwyth Grits (Upper Llandoverian). *Q. Jl geol. Soc. Lond.* **114,** 163-195.

6
THE PLYNLIMON AREA

by DENIS BATES

Maps	*Topographical:*	1 : 50 000	Sheet 135 Aberystwyth
		1 : 25 000	Sheets SN78, SN77, SN87
	Geological:	1 : 100 000	Central Wales Mining Field (IGS)

THE rocks of the Plynlimon area (Pumlumon Fawr) of northern Dyfed (Fig. 1) comprise a sequence of deep water sedimentary rocks, made famous by the work of O. T. Jones (1909, 1922; Jones & Pugh 1915, 1935), who mapped the area during the first decade of this century. The succession is of Ashgill (upper Ordovician) and Llandovery (lower Silurian) age, but with neither the base nor the top exposed; the sediments are predominantly fine grained, consisting of mudstones and shales (many now poorly cleaved slates) and graded siltstones, with the occasional development of sandstones and turbidites. Based on the work of Jones (1909), the general succession is as follows:

Group	Formation	Thickness	Series
YSTWYTH GROUP	Rhuddnant Formation	46 m+	LLANDOVERY SERIES
	Myherin Formation	320 m	
	Devil's Bridge Formation	460 m	
PONTERWYD GROUP	Castell Formation	80 m	
	Rheidol Formation	120 m	
	Eisteddfa Formation	90 m	
PLYNLIMON GROUP	Brynglas Formation	274 m	ASHGILL SERIES
	Drosgol Formation	460 m	
	Nant-y-moch Formation	370 m	

There is some local variation in nomenclature across the Plynlimon dome, but the above succession is applicable to the area of this excursion. Cave (1980) has provided a modern interpretation of the sequence as comprising turbiditic and pelagic sediments. The turbidite units are mainly formed of Bouma $T_{c\text{-}e}$ divisions, the pelagic shales and mudstones of dark coloured anoxically deposited graptolitic sediments, and lighter oxically deposited bioturbated mudstones without graptolites. The thick sandstones of the Drosgol Formation are described as fluxoturbidites, attributed to unusual conditions during the Ashgill ice age. The succeeding lower Silurian rocks record anoxic graptolitic shales, oxic inter-turbidite mudstones, and thin turbidites typical of

[pp. 91-102 *In* BASSETT, M. G. (ed.). 1982. Geological excursions in Dyfed, south-west Wales.]

the outer region of a submarine fan, and generally having a westerly current direction. In the upper Llandovery the coarse turbidites of the area, with a southerly derivation, record a major change in conditions, perhaps caused by tectonic events in the Pembrokeshire region to the S.

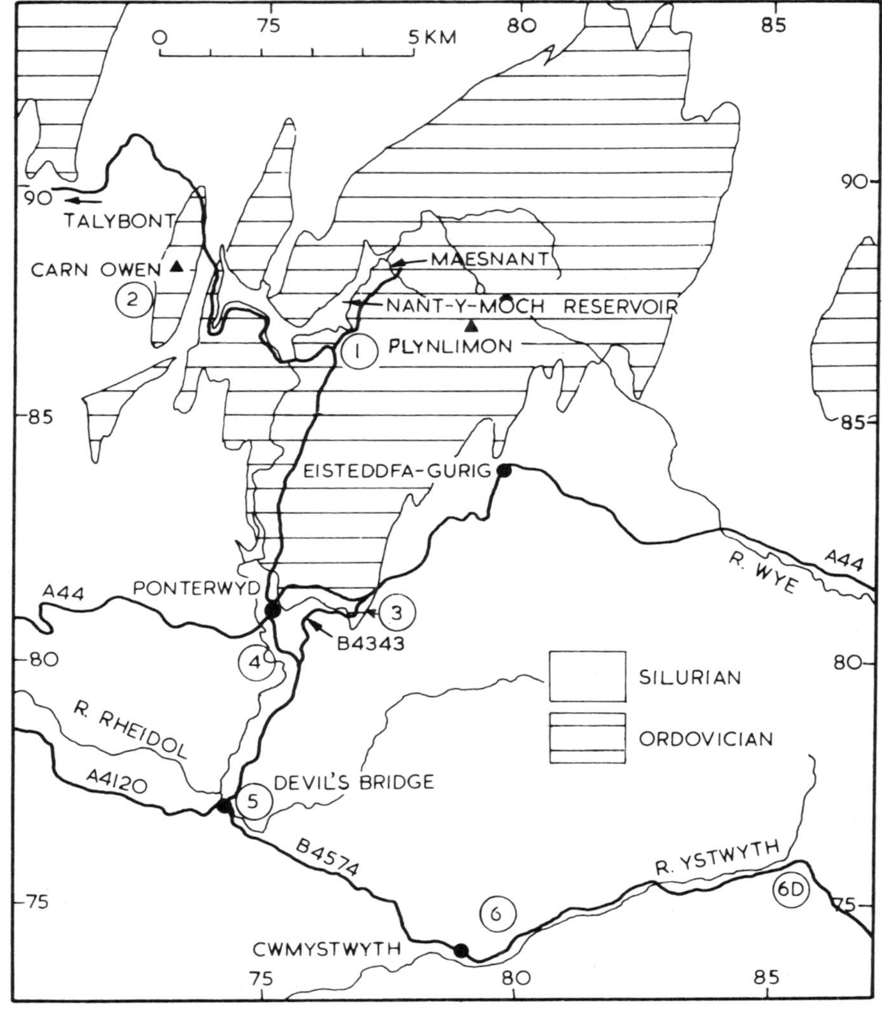

Fig. 1. Sketch map of the Plynlimon area showing the position of localities described in the text.

The fossils present throughout the area are dominantly graptolites, though trace fossils are common, particularly on the undersurfaces of thin siltstones. The complete sequence in the area described here extends from the *anceps* Zone of the Ashgill to the *crispus* Zone at the base of the upper Llandovery, though slightly younger zones are also present in adjacent areas.

The whole succession has been folded along NNE-SSW axes into a complex anticlinorium, with a plunge culmination forming the Plynlimon Ordovician inlier (Fig. 1). ENE-WSW normal faulting postdated the folding, and associated lead-zinc mineralisation was formerly exploited in numerous mines. This has been associated traditionally with a concealed granite body at depth, but recently Phillips (1972) has proposed an alternative model for the faulting and the mineralisation. In this the ore and gangue minerals are considered to be derived from the country rock by solution in the pore water at high pressure. Faulting was then caused by a process of hydraulic fracture, brecciating the adjacent rock, lowering pore pressure, and allowing the minerals to precipitate in the spaces (Raybould 1974).

The mountains are regarded by most authors as being a dissected plateau, with a largely superimposed river system. In detail, however, strike ridges are common, the ridge of Carn Owen (locality 2) being a particularly good example, and the harder horizons often form prominences on the hill sides (e.g. just E of Eisteddfa Gurig). Deep gullies and ravines are formed along parts of the major faults, good examples being the Hafan Fault at Carn Owen quarry (locality 2) and the Castell Fault just N of Parson's Bridge (locality 4).

Glacial features are not prominent, by comparison with those found further to the N, though there is a mantling of boulder clay over much of the area. The most striking features are the glacial diversions of the River Rheidol in the region just S of Ponterwyd (locality 4).

ITINERARY

The localities (Fig. 1) are arranged in stratigraphical order, to give reasonably complete coverage of the stratigraphy and structure of the area. However, a one day excursion can be filled amply by visiting localities 2 and 4, with a brief visit to see the view from the road at the Hafod Arms hotel (locality 5). All the roads used are suitable for motor coaches.

1. Nant-y-môch. This locality is best approached from Ponterwyd, at the juntion of the A44 and A4120 roads 20 km E of Aberystwyth. From the centre of Ponterwyd (SN 7495 8086) take the minor road to the N signposted to **Nant-y-môch reservoir.** This follows the E slopes of the Rheidol Valley, and also a series of NNE-SSW strike ridges formed in the strongly folded Ashgill rocks of the Plynlimon inlier. The oldest formation in the inlier is the Nant-y-moch Formation (James 1971), which is exposed in a number of **stream sections along the E side of the reservoir.** If time is limited, the upper member of the Formation may be examined in **road side exposures** at SN 7635 8620 or SN

7600 8640. The most complete section through the formation is in the Maesnant stream, from SN 7780 8770 to SN 7735 8822, the lower member cropping out from SN 7765 8778 downstream. All these exposures are of distal turbidites, comprising coarse siltstones with local sandstones and interbedded mudstones. Burrows are common locally on the bases of some coarser beds. The mudstones and siltstones are generally regularly banded, with faint parallel lamination and sharp margins (James 1971). Grading is not common. Sedimentary structures include ripple lamination, convolute lamination, flute moulds, and weak scours. In the lower beds transport direction appears to have been towards the NW, but in the higher beds the ripple laminae suggest a change in direction towards the SSW (James 1971, fig. 1).

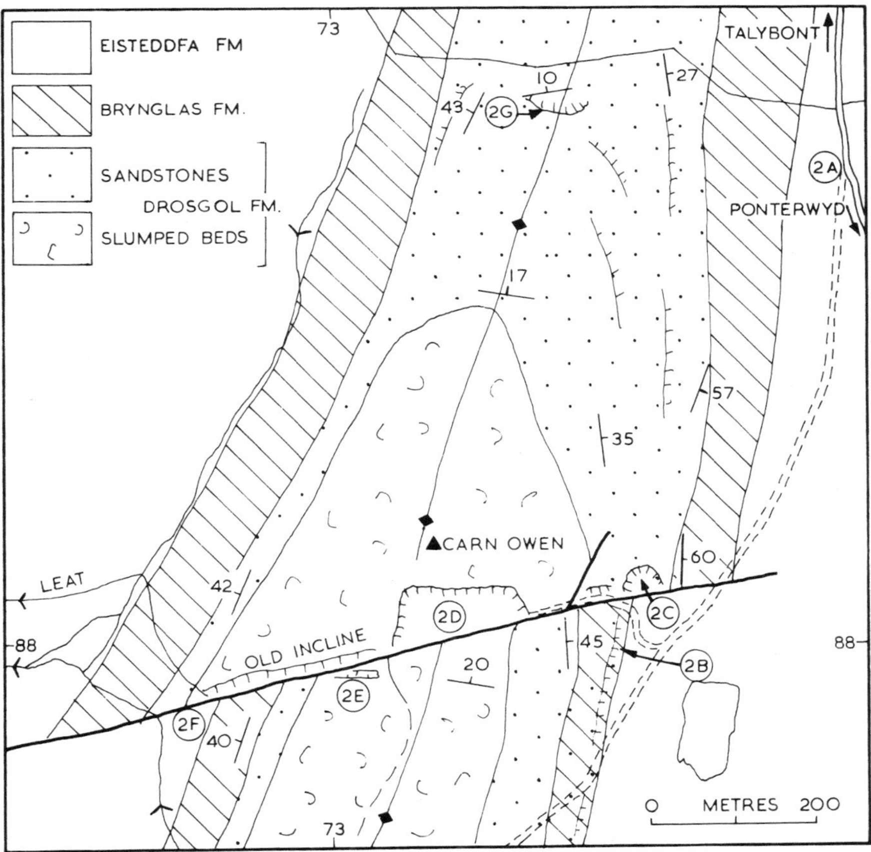

Fig. 2. The area around Carn Owen quarry (locality 2).

2. Carn Owen. Follow the road across the Nant-y-môch dam, then NW to SN 7362 8854 (Fig. 2. locality **2A**) where a track and bridleway joins the road. This point can also be reached by following the road E and then S from Talybont, on the A487 N of Aberystwyth. This area is formed of a pericline in the upper Ordovician and lower Silurian, cut by the Hafan Fault. Follow the track SW and then WSW to a **small strike ridge (a dip slope)** at SN 7343 8802 (locality **2B**). Biserial graptolites can be collected from the screes along this outcrop, from the basal Silurian shales of the Eisteddfa Formation.

Just N of this ridge the **track leading W to Carn Owen quarry** follows a striking topographical depression formed along the Hafan Fault. At the E end the uppermost beds of the Drosgol Formation are exposed in a small quarry (locality **2C**) in which graded sandstones, with an 8 m intercalation of shales, dip steeply to the E. Some beds are lenticular; loadcasting is strikingly shown on some of the quarried blocks.

Walk W along the track, noting to the N that the bedding, which is conspicuous in the quarry, disappears as one descends stratigraphically into the slumped lower member of the formation here. This is exposed dramatically in the main **Carn Owen quarry** (SN 7320 8806, locality **2D**) which exposes a chaotic mass of enormous rafts of bedded sandstones, measuring up to 20 m x 10 m, in a shale matrix. Some of the sandstone inclusions are partially folded; sandstone dykelets can be found adjacent to them; prominent quartz veins cut the sandstones but not the shales.

Descend the **old tramway** incline on the W side of the quarry, which follows the Hafan Fault (Fig. 2). On its N side are cliffs of slumped sandstones and shales, while to the S are small adits and opencast workings in the Hafan lode (locality **2E**). Lead and zinc sulphide ores can be collected from the extensive tips. **N of the foot of the incline** the upper bedded sandstones are again exposed, this time dipping W, and overlain by mudstones of the Bryglas Formation (locality **2F**). On the S side of the fault the succession is less clear, but mapping shows that the Hafan Fault has principally a normal movement, downthrowing to the S.

If time permits, walk N following the top of the Drosgol Formation to the forestry fence at SN 7315 8875, and then traverse E across the anticline back to the road via **Whitestone quarry** (SN 7330 8870, locality **2G**). Only bedded sandstones are exposed; in the quarry the beds dip N in the core of the anticline, demonstrating that it plunges to the N. The sandstones here are very pure, almost quartzites, and display a number of sedimentary features which suggest, somewhat enigmatically, a shallow water origin.

3. Castell Lode (SN 7743 8119). E of Ponterwyd, the ruins and spoil heaps of the Castell Mine are easily seen on the S side of the valley 200 m S of the junction of the A44 and the B4343 roads. This locality forms an alternative to locality 6 (Cwm Ystwyth) in which to study the mineralisation of the region.

Leave transport near the road intersection, and cross the Afon Castell to reach the **old opencast pits,** S of the spoil heaps. Mining and quarrying were carried out in a brecciated zone some 3 m wide, which marks the outcrop of the Castell Fault, running ENE-WSW along the valley, downthrowing to the S. The brecciated zone is particularly well exposed in the **most easterly pit.** It both forms a roof over flooded workings, and also a wall of unworked material on the N side. The gangue minerals here are predominantly carbonates, including ankerite, while sphalerite is the dominant ore mineral.

4. **Rheidol Gorge** (Figs. 3, 4). This area makes a convenient half day excursion in itself, but longer if serious fossil collecting is contemplated. If a coach is being used, it can be sent empty from the George Borrow hotel to Ysbyty Cynfyn, and the traverse made from N to S. However, if it is not possible to send transport round, then vehicles must be left at one end or the other; geologically and scenically it is more spectacular to start and finish at Ysbyty Cynfyn. The excursion is described, however, as a traverse from N to S.

Leave the transport at the George Borrow hotel, at the W end of Ponterwyd (SN 7467 8055). In the front of the hotel the River Rheidol flows through a vertical-sided ravine (Fig. 3, locality **4A**). This is a glacial diversion (Challinor 1933) the original valley, now partly exhumed, lying to the E (well seen from the A44 road bridge in Ponterwyd). Follow the track S from the hotel towards Bryn Brâs farm, and through the farm yard, turn S across a boggy depression and then skirt the fields beyond to descend to the Rheidol at SN 7507 7990.

This region was described very carefully and fully by Jones (1909) whose map and measured section form the basis of Fig. 4. The anticline in the NW corner of the map is the main axis of the Plynlimon Ordovician inlier. In the traverse within the gorge, the entire sequence is within the Rheidol Formation, spanning the *cyphus* to *argenteus* graptolite zones of the lower to middle Llandovery Series; the base of the overlying Castell Formation crops out along the sides of the gorge (Figs 3, 4). The main graptolitic horizons are indicated by Jones' locality numbers, and can be found by reference to the map, and for F14-18 (locality **4D**) by measuring the section with reference to the upper nodule band. The two nodule bands form distinctive marker horizons; they weather into small hollows, and the upper horizon has larger nodules, about 30 cm in diameter. The graptolitic horizons are formed of darker and rusty weathering shales, which contrast with largely unfossiliferous paler strata. The faunas recorded from each locality are given below (c = common; vc = very common):

F12. *Monograptus 'acinaces'* (c), *M. attenuatus, Orthograptus mutabilis* (c), *Glyptograptus tamariscus, Dimorphograptus confertus swanstoni, Climacograptus rectangularis, Cl. scalaris normalis* (c), *Rhaphidograptus toernquisti* (v. c.).

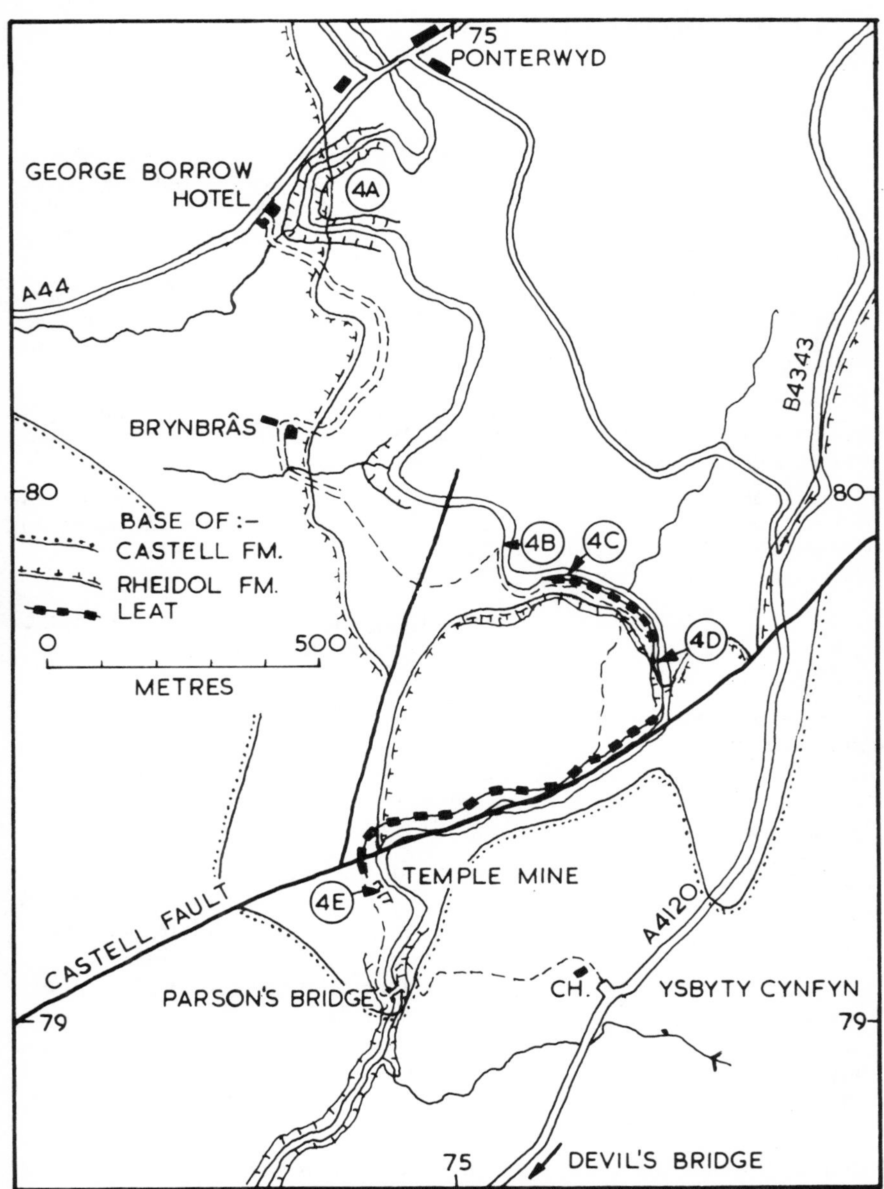

Fig. 3. Locality map for the Ponterwyd-Parson's Bridge area (locality 4)

F13. *M. atavus* (v. c.), *M. cyphus, M. revolutus, M. acinaces, M. sandersoni normalis, R. toernquisti* (c).

F14. 1.8 m below the upper nodule layer: *M. atavus* (c), *M. attenuatus, M. cyphus, M. gregarius, M. inopinus* (?), *M. revolutus austerus, M. sandersoni, O. mutabilis* (v. c.), *Cystograptus* cf. *penna, Gl. tamariscus* (c), *Cl. hughesi, R. toernquisti* (c).

F15. 1.9 m above the uper nodule layer: *M. atavus* (c), *M. attenuatus, M. communis, M. concinnus* (c), *M. cygneus, M. fimbriatus, M. gregarius, M. revolutus* (v. c.), *M. sandersoni, M. triangulatus* (c). *O.* cf. *bellulus, Gl. tamariscus, Petalograptus palmeus, Cl. hughesi, R. toernquisti* (v. c.) *Orthis?*, fragments of *Orthoceras*, bivalves.

F16. 9.1 m above the upper nodule layer: *Rastrites approximatus, R. longispinus, M. atavus, M. communis* (c), *M. concinnus* (c), *M. fimbriatus, M. gregarius, M. revolutus* (?), *M. triangulatus* (c), *O. bellulus, O. insectiformis* (c), *Gl. sinuatus, Gl. tamariscus, Cl. hughesi, R. toernquisti* (v. c.).

F17. 10.0 m above the upper nodule layer: *Diplograptus magnus, M. argutus?, M. attenuatus, M. concinnus, ?M. communis, M.* cf. *millepedia, M.* cf. *triangulatus, Rastrites approximatus, Rastrites longispinus, R. toernquisti.*

F18. 17 m above the upper nodule layer: *M. argenteus, M. argutus* (c) *M. communis, M. concinnus, M. cygneus, M. gregarius, M. leptotheca* (c), *M.* cf. *millepeda* (v. c.), *M. revolutus?, M.* cf. *urceolus, Diplogr. mangus, Gl. tamariscus, P. palmeus, P. palmeus tenuis, Cl. hughesi* (v. c.), *Cl. normalis?*

At SN 7507 7990 (locality **4B**, Jones F12) where the fence bounding the fields leaves the river, the low cliffs are cut in shales of the *A. atavus* Zone, yielding diplograptids and dimorphograptids.

Follow the river bank downstream for about 200 m, where an old water course leaves the river to run downstream alongside it. This was a leat to supply water for the Temple lead mine further downstream. In the outcrops along this leat, particularly at its upper end, graptolites of the *M. cyphus* Zone are common (locality **4C,** Jones F13).

Continuous outcrops can be followed for the next 300 m downstream, at which point the river plunges into a ravine and the leat was carried in a wooden trough. Note the variations in dip outlining minor folding plunging S as one goes along this section. At the downstream end the river bank widens, and a number of horizons of dark blue-rusty weathering shale are interbedded with pale shales and siltstones (locality **4D**, Jones F14-18). Careful collecting from the dark shales will yield a succession of monograptid faunas of the *M. gregarius* Zone (divided into the *triangulatus, magnus* and *argenteus* subzones) including triangulate monograptids and *Rastrites,* together with *Petalograptus* and *Rhaphidograptus.*

Climb up over the scarp, which is formed in the succeeding Castell Formation, and then descend again through scrub oak trees to the leat, which now forms a ledge in the hillside, well above river level. The river here has excavated its valley along the Castell Fault. Further SW, the valley and the path turn abruptly S, with the mine ruins and spoil tips of the **Temple Mine** just beyond. The tips yield ore and gangue minerals typical of the Cardiganshire ore field (locality **4E,** Fig. 3).

Follow the path S to **Parson's Bridge,** and pause to examine the nature of the ravine here, with its gigantic potholes. River flow is normally much less than before, since much of the water is abstracted above Ponterwyd to feed the hydro-electric power station in Cwm Rheidol. The path leads up from the bridge to the church at Ysbyty Cynfyn (SN 7530 7905).

5. Devil's Bridge. Drive S along the A4120 to Devil's Bridge. Note the open nature of the Rheidol Valley here; the gorge is cut as a narrow notch into it, ascribed to rejuvenation during the Pleistocene.

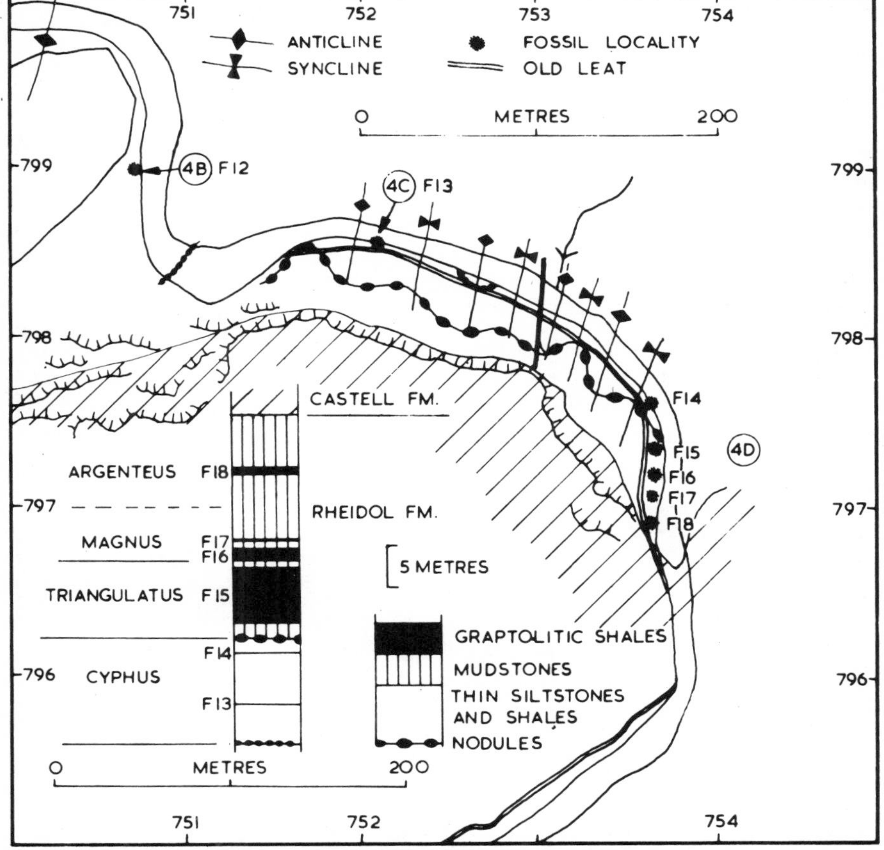

Fig. 4. The graptolite localities of the Rheidol Gorge (localities 4B-4D)

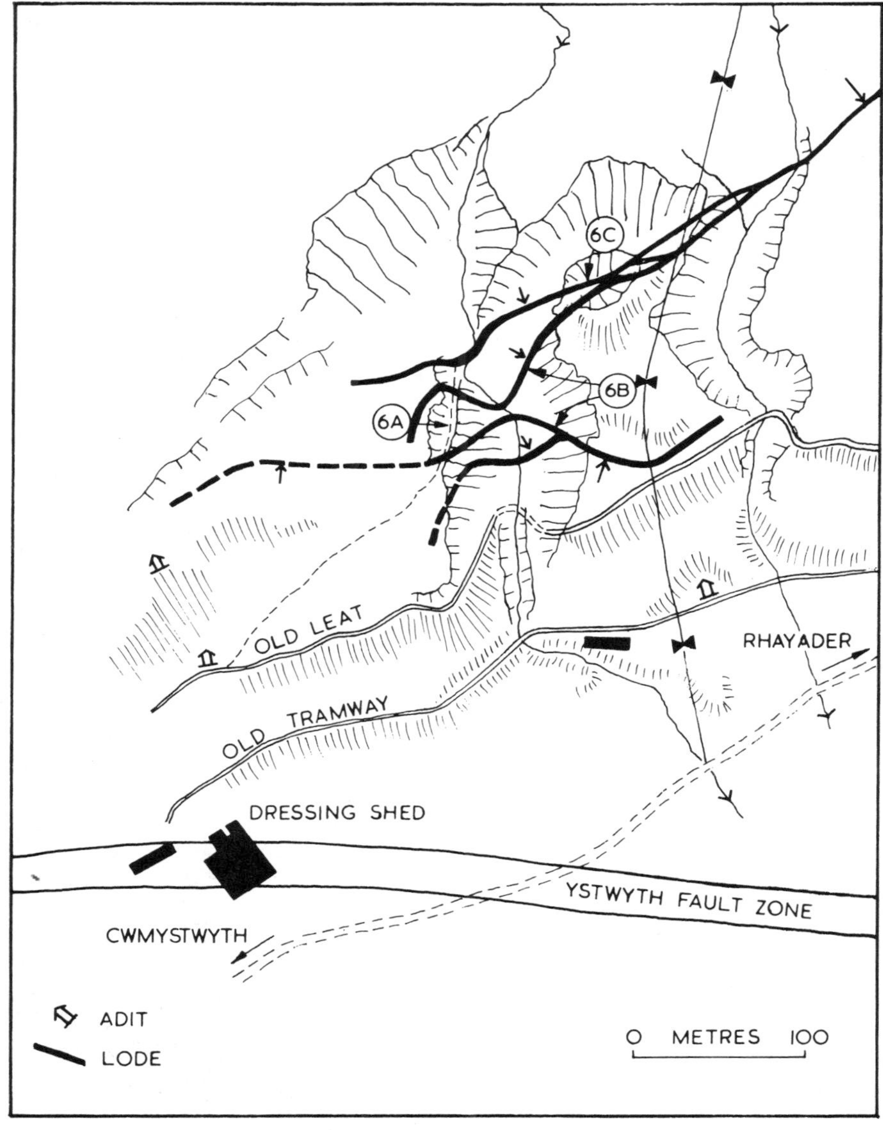

Fig. 5. The mineralised veins of the Cwmystwyth lead mines (locality 6).

At Devil's Bridge (SN 7415 7703) the Rheidol turns sharply to the W, and the Mynach, a river graded to the higher open valley of the Rheidol, plunges through a dramatic gorge and down a series of waterfalls to join it. These relationships can be seen both from the terrace opposite the Hafod Arms hotel, and from the bridge itself, while a closer view is possible by passing through the tourist turnstiles.

6. Cwm Ystwyth (SN 802 744 Fig. 5). Drive to Cwmystwyth, via the B4574 SE from Devil's Bridge. The road passes through an arch erected for the Jubilee of George III, at the watershed dividing the Mynach and Ystwyth catchment areas. The Cwmystwyth mines lie 1.5 km E of the village, and this section of the road is narrow, but passable by coach, which can be turned and parked at the mines, below the corrugated iron dressing shed. At this locality the major E-W Ystwyth Fault (unexposed) passes beneath the shed. The mineralisation occurs in ENE-WSW trending lodes to the N emplaced in the upper Llandovery Cwmystwyth Grits, disposed in a N-S trending syncline, whose axis lies E of the main opencast.

Look due N from here, to the skyline. A stream can be seen here, plunging down a ravine in a series of cascades past the upper opencast workings (locality **6C**) and lower spoil tips. Ascend the hillside towards the ravine, eventually reaching the **level path** at locality **6A**. From this point the outcrop of some of the lodes can be seen in the **opposite river bank** (locality **6B**). The path eventually peters out, at a point where there was formerly a small bridge across the river. Scramble across at this point and ascend to the **opencast** (locality **6C**). In the opencast, which is somewhat dangerous, are the outcrops of two brecciated fault zones. In these the sequence of mineralisation can be studied.

Drive to the car park (SN 855 758) at the head of the Ystwyth valley (locality **6D**), and walk back down the road to the **cutting 200 m to the W.** This is cut in the uppermost beds of the Cwmystwyth Grits, a facies equivalent of the Aberystwyth Grits. These show typical turbidite features and dip east. They are succeeded, in the **stream to the N of the car park** by the pale shales of Cwmystwyth (Jones 1945), soft green and maroon mudstones, which can be correlated lithologically with similar beds to the E and N of the region.

REFERENCES

CAVE, R. 1980. Sedimentary environments of the basinal Llandovery of mid-Wales. *In* HARRIS, A. L., HOLLAND, C. H. & LEAKE, B. E. (eds.). The Caledonides of the British Isles — reviewed. *Spec. Publs geol. Soc. Lond.* **8,** 517-526.

CHALLINOR, J. 1933. The 'incised meanders' near Ponterwyd. *Geol. Mag.* **70,** 90-92.

JAMES, D. M. D. 1971. The Nant-y-Moch Formation, Plynlimon inlier, West Central Wales. *J. geol. Soc. Lond.* **127,** 177-181.

JONES, O. T. 1909. The Hartfell-Valentian succession in the district around Plynlimon and Ponterwyd (north Cardiganshire). *Q. Jl geol. Soc. Lond.* **65,** 463-537.

JONES, O. T. 1922. The mining district of north Cardiganshire and west

Montgomeryshire. *Mem. geol. Surv. spec. Rep. Miner. Resour. Gt. Br.* **20,** 205 pp.

JONES, O. T. & PUGH, W. J. 1915. The geology of the district around Machynlleth and the Llyfnant Valley. *Q. Jl geol. Soc. Lond.* **71,** 343-385.

JONES, O. T. & PUGH, W. J. 1935. The geology of the districts around Machynlleth and Aberystwyth. *Proc. Geol. Ass.* **46,** 247-300.

JONES, W. D. V. 1945. The Valentian succession around Llanidloes, Montgomeryshire. *Q. Jl geol. Soc. Lond.* **100,** 309-332.

PHILLIPS, W. J. 1972. Hydraulic fracturing and mineralisation. *J. geol. Soc. Lond.* **128,** 337-359.

RAYBOULD, J. G. 1974. Ore textures, paragenesis and zoning in the lead-zinc veins of mid-Wales. *Trans. Inst. Min. Metall.* **B, 83,** B111-B120.

7
SILURIAN ROCKS OF THE MARLOES AND PEMBROKE PENINSULAS

by MICHAEL G. BASSETT

Maps	*Topographical:*	1 : 50 000	Sheets 157 St David's and Haverfordwest, 158 Tenby
		1 : 25 000	Sheets SM70, SM80, SR89, SS09
	Geological:	1 : 50 000	Sheets 226/227 Milford, 244/245 Pembroke and Linney Head

THE southern coast of SW Dyfed, from Skomer eastwards across Milford Haven to Tenby and Amroth, displays almost continuous sections ranging from early Silurian to late Carboniferous in age, together with minor outcrops of Ordovician and Triassic strata. This excursion is designed to demonstrate the sequence of Silurian rocks and faunas below the Old Red Sandstone facies, to give a general picture of the depositional environments, and to point out the evidence for correlation with sections outside Dyfed, particularly with those in the Silurian type areas further to the E in Wales and in the Welsh Borderland. Two itineraries are described, covering all the coastal Silurian outcrops plus a few nearby inland localities; the first is on the N side of Milford Haven and covers the Marloes or Wooltack peninsula (Fig. 1); the second is S of the Haven in the Pembroke peninsula, where localities are described at Freshwater East and Freshwater West.

Following early work in the 19th century, the Silurian rocks were mapped and described in detail by Cantrill *et al.* (1916) and Dixon (1921); more recently Ziegler *et al.* (1969) revised the lower part of the sequence and Walmsley & Bassett (1976) redescribed the upper part, while Sanzen-Baker (1972) discussed regional structural and facies relationships. At the top of the marine Silurian sequence the beds are overlain by Old Red Sandstone facies, still in part of Silurian age, which have been revised by Allen & Williams (1978; see also excursions 8 and 9, this volume).

A summary of the succession to the N of Milford Haven is as follows:

	Thickness
RED CLIFF FORMATION (of Milford Haven Group - Old Red Sandstone facies)	up to 52 m
Red, purple and pink mudstones, sandstones and fine	

[pp. 103-122 *In* BASSETT, M. G. (ed.). 1982. Geological excursions in Dyfed, south-west Wales.]

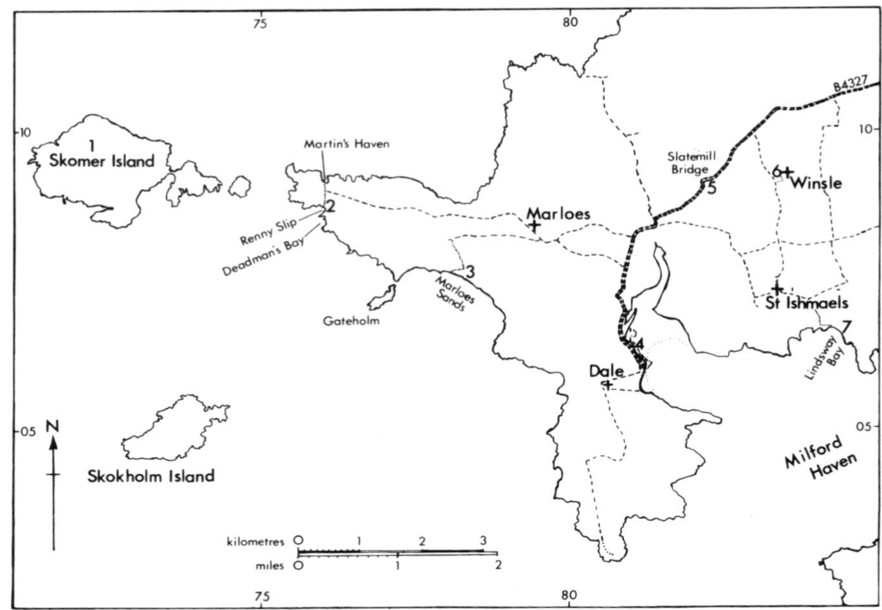

Fig. 1. The Marloes peninsula, showing the position of localities 1-7.

quartzites, with calcretes and rare intraformational conglomerates and fine tuffs. Mud cracks, scours, channels and cross bedding common. Grey-green intercalations common in basal beds, which are unfossiliferous but probably of Silurian age.

GRAY SANDSTONE GROUP 300 m

Grey, buff, and yellow-green sandstones with grits, sandy siltstones, and thin 'rottenstones'. Early to mid Wenlock in age at base, with upper beds probably no younger than late Wenlock.

CORALLIFEROUS GROUP up to 100 m

Olive-green and grey shales, mudstones, and sandy siltstones with 'rottenstones', thin grits and muddy calcareous lenses. Basal beds of late Upper Llandovery (C_6) age, passing conformably into the Wenlock Series within the division.

UNCONFORMITY

SKOMER VOLCANIC GROUP 1000 m+

Higher beds include Conglomerate 'Series' of early accounts. Grits, conglomerates, sandstones, shaley and sandy mudstones, with thick basalts and tuffs. Fossils near top indicate an early Upper Llandovery (C_{1-2}) age.

Lower beds include Skomer Volcanic 'Series' of early accounts. Thick basalts, rhyolites, tuffs and an ignimbrite, with coarse conglomerates, sandstones, and siltstones. Probably all of Llandovery age.

South of Milford Haven there is a maximum stratigraphical thickness of 60 m of marine/deltaic Silurian beds exposed below Old Red Sandstone facies, and all the beds appear to belong within the Gray Sandstone Group. The correlation between the various sequences in the tectonically separated sections is shown in Fig. 2, based mainly on the five successive faunas (I - V) traced throughout the region by Walmsley & Bassett (1976). All the sections have been subjected to both Caledonian and Variscan (Hercynian) deformation, and all fall within Hancock's (1973) Variscan Zone 1 (see also fig. 1 in excursion 12, this volume). On the Marloes peninsula the sections between the Ritec and Musslewick faults (Fig. 2) are within Hancock's Variscan Zone 1b, equivalent to the Marloes Block of Sanzen-Baker (1972); to the N of the Musslewick Fault the Winsle inlier is also within structural Zone 1b, in what Sanzen-Baker termed the Winsle Block. On the Pembroke peninsula S of Milford Haven the Silurian sections are entirely within Hancock's (1973) structural Zone 1a (Freshwater Block).

At all the coastal localities described in this excursion strict attention must be paid to tidal timetables. A number of the bays become cut off at high water, and in itinerary 1 especially the cliffs are steep and dangerous, making access unsafe other than along the marked paths. Itinerary 1 is described as starting from Haverfordwest and itinerary 2 from either Tenby or Pembroke. At least one full day should be allowed for the former, but for a detailed study 2 or 3 days may be necessary.

ITINERARY 1

From Haverfordwest take the Dale road (B4327) as far as Mullock Bridge (SM 8120 0830), then turn right onto the minor road to Marloes village and continue straight on to Martin's Haven (SM 7605 0915). Cars can be parked in the car park at Martin's Haven, but as the lane through to this point is narrow, coaches should be left in Marloes.

1. Skomer (SM 725 095). The island of Skomer is an outstanding National Nature Reserve owned and administered jointly by the Nature Conservancy and the West Wales Naturalists' Trust. From mid March to mid October a boat leaves Martin's Haven daily at 10 a.m. and there is a small landing fee (sailing times should be checked beforehand). Parts of the island are out of bounds in order to protect the wild life and visitors are urged to keep to the marked paths or to seek permission from the warden to visit special study areas (the paths are clearly marked and described in a guide to the natural history of the island published by the West Wales Naturalists' Trust, available from the warden).

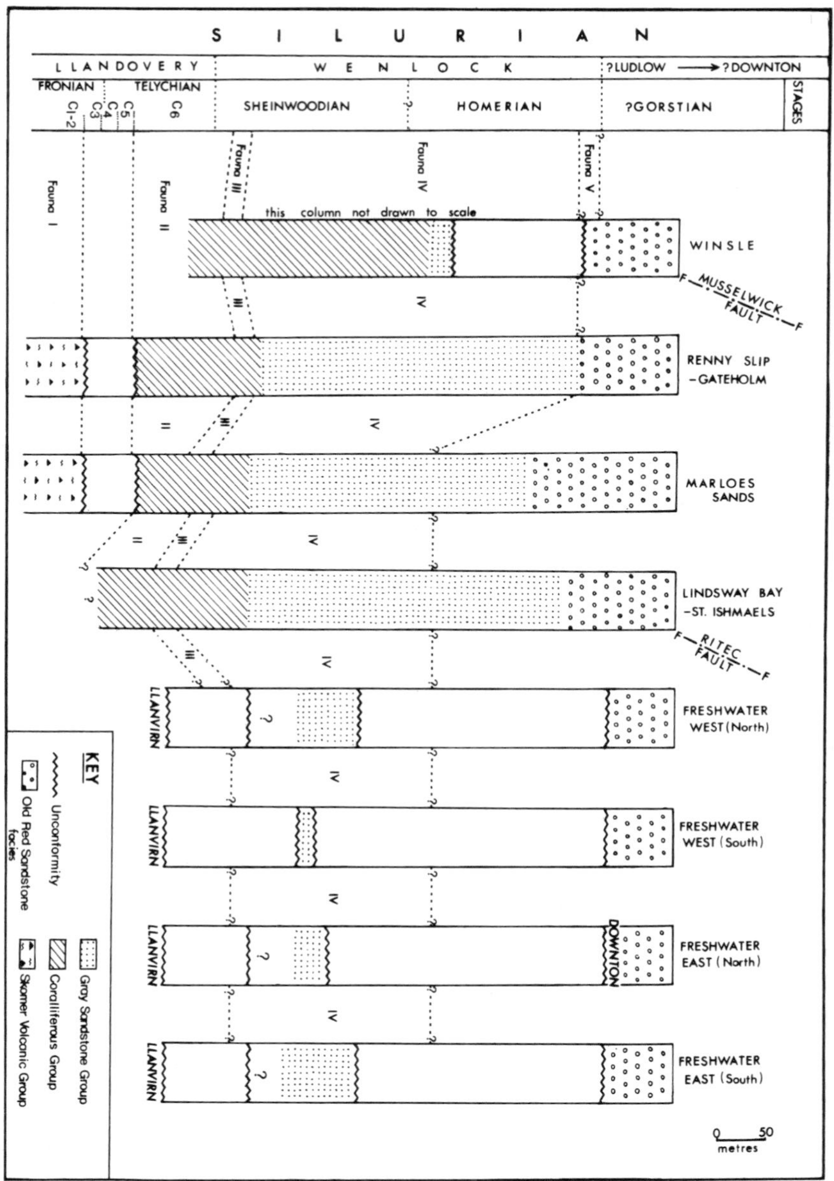

Fig. 2. Correlation of Silurian sequences in the Marloes and Pembroke peninsulas based on Faunas I-V of Walmsley & Bassett (1976).

Because of the restrictions of access throughout the island, Skomer is not suitable for a visit by large parties or for those with only a general geological interest, and a detailed itinerary will therefore not be described here. Specialist students who do wish to spend some time on Skomer should consult the publication by Ziegler *et al.* (1969), which includes a map and detailed account of the geology. This account is fundamental to the interpretation and correlation of much of the succession on the mainland as well as on the island itself; its main conclusions are therefore outlined here for those who wish to proceed immediately to subsequent localities.

Skomer is made up largely of volcanic rocks with relatively minor interbedded sediments, the whole totalling over 1000 m in thickness. The volcanics are mainly basaltic in composition, but rhyolite flows are developed at three levels and there is an ignimbrite horizon some 125 m below the top of the succession. A number of the volcanic horizons can be traced laterally on to the mainland, including the ignimbrite which forms a distinctive and important datum in the correlation across from Skomer. Early workers in the area, notably Thomas (1911) and Cantrill *et al.* (1916), considered that on the mainland the Skomer Volcanic Group was overlain unconformably by sediments of Upper Llandovery age belonging to the Conglomerate 'Series'; although the age relationships of the Skomer volcanics were not obvious, these authors considered that on balance an Arenig age (lowest Ordovician) was most probable, based partly on a correlation with volcanic rocks known to be of Arenig age at Trefgarn and on Ramsey Island to the N, and at Llangynog in E Dyfed.

Ziegler *et al.* (1969) re-examined the whole sequence and demonstrated that the Skomer volcanics pass conformably upwards and grade laterally into sediments containing lower Silurian faunas. They extended the Skomer Volcanic 'Series' of earlier authors to include the overlying Conglomerate 'Series', and redefined both units within the Skomer Volcanic Group; there is thus no major unconformity within the Group. The highest beds of this redefined unit can be dated as early Upper Llandovery (C_{1-2}) (see below, p. 109); the dating of the lower volcanic beds is not so precise, but definitely excludes an Arenig age. Fossils have not been recorded from Skomer itself, but Ziegler *et al.* collected poorly preserved ostracodes on the S of Midland Island, between Skomer and the mainland, from beds which they correlate with sediments at the Mew Stone, near the top of the sequence on Skomer. The ostracodes did not allow a definite identification but were considered to be closely allied to the genus *Herrmannina,* which occurs in the Llandovery and Wenlock Series. Similar forms possibly might have occurred in the latest Ordovician but none have been recorded from earlier beds.

The palaeontological evidence for re-dating the Skomer volcanics is supported by structural and regional environmental evidence. Detailed studies of both sedimentary and volcanic rocks within the Skomer Volcanic

Group allowed Ziegler *et al.* to demonstrate that they were laid down under very shallow water, paralic, and at times terrestrial conditions, whereas the known Arenig igneous rocks further to the N and E were extruded into a relatively deep water basin, which palaeogeographical constructions suggest to have extended over the Skomer area throughout the early Ordovician. The structural evidence is based mainly on the sections at Musselwick Sands on the N of the Marloes peninsula (SM 781 089), where the Skomer Volcanic Group is faulted against sediments of Llandeilo age. Ziegler *et al.* (p. 413) interpret the fault as downthrowing the Skomer Group against the Llandeilo beds, which thus provide a lower age limit for the volcanics.

On the mainland the lower beds of the Skomer Volcanic Group are best exposed in the cliffs of Wooltack Park, notably at Wooltack Bay (SM 756 094), Wooltack Point (SM 755 095), Mouses Haven (SM 755 092), Jeffry's Haven (SM 756 091), Cable Bay (SM 755 089), and Anvil Bay (SM 756 088) (see Ziegler *et al.* 1969, fig. 2). At all these localities the cliffs are very steep and descent is usually impossible without the aid of a rope. The remainder of this itinerary will thus be confined to a description of more accessible localities in the upper part of the Skomer Volcanic Group and in younger beds.

2. Renney Slip and Deadman's Bay. From Martin's Haven follow the path S alongside the wall of the Deer Park to the head of the bay known as Renney Slip (SM 7600 0875). Descend to beach level by means of a steep path at the NE corner of the bay. The sections exposed include the highest beds of the Skomer Volcanic Group and the overlying Coralliferous Group.

The prominent line of sea stacks known as Limpet Rocks (SM 7550 0869), some 200 m off the W promontory of the bay, is composed of the highest of the basalt flows in the Skomer Volcanic Group and this horizon forms a useful datum to begin the examination of the upper part of the sequence. The basalt, which is some 7 m thick, extends from Limpet Rocks through the promontory dividing Renney Slip from Anvil Bay to the NW, where it is underlain by a prominent tuff band (Ziegler *et al.* 1969, fig. 4). The sequence in the promontory is inaccessible, but it is repeated twice by faulting in the cliffs forming the **E wall of Renney Slip.** The easternmost of the two exposures is **directly below the end of the wall of the Deer Park** (SM 7604 0876), some 10 m to the E of the path leading to the beach. Here the base of the basalt is cut out by faulting, but it can be seen to have a vesicular top and an uneven upper surface, and is followed by a bed of silty mudstone containing *Lingula* sp. and pebbles of igneous rock. Ziegler *et al.* (1969, p. 429) also recorded eurypterids from this section. **60 m to the NW** of these exposures (SM 7598 0877) the basalt is again faulted in, this time exposing its complete thickness and indicating that both the base and top are vesicular; here the basalt passes down into the tuff horizon, which in turn is underlain by coarse grey-green and brown sandstones with silty partings. Above the basalt the *Lingula* bearing mudstones of the section to the SE are replaced by coarse, unfossiliferous sandstones.

The beds following the basalt horizon and its immediately overlying sediments are best studied in the **steep dip faces forming the N side of Renney Slip.** They form a distinct unit, some 10-12 m thick, composed of conglomerates, quartzites, and coarse sandstones which display cross bedding, ripple marks, and the effects of small scale scouring. Specimens of *Lingula* sp. occur near the base of the unit but much of the sequence is unfossiliferous. The highest beds, forming the top dip slopes, include grey-green grits in which *Tentaculites* sp. is fairly common in association with the brachiopods *Eostropheodonta* sp., *Stegerhynchus*? aff. *decemplicatus*, and *Atrypa* sp.

Succeeding this dominantly arenaceous unit is a sequence of green and grey silty micaceous shales with thin sandstones. These beds form the **sea stacks in the centre and south-centre of the bay,** as well as the cliffs in the **small embayment** immediately S of the easternmost faulted-in basalt section. The silty beds are exposed to a thickness of approximately 45 m but a true estimate is difficult to obtain as they are cut by numerous small faults, and as the upper part of the sequence was eroded before the deposition of the overlying Coralliferous Group. *Lingula* sp. occurs in the lowest beds, but throughout most of the sequence there is a more diverse fauna occurring in shelly lenses and bands of decalcified sandstone. *Eocoelia hemisphaerica* is the dominant brachiopod species, especially in the highest beds, while *Leptostrophia* cf. *compressa* and *Microsphaeridiorhynchus*? sp. are also common. Associated fossils are commonly too fragmentary to allow a definite identification but specimens of *Leptaena* sp., *Atrypa* sp. and favositid corals may also be obtained. The complete fauna is typical of Walmsley & Bassett's (1976) Fauna I (Fig. 2), with the presence of *E. hemisphaerica* throughout the unit being particularly important in dating since this species is known only from beds of early Upper Llandovery (C_{1-2}) age (Ziegler 1966, p. 540, fig. 6). The *Eocoelia* specimens are also indicative of the *Eocoelia* community (Ziegler 1965; Ziegler *et al.* 1968), representing a slightly deeper water environment than the in-shore *Lingula* community of the underlying sandy unit; the faunas thus complement the sediments in suggesting a deepening upward sequence through the bay.

Along the **S side of Renney Slip** (SM 7600 0865) the topmost beds of the Skomer Volcanic Group are overlain unconformably by the basal conglomerates and sandstones of the Coralliferous Group. The angular discordance of 5° - 10° is well exposed. Below the unconformity the shales and silts are deeply weathered and reddened to a depth of some 0.5 m, 'probably due to subaerial weathering during the period of erosion represented by the break' (Ziegler *et al.* 1969, p. 430).

Fossils are scarce in the lowest 20 m of the Coralliferous Group, which comprises thin horizons of conglomerate and grit interbedded with coarse reddish-brown sandstones, with thin limestones and reddened argillaceous partings. The arenaceous units are cross bedded and graded, and some display basal load cast structures. These beds contrast sharply with the succeeding blue-grey and green coloured shaley siltsones and mudstones, which make up the bulk of the Coralliferous Group. The mudstones are cleaved to varying degrees and are highly fossiliferous; they can be examined first in the **steep spit separating Renney Slip from Deadman's Bay** to the S (SM 7600 0862). The bedding planes on the S face of this spit are crowded with specimens of the brachiopod *Costistricklandia lirata lirata,* and slightly higher beds contain the coral *Palaeocyclus porpita;* both species are indicative of Walmsley & Bassett's Fauna II and allow a firm correlation with the topmost Upper Llandovery (C_6), thus indicating that the break at the base of the Coralliferous Group cuts out beds of C_3 to C_5 age inclusive (Fig. 2). The associated fauna in Deadman's Bay includes the brachiopods *Eospirifer radiatus, Clorinda* sp., *Atrypa reticularis* (Linnaeus), *Leptaena* sp., and favositid and phaulactid corals. The common occurrence of *Costistricklandia* indicates the presence of the *Costristicklandia* community, and the full fauna suggests a relatively offshore position in Boucot's (1975) Benthic Assemblage 3 or 4; the incoming of this assemblage close to the base of the Coralliferous Group supports the view of a deepening upward, transgressive sequence above the unconformity.

The Coralliferous Group in Deadman's Bay has a thickness of 90 - 100 m, with the brachiopod *Eocoelia angelini* appearing in the top 30 m as an indicator of Walmsley & Bassett's Fauna III within the Sheinwoodian Stage of the lower Wenlock Series. The base of the Gray Sandstone Group is exposed in the SE corner of the bay. On the SE side of Pitting Gales Point (SM 7609 0835) the early to mid Wenlock Fauna IV appears close to the base of the Gray Sandstone Group, dominated by the Brachiopod *Pembrostrophia freshwaterensis;* this Group then occupies the coastline for some 1.5 km to the SE, before passing into Old Red Sandstone facies in the cliffs N of Gateholm. Although the Coralliferous and Gray Sandstone groups can be studied between Deadman's Bay and Gateholm, access is difficult in many places. Since the same succession can be examined with ease at locality 3 parties are advised to return to Martin's Haven via Renney Slip.

3. Marloes Sands. Those on foot can walk SE from the head of Renney Slip along the cliff tops for about 2.4 km to Marloes Sands; from the cliffs there are magnificent views NW to Skomer, SW to Skokholm, and SE across the [Pembrokeshire] 60 m wave cut platform. Parties with transport should return to the E end of Marloes village and take the sharp fork back to the SW which is signposted to Marloes Sands. Vehicles can be left in the large car park at the end of the metalled road (SM 7800 0820); a track known as Sandy

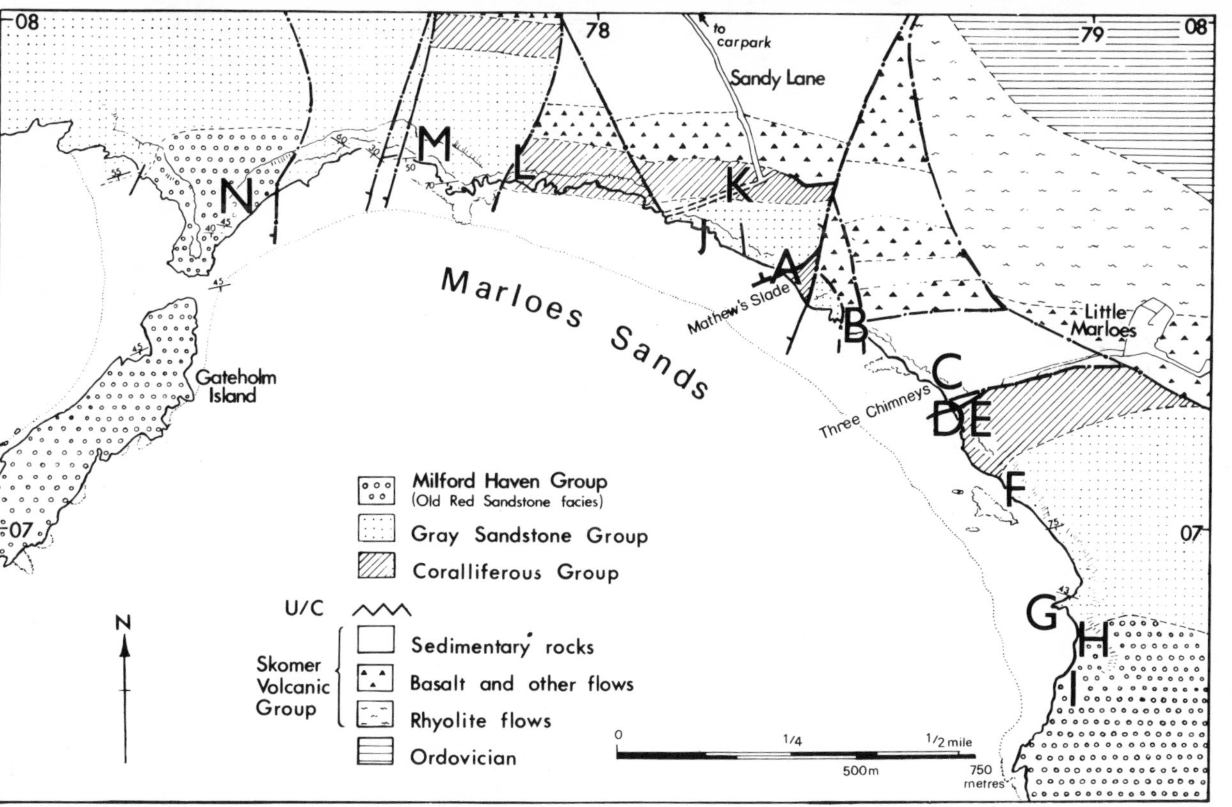

Fig. 3. The geology of Marloes Sands, showing the position of localities 3A-3N.

Lane runs from just E of the car park to the beach.

At Marloes Sands the Silurian rocks are superbly exposed and can be studied almost continuously at beach level. At least a full day should be allowed to study the sections in detail, and parties with limited time available are therefore advised to visit this locality first in preference to others. Fig. 3 illustrates the geology of the bay, with the letters A to N indicating selected points in an itinerary for those with insufficient time to study the complete sequence in detail. Structural details at this locality are described in excursion 12, locality 9, this volume.

An easily located point from which to commence a traverse is the broad grassy hollow in the cliff line known as **Mathew's Slade (3A)** (SM 7840 0750), 350 m to the E of the path from the car park. The beds forming the hollow belong to the Coralliferous Group, included here in a faulted slice and therefore out of their normal sequence. The fauna is limited but includes the brachiopods *C. lirata lirata, E. radiatus, A. reticularis, Howellella* sp., and *Isorthis mackenziei,* as well as fragmentary corals referable to *Favosites* sp. and ?*Rhabdocyclus* sp.; the association is typical of Fauna II (Fig. 2).

On the E side of Mathew's Slade the beds of the Coralliferous Group are faulted against a sequence of yellowish-grey feldspathic sandstones with an exposed thickness of about 6 m. The sandstones are the oldest beds exposed along Marloes Sands, belonging within the upper half of the Skomer Volcanic Group; they are cut and brecciated by numerous minor faults. At **3B, 100 m E of Mathew's Slade** the sandstones are followed by two basaltic lava flows which are best studied along the **N face of a steep gully** in the cliffs (SM 7852 0740). The basalts are cut by numerous faults, but in the **cliffs to the N of the gully** the lower flow can be seen to sit, with a vesicular base, on a bed of grey sandstone; this flow has a thickness of over 20 m and it has an uneven, red-weathered upper surface. The upper flow rests on this surface, also has a vesicular base, and reaches a thickness of 19 m. Ziegler *et al.* (1969, p. 433) correlate these basalts with those exposed at the Anvil (SM 7555 0885) on the S side of Cable Bay in the Wooltack sections opposite Skomer; the Anvil basalts are some way below, and hence older than, those exposed at Limpet Rocks and in Renney Slip, described at locality 2.

Between localities 3B and 3C the basalts are succeeded by a distinctive group of sediments some 90 m in thickness, consisting mainly of sandstones, silty mudstones and conglomerates with numerous tuffaceous bands. Fossils are scarce, but *Lingula* sp. occurs in some of the tuffaceous mudstone bands towards the top. The sandstones and siltstones are mainly grey and green, and many of the beds display cross bedding, ripple marks, scour structures and burrows. The conglomerates and coarse pebbly sandstones contain a wide variety of pebbles, dominated by quartz and igneous rocks. Tuffaceous bands occur throughout the succession, with the most distinctive horizon occurring approximately 70 m above the basalt flows; this horizon is a 6 m thick brecciated tuff, the top 0.5 m of which is reworked and rippled. Ziegler *et al.* (1969, p. 433) correlate this tuff with that exposed below the basalt at Limpet Rocks and Renney Slip (see locality 2). At Marloes the basalt itself is not developed, the flow presumably not having spread over that distance. The 15 - 20 m of sediments following the thick tuff are considerably finer than those below, with siltstones and sandy mudstones as the dominant rock types. In addition to *Lingula,* favositid corals, *Leptaena* sp. and rhynchonellid brachiopods occur rarely.

At locality **3C** is the distinctive landmark known as the **Three Chimneys** (SM 7860 0732), formed by three near-vertical beds of sandstone which stand out in the cliff from the softer, weathered, interbedded siltstones. Above this horizon the topmost beds of the Skomer Volcanic Group are represented by about 60 m of flaggy bedded silty mudstones with thin sandstones and decalcified fossil bands; the fauna of these bands includes *Favosites* sp., ?*Rhabdocyclus* sp., *Leptaena* sp., rhynchonellids, broken crinoid columnals, *Tentaculites* sp., and indeterminate bivalves. A small fault visible in the cliffs and near the top of the unit 'cuts out no great thickness of strata' (Ziegler *et al.* 1969, p. 434). The whole of the sequence of the Skomer Volcanic Group, from the fault along the E of Mathew's Slade to locality 3D, is interpreted (Ziegler *et al.,* 1969) as being of shallow water, near shore origin, probably deposited around the coast of an island separated from the mainland which lay to the SE around Skomer. Regional evidence from thickening of the lavas, flow banding, and structures in the volcanically derived sediments suggest that the island was a volcanic island only a short distance to the NW (Sanzen-Baker 1972, p. 141).

A **broad embayment in the cliffs** (SM 7800 0725) marks the line of the fault in the top beds of the Skomer Volcanic Group, a few metres to the E of which (locality **3D**) they are overlain unconformably by the Coralliferous Group. The angular discordance of 5° - 10° between the two units is best seen by standing back a little way from the cliffs. The basal 10 m of the Coralliferous Group consist of sandstones and conglomerates, which then pass up into blue-grey, cleaved silty mudstones with thin sandstones and shelly, calcareous lenses. About 10 m S of the unconformity the first richly fossiliferous beds are exposed in the **roof of a small cave** (locality **3E,** SM 7872 0724). The coral *Palaeocyclus porpita* and the brachiopod *Eocoelia sulcata* are especially common, the association of the two species indicating the presence of beds low in Fauna II (Fig. 2; Walmsley & Bassett 1976, figs. 4, 8, 9) and providing a firm correlation with the topmost Upper Llandovery (C_6), while the abundance of *Eocoelia* is indicative of an *Eocoelia* community in an inshore Benthic Assemblage. This fauna is also important in demonstrating that the base of the Coralliferous Group above the unconformity is synchronous from Renney Slip (locality 2) to Marloes, and that the unconformity can therefore be taken as a regional datum in correlation. Slightly higher beds yield abundant *C. lirata lirata,* still indicating a C_6 age but now providing evidence of deepening water conditions to accommodate the *Costistricklandia* community in a further offshore assemblage (Ziegler 1965; Ziegler *et al.* 1968; Boucot 1975).

From the cave at 3E the Coralliferous Group crops out for about 150 m to the SE along the beach, through a total stratigraphical thickness of close to 100 m. The section is cut by numerous minor faults. In addition to the species already mentioned the following fossils occur:— *Favosites* sp. and numerous small corals, *A. reticularis,* ?*Isorthis* sp., *E. radiatus, Howellella* sp., *Microsphaeridiorhynchus nucula, Mclearnites coralli,* and *Tentaculites* sp. Bentonites and tuffaceous bands occur throughout the succession.

Costistricklandia and *Palaeocyclus* continue to occur for about 30 m above the base of the Group, but for about 10-20 m above that *Costistricklandia* is rare and finally disappears. This genus occurs rarely in the Woolhope Limestone, of basal Wenlock (Sheinwoodian) age, in the Welsh Borderland so that a general correlation with that horizon is suggested; there is thus a conformable Llandovery-Wenlock transition within the lower half of the Coralliferous Group, and throughout the remainder of its thickness it is of Wenlock age. Unlike at Deadman's Bay, *Eocoelia angelini,* the diagnostic element of Fauna III, has not yet been found at Marloes, but the general similarity of the sequence suggests that the upper beds of the Coralliferous Group are still of Sheinwoodian age (Fig. 2).

Both at Renney Slip and Marloes the basal conglomerates and sandstones of the Coralliferous Group have a similar composition to those of the underlying Skomer Volcanic Group, and were thus probably from the same source. Large symmetrical ripples oriented from NW to SE suggest a nearby shoreline of similar trend. Thin sandstone and siltstone units in mudstones of the middle of the Coralliferous Group display scours and cross bedding structures, which may indicate intermittent wave agitation during storms (Sanzen-Baker 1972, p. 145). Higher beds include graded sandstones with some sole marks indicating flow from the S, and towards the top of the Group a gradual coarsening indicates the onset of shallowing conditions.

Slightly to the N of locality **F** the Coralliferous Group passes upwards into the Gray Sandstone Group, but the transitional beds are obscured by a large mass of fallen blocks. Lithological differences between the two units involve a change from hard, blue-grey cleaved mudstones into flaggy bedded sandstones and siltstones and softer brown and grey sandy mudstones with thin rottenstone bands. Fossils are rare in the lowest beds of the Gray Sandstone Group, but include the brachiopods *M. coralli, A. reticularis, P. freshwaterensis* and *Howellella* sp., together with favositid corals. Although limited, these elements indicate the presence of Fauna IV, whose conformable superposition above an early Wenlock horizon at Deadman's Bay (locality 2) suggests that it too is of early to mid Wenlock age, thus providing a correlation for the base of the Gray Sandstone Group.

From locality F, which displays a number of thin fossil bands in the lowest beds, the Gray Sandstone Group then extends some 350 m to the SE, occupying a total thickness approaching 320 m. The higher beds include more sandstones than those at the base, with a distinctive unit of relatively soft grey sandy mudstones and sandstones in the middle division. The top 60 m or so comprise hard, greenish-grey quartzitic sandstones and tough, olive-yellow weathering mudstones which show evidence of bioturbation; *Lingula* sp., broken crinoid columnals, *Cornulites* sp., and indeterminate bivalves appear to be the only fossils present. This restricted fauna forms Fauna V of Walmsley & Bassett (1976), and its paucity through the middle and upper divisions of the Gray Sandstone Group makes their correlation and age determination difficult. However, since the beds were probably deposited fairly rapidly, their continuity above mid Wenlock horizons suggests that they are probably entirely of Wenlock age.

The gradual upward coarsening facies of the Gray Sandstone Group indicate increasing current activity and greater sand supply. Ripples, scours and cross bedding are common throughout. Sanzen-Baker (1972, p. 145) has interpreted the lower part of the sequence as being of coastal marine origin, passing up into higher beds which retain marine facies between deltaic distributary bar deposits; channelling becomes increasingly common through the uppermost 60 m of the section and there is some evidence of slumping. Air heave structures suggest the presence of intertidal deposits, and the complete sequence suggests the advance of a delta building up through an intertidal zone and into the fluviatile floodplain represented by the succeeding Old Red Sandstone.

The **sea stacks S of the cliff line** at locality **3G** display the highest beds of the Gray Sandstone Group in which there are interbedded red sandstones heralding the onset of the Old Red Sandstone facies a few metres higher. At locality **3H** the transitional base of the Old Red Sandstone facies is clearly marked in the **main cliff section** (SM 7896 0678) by a broad arrow, cut in the rock by the officers of the Geological Survey; this horizon marks the major change in the colour of the sediments from greenish-grey to red, though as noted above there is some alternation slightly below. The red beds belong to the Red Cliff Formation of the Milford Haven Group (Allen & Williams 1978). The age of the transition from the Gray Sandstone Group to the red beds remains in some doubt. Allen & Williams (1978, p. 131) point out that within the transitional sequence there are sandstones with sharp, erosional bases which might point towards a substantial break. Walmsley & Bassett (1976, p. 208) had previously considered that the basal red facies could be of late Wenlock age (or at the youngest early Ludlow), based on the view that the transitional sequence is conformable and follows above lower horizons that can be dated as no younger than Wenlock; certainly the scouring within the transitional zone is no more severe than within much of the underlying Gray Sandstone Group itself and the sedimentary structures are consistent with those produced in an upward transition from marine through deltaic to fluviatile facies; in the absence of firm faunal control in the boundary sequence the question of age remains equivocal. One important point to note is that no undoubted Ludlow faunas have been identified anywhere in Dyfed.

From locality 3H the Red Cliff Formation and succeeding Albion Sands Formation can be examined for a few hundred metres to the S **(3I).** The succession is similar to that described at the opposite (NW) end of Marloes Sands in excursion 8 of this volume.

Returning to Mathew's Slade (3A) much of the sequence outlined above can be followed W and SW to the **cliffs N of Gateholm. Immediately W of Mathew's Slade** sediments at the top of the Gray Sandstone Group **(3J)** correspond closely in position to those described at 3F. The **valley leading from the beach to the car park** is cut in beds of the Coralliferous Group, outcrops of which can be examined in the **path around 3K.** On the N side of the **sharp bend in the path above 3K,** basaltic lava can be traced, apparently underlying the Coralliferous Group directly; the flow probably correlates with one in the higher part of the Skomer Volcanic Group, and as there appears to be no evidence of a faulted junction it has been suggested (Cantrill *et al.* 1916, p. 65; Ziegler *et.al.* 1969, p. 431) that the Coralliferous Group here provides evidence of overlap across the underlying beds.

Outcrops of the Coralliferous Group can be followed in the **foreshore** for just over 200 m to the SW from the path on to the beach, as far as **3L,** where there is a faulted junction with the overlying Gray Sandstone Group. The latter division is especially well displayed around locality **3M,** where there are large bedding surfaces exposed in steep, seaward dipping sandstone units. At **3N** the Gray Sandstone Group passes into Old Red Sandstone facies of the Red Cliff Formation, the junction beds apparently being slightly faulted. The cliffs S of this point, and the whole of the island of Gateholm, are in red bed facies and are described in detail in excursion 8, this volume.

4. Dale. From Marloes return E to the B4327 S of Mullock Bridge (SM 8090 0770) and take the road S to Dale village. On the **foreshore on the W side of the Dale estuary,** 760 m NE of Dale Church (SM 8100 0646), there is a further transitional sequence from the upper Gray Sandstone Group into the Red Cliff Formation; the general relationships and facies are similar to those described at locality 3.

5. In contrast to the extensive coastal sections at localities 2, 3, and 4 marine Silurian rocks are poorly exposed inland in the Marloes peninsula. However, a narrow strip known as the Winsle inlier, extending from Sandyhaven Pill near Tucking Mill (SM 863 088), via Upper Winsle (SM 835 093) to Orlandon (SM 811 094) has a few localities that are easily accessible and worthy of examination. Locality **5** is on and adjacent to the B4327 road at **Slatemill Bridge** (SM 8215 0917), where there are exposures in the **stream bed** and in the **road bank at the sharp bend** N of the bridge. In recent years there have also been a number of good temporary exposures in the foundation of buildings on the W side of the road. The beds belong to the Coralliferous Group and the temporary exposures especially have proved to be richly fossiliferous; unlike the coastal sections the fossils are hardly distorted by cleavage. The following fauna has been obtained:— *Mclearnites coralli, Atrypa reticularis, Leptaena melinae, Howellella* cf. *elegans,* ?*Isorthis* sp., *Favosites* sp., ?*Rhabdocyclus sp., Calymene* cf. *blumenbachi,* beyrichiid ostracodes, crinoid stems and bivalves. This assemblage belongs to Fauna IV of Walmsley & Bassett (1976), indicating that the beds correlate with a high horizon of the Coralliferous Group on the coast.

The beds of the Coralliferous Group around Slatemill Bridge dip to the S as part of the southern limb of an anticline through the Winsle inlier, but only some 120 m to the SW **among the old buildings of Slatemill Farm** (SM 8201 0913) there are thick sandstones which both dip and young to the N. These are the basal beds of the Gray Sandstone Group in the southern limb of a tight syncline along the southern margin of the Winsle inlier (Walmsley & Bassett 1976, fig. 10; Allen *et al.* 1976, p. 223). Red soils indicating the outcrop of Old Red Sandstone facies appear about 50 m farther S, but no junction is exposed. Red beds of the Sandy Haven Formation crop out in an old quarry on the S side of the B4327 road at SM 819 088, and since these dip steeply to the S they indicate that the contact with the marine Silurian is not conformable.

6. Winsle Valley (Fig. 4). Beds in the central part of the Winsle inlier are exposed in an **old quarry** (SM 8330 0935, locality **6A) along the side of the reservoir** at the site of the old mill in the small valley 200 m W of Upper Winsle. Access to the reservoir is along a narrow track off the minor road just W of Upper Winsle (SM 8339 0921), and **permission to examine the exposures** should be obtained from the occupants of the house at the end of the track. The rocks again belong to the Coralliferous Group, but unlike the Slatemill exposures (locality 5) the beds are here strongly cleaved and the fossils are distorted and flattened; however a rich fauna can be obtained, including *M. coralli, Coolinia* cf. *pecten, L. melinae, E. radiatus, Howellella* sp., *Atrypa reticularis, Meristina* sp., *Microsphaeridiorhynchus* sp., ?*Sphaerirhynchia* sp., *Rhynchotreta* sp., *Calymene* cf. *blumenbachi, Dalmanites* sp.. *Proetus* sp., *Favosites* sp., *Rhabdocyclus* sp., gastropods and bivalves; this fauna is

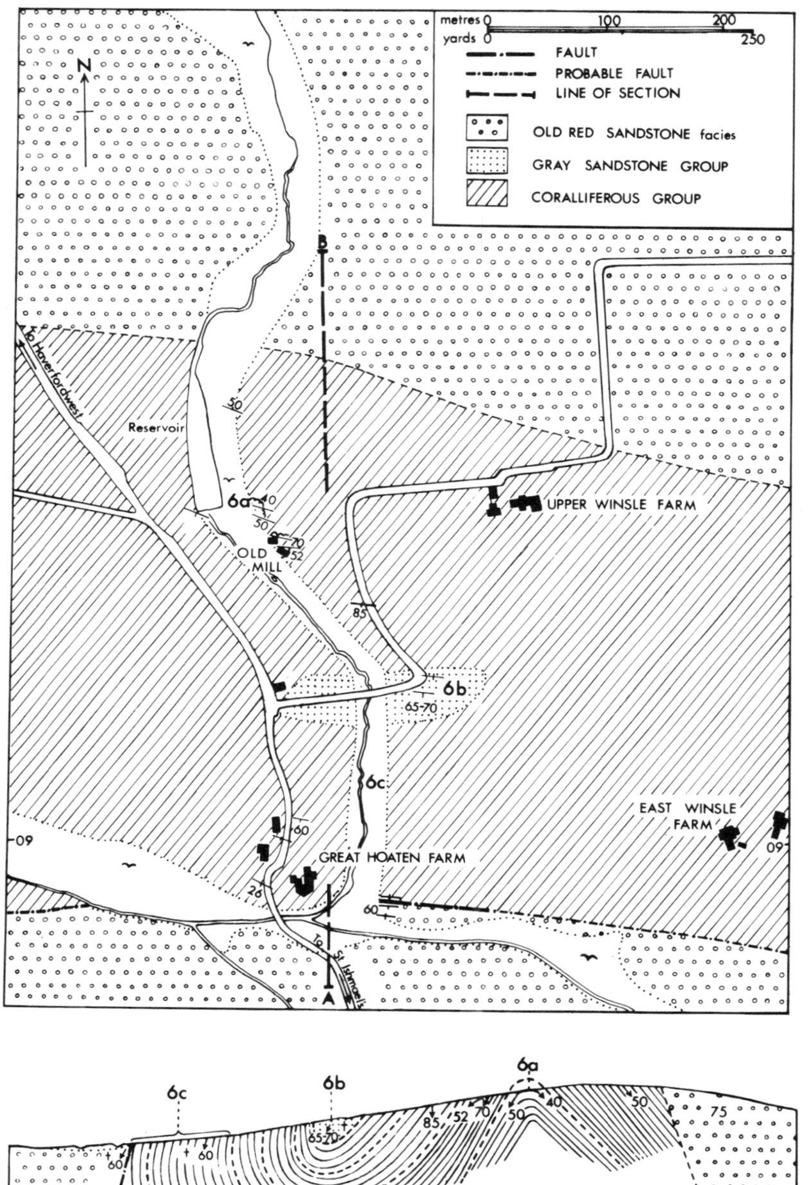

Fig. 4. Geological map and section through the Winsle Valley (locality 6); based on Walmsley & Bassett (1976, fig. 11) and Allen *et al.* (1976).

again part of Fauna IV of Wenlock age.

At locality **6A** the beds form the core of an anticline, which although not obvious at first examination because of the strong cleavage, can be confirmed by careful tracing of bedding relationships. To the **N of the quarry** exposure is poor, but within a short distance the soil indicates the presence of Old Red Sandstone facies (Fig. 4); the anticline appears to be a structure whose core runs close to the N margin of the Winsle inlier throughout its length, with the red beds to the N probably resting unconformably on the northern limb (Allen *et al.* 1976).

From locality 6A at the Old Mill, return along the track to the minor road and proceed S for about 100 m to the **sharp bend in the road** at SM 8343 0916 (locality **6B,** Fig. 4). Here vertical beds of the Gray Sandstone Group crop out. Within a few metres to the S the Coralliferous Group then reappears, and from there extends through the **abandoned mill race** (locality **6C**) to the S margin of the inlier opposite Great Hoaten Farm (SM 8343 0898). In the mill race the Coralliferous Group is near vertical or dips steeply to the S, but bedding/cleavage relationships indicate that younging is to the N; together with the evidence of younger, Gray Sandstone beds to the N at locality 6B, this shows therefore that the southern half of the inlier comprises an overturned syncline (Fig. 4). At the **S end of the mill** race the contact with the Old Red Sandstone appears to be a fault (Allen *et al.* 1976, p.225); the red beds both dip and young consistently to the S.

7. Lindsway Bay. S of the village of St. Ishmael's the Silurian is again exposed on the coast in the seies of bays between Watch House Point and Great Castle Head. The outcrop is generally referred to as Lindsway Bay, but also includes Wenall Bay and Watch House Bay, all of which may be reached by taking the footpath to the SE across the fields from the road-fork 200 m E of St. Ishmael's School (SM 8326 0720). The cliffs are steep and a boat is needed for a full examination, but access to the inlets can be gained at a number of points. Beds of the Coralliferous Group and Gray Sandstone Group occupy the central part of the section, flanked in the headlands on either side by Old Red Sandstone facies. As all these horizons have been described in the Marloes Bay sections (locality 3), a detailed itinerary here is not necessary; students who wish to visit the area should be guided by the account and map in the Geological Survey Memoir (Cantrill *et al.* 1916, pp. 77-83, text-figs. 16, 17), and by the map of Walmsley & Bassett (1976, fig. 5). The sequence through the Old Red Sandstone facies at this locality is described in excursion 8, this volume.

8. Spreadeagle Pill and Sandyhaven Pill. Important evidence bearing on the nature of the contacts between marine Silurian rocks and Old Red Sandstone facies on both margins of the Winsle inlier can be examined at the E extremity of the inlier; the sections on the **N side of the road** (SM 861 088) **W**

of Spreadeagle Pill and on the **NW shore of Sandyhaven Pill** (SM 863 088) are described in excursion 8, this volume (see also Allen *et al.* 1976, p. 224; Walmsley & Bassett 1976, fig. 12).

ITINERARY 2

9. Freshwater East is reached by taking the A4139 road E from Pembroke or W from Tenby, and turning S on the B4584 in Lamphey; a minor road off the B4584 at SS 0188 9845 descends sharply to the head of the bay, where there is ample parking space for vehicles.

The solid geology in the valley running down to the bay, and much of the foreshore itself, is obscured by blown sand and alluvium. Systematic geological mapping (Dixon 1921) indicates that beneath the drift cover the structure is broadly anticlinal, with Ordovician sediments of Llanvirn age (*bifidus* Shales) in the core of the fold being overlain unconformably by shallow marine to deltaic Silurian and then Old Red Sandstone rocks. The junction of the Ordovician and Silurian is not exposed, but the higher Silurian rocks crop out on both sides of the bay. Structural details of this locality are described in excursion 12, locality 1, this volume.

The sequence is best examined in the **southern outcrop** (SS 015 975), along the **foreshore and in the cliffs** of the NW side of the promontory which extends seawards to terminate at Trewent Point. Here some 60 m of Silurian beds dipping to the SSW at 40 - 50° are exposed below Old Red Sandstone facies.

The lowest 10 m at present exposed consist of grey-green sandy siltstones and mudstones with included shale fragments, and thin decalcified sandstone or 'rottenstone' bands. Fossils are fairly common, especially brachiopods, which include *Pembrostrophia freshwaterensis, Atrypa reticularis, Leptaena* sp., *Howellella* sp., ?*Obturamentella* sp., ?*Microsphaeridiorhynchus* sp. and *Salopina conservatrix* (Mclearn). Favositid corals, the trilobite *Acaste subcaudata,* and bivalves, cephalopods and gastropods also occur.

The overlying 50 m of beds include more sandstones and sandy mudstones, with subordinate bands of grit and shale. Decalcified 'rottenstones' are numerous, most of them being very fossiliferous. All the fossils listed above from the underlying beds are present, with the addition of *Marklandella giraldi, Lingula* sp., *Nucleolites* sp., *Holopella* sp., tentaculitids, and *Trimerus* sp. Lithologically the complete sequence equates with the Gray Sandstone Group as developed N of Milford Haven, and the fauna belongs to Fauna IV of Walmsley & Bassett (1976), indicative of a middle Wenlock age. Hurst *et al.* (1978, p. 207) have suggested that the transgression of Gray Sandstone rocks over the Ordovician may have coincided with a more widespread deepening in earliest Ludlow times, but this view is at variance with the faunal evidence. The whole of the Skomer Volcanic Group, Coralliferous Group, and the lower part of the Gray Sandstone Group are missing at Freshwater.

The highest marine Silurian beds are succeeded by basal conglomerates and sandstones of the Old Red Sandstone, but the junction here appears to be along the line of a minor strike fault. The conglomerates are red and grey-green, with large pebbles of quartzite and milky quartz; they pass rapidly up into red sandstones and marls which form the remainder of the headland out to Trewent Point.

The **foreshore and cliffs on the N side of Freshwater East** bay (SS 022 981) again expose a thin sequence of Gray Sandstone Group overlain by Old Red Sandstone rocks. Some 20 m of shallow marine Silurian beds are present, consisting of alternating beds of sandstones, 'rottenstones', mudstones and siltstones, with a few prominent beds of tough, grey-green micaceous sandstone. The rottenstones contain a similar fauna to those of the southern outcrop. A few of the sandstone beds are current bedded and a number show scouring and minor channelling into the underlying units.

The basal Old Red Sandstone comprises a thick conglomeratic unit sitting unconformably on the Gray Sandstone Group, but with no angular discordance. From the green-grey micaceous sands and silts within the lower part of the Old Red Sandstone facies, Richardson & Lister (1969) have reported a spore flora of Downton age, suggesting that on the S side of Milford Haven the basal Old Red facies are younger than those to the N (see Fig. 3). From slightly higher beds Edwards (1979) has collected a rich Downton macroflora including species of *Cooksonia, Hostinella,* and *Torticaulis*.

10. Freshwater West. From Freshwater East continue SE along the minor road via Stackpole to join the B4319 leading to Castlemartin and Freshwater West. At the **S end of the bay** there is a section on the **foreshore** (SR 885 995), beginning just to the N of Little Furzenip. When the sand has been scoured by strong tides, black graptolitic shales of the Ordovician Llanvirn Series are sometimes exposed at the base of the exposed sequence; the shales contain *Didymograptus bifidus*. Unconformably overlying the Llanvirn shales are 11 m of Gray Sandstone beds dipping to the S, with similar facies and restricted faunas (Fauna IV, see Fig. 2) to those described at other localities in this excursion. The Gray Sandstone Group is followed unconformably by Old Red Sandstone facies, which are described in excursion 9, this volume. Structural details at this locality are described in excursion 12, locality 3, this volume.

A few metres of the Gray Sandstone Group are also exposed on the **foreshore on the N side of Freshwater West** (SM 879 006), again succeeded unconformably by Old Red Sandstone facies which are described in excursion 9, this volume; dips are constantly to the N, indicating that the bay is eroded in an anticline whose core is occupied by the soft Llanvirn shales.

REFERENCES

ALLEN, J. R. L., BASSETT, M. G., HANCOCK, P. L., WALMSLEY, V. G. & WILLIAMS, B. P. J. 1976. Stratigraphy and structure of the Winsle Inlier, south-west Dyfed, Wales. *Proc. Geol. Ass.* **87,** 221-230.

ALLEN, J. R. L. & WILLIAMS, B. P. J. 1978. The sequence of the earlier Lower Old Red Sandstone (Siluro-Devonian), north of Milford Haven, south-west Dyfed (Wales). *Geol. J.* **13,** 113-136.

BOUCOT, A. J. 1975. *Evolution and extinction rate controls.* 427 pp., Elsevier, Amsterdam, Oxford, New York.

CANTRILL, T. C., DIXON, E. E. L., THOMAS, H. H. & JONES, O. T. 1916. The geology of the South Wales Coalfield, Part 12. The country around Milford. *Mem. geol. Surv. U.K.* i-vii, 185 pp., 7 pls.

DIXON, E. E. L. 1921. The geology of the South Wales Coalfield. Part 13. The country around Pembroke and Tenby. *Mem. geol. Surv. U.K.* i-vi, 220 pp., 5 pls.

EDWARDS, D. 1979. A late Silurian flora from the Lower Old Red Sandstone of south-west Dyfed. *Palaeontology,* **22,** 23-52.

HURST, J. M., HANCOCK, N. J. & McKERROW, W. S. 1978. Wenlock stratigraphy and palaeogeography of Wales and the Welsh Borderland. *Proc. Geol. Ass.* **89,** 197-226.

RICHARDSON, J. B. & LISTER, T. R. 1969. Upper Silurian and Lower Devonian spore assemblages from the Welsh Borderland and South Wales. *Palaeontology,* **12,** 201-252.

SANZEN-BAKER, I. 1972. Stratigraphical relationships and sedimentary environments of the Silurian-early Old Red Sandstone of Pembrokeshire. *Proc. Geol. Ass.* **83,** 139-164.

THOMAS, H. H. 1911. The Skomer Volcanic Series (Pembrokeshire). *Q. Jl geol. Soc. Lond.* **67,** 175-214.

WALMSLEY, V. G. & BASSETT, M. G. 1976. Biostratigraphy and correlation of the Coralliferous Group and Gray Sandstone Group (Silurian) of Pembrokeshire, Wales. *Proc. Geol. Ass.* **87,** 191-220.

ZIEGLER, A. M. 1965. Silurian marine communities and their environmental significance. *Nature, Lond.* **207,** 270-272.

ZIEGLER, A. M. 1966. The Silurian brachiopod *Eocoelia hemisphaerica* (J. de C. Sowerby) and related species. *Palaeontology,* **9,** 523-543, pls. 83, 84.

ZIEGLER, A. M., COCKS, L. R. M. & BAMBACH, R. K. 1968. The composition and structure of Lower Silurian marine communities. *Lethaia,* **1,** 1-27.

ZIEGLER, A. M., McKERROW, W. S., BURNE, R. V. & BAKER, P. E. 1969. Correlation and environmental setting of the Skomer Volcanic Group, Pembrokeshire. *Proc. Geol. Ass.* **80,** 409-439.

8
THE OLD RED SANDSTONE NORTH OF MILFORD HAVEN

by J. R. L. ALLEN, R. G. THOMAS, *and* B. P. J. WILLIAMS

Maps	*Topographical:*	1 : 50 000 Sheet 157 St David's and Haverfordwest
		1 : 25 000 Sheets SM70, SM80, SM90, SN00
	Geological:	1 : 50 000 Sheets 226/227 Milford Haven, 228 Haverfordwest

THE Old Red Sandstone (ORS) to the N of Milford Haven (Fig. 1) presents a continuous succession several kilometres thick, but was described only in very general terms by the early surveyors of the Geological Survey (Strahan *et al.* 1914; Cantrill *et al.* 1916), who subdivided the rocks merely into the Red Marls below and the Cosheston Group above. Consequently the beds have been little studied by geological parties, in contrast to the much more often demonstrated ORS rocks exposed S of Milford Haven (Dixon 1921). Recent work, however, has gone some way towards redressing the imbalance of knowledge. From N of the Haven Allen & Williams (1978) described a succession of Red Marls (renamed the Milford Haven Group) that is much thicker and more diverse than that to the S. Thomas (1978) gave for the first time a detailed stratigraphical and sedimentological account of the Cosheston Group, and showed from palynological evidence that this lithostratigraphical unit is a correlative of the Senni Beds in the Brecon Beacons, ranging in age between mid Siegenian and ?early Emsian.

The ORS succession in the area (Fig. 1) is as follows:

Cosheston Group (mid Siegenian to ?early Emsian)

Formation	Thickness
New Shipping Formation	320-400 m
Lawrenny Cliff Formation	210-250 m
Mill Bay Formation	540-600 m
Burton Cliff Formation	170-210 m
Llanstadwell Formation	265-340 m

Milford Haven Group (?Ludlow to early Siegenian)

Formation	Thickness
Gelliswick Bay Formation	1000-1500 m
Sandy Haven Formation (with Townsend Tuff Bed)	850-900 m

[**pp. 123-149** *In* BASSETT, M. G. **(ed.). 1982. Geological excursions in Dyfed, south-west Wales.**]

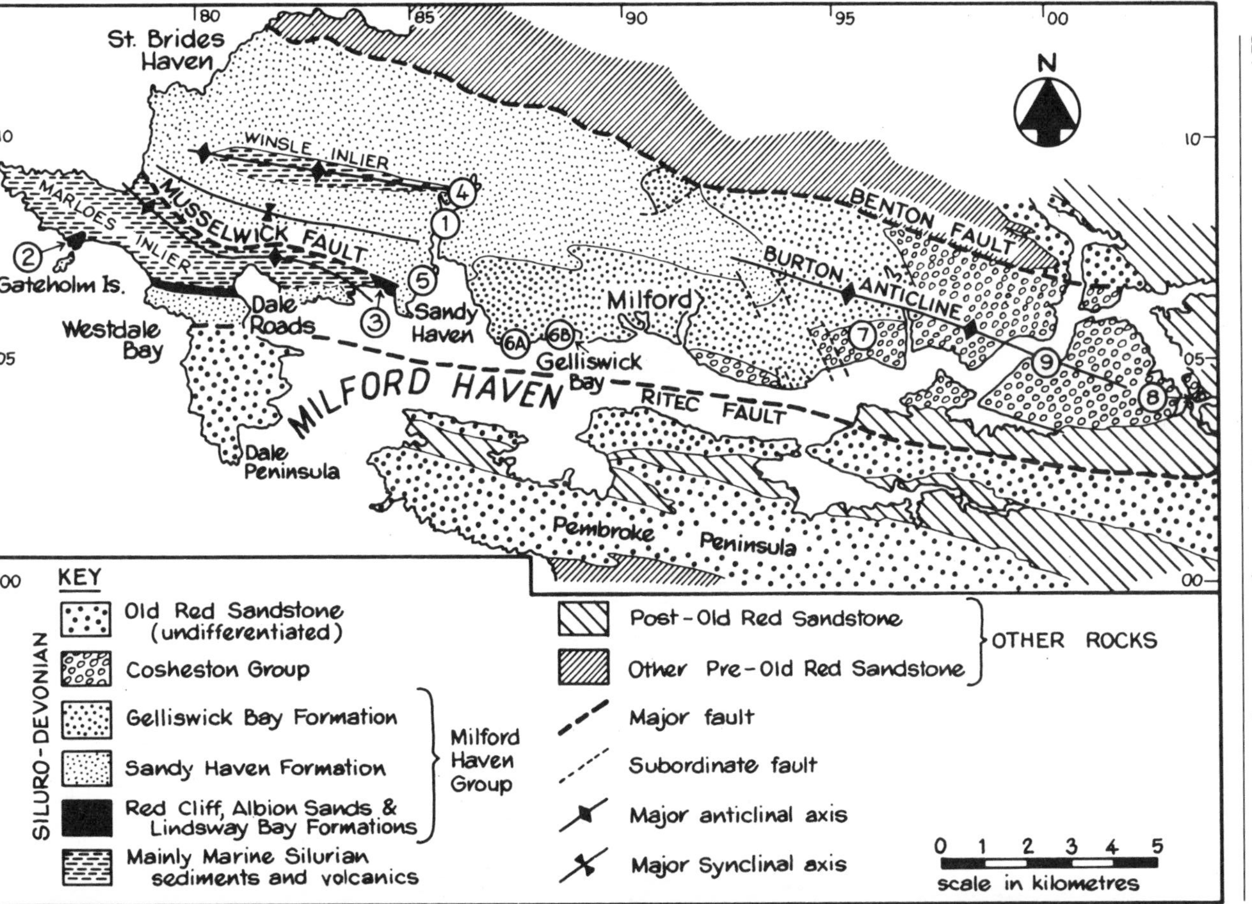

Fig. 1. Localities described in the text and the general distribution of Lower Old Red Sandstone rocks N of Milford Haven

Lindsway Bay Formation (interfingers with adjacent formations)	up to 81 m
Albion Sands Formation	up to 103 m
Red Cliff Formation	up to 52 m

Locally, the Red Cliff Formation at the base of the sequence rests unconformably on the underlying Silurian (see excursion 7, this volume), while the uppermost ORS in the area is succeeded unconformably by the Lower Carboniferous Lower Limestone Shales.

The name Milford Haven Group is assigned to distinctive formations characterised by substantial to predominating amounts of red to brown siltstones, accompanied in most instances by red to brown or purple sandstones. The Group is thickest and most complete in the Marloes Inlier, where the Red Cliff Formation (locality 2), apparently conformably overlying the grey and green, supposedly deltaic Gray Sandstone Group (Sanzen-Baker 1972; Walmsley & Bassett 1976), is overlain by the Albion Sands Formation (localities 2, 3), in turn succeeded by the Sandy Haven Formation (locality 1). The Red Cliff Formation comprises red siltstones with subordinate sandstones, occasional calcretes (fossil soils), and very rare air-fall tuffs. The Albion Sands Formation is a rapid interbedding of bundles of white, cross bedded quartzites with thinner red to brown siltstones and occasional air-fall tuffs and calcretes. Above come the thick red siltstones of the Sandy Haven Formation, associated with numerous sandstones, beds of very coarse sandstone and vein quartz conglomerate, abundant calcretes, and plentiful air-fall tuffs. In the middle of this Formation is a distinctive complex of tuffs, the Townsend Tuff Bed (about 4 m thick) (localities 1, 5) which serves as a marker horizon throughout the Lower Old Red Sandstone of SW Dyfed. The Lindsway Bay Formation (locality 3), in the Marloes Inlier, is the lateral equivalent of the middle and upper part of the Albion Sands Formation and the lowermost beds of the Sandy Haven Formation. Northwards from the Marloes Inlier, an unconformity develops at the base of the red beds. The Lindsway Bay Formation rests directly on the Silurian Coralliferous Group in the Winsle Inlier (locality 4), the Red Cliff and Albion Sands Formations being overlapped. The Lindsway Bay Formation is dominated by conglomerates rich in clasts of volcanic rocks, but includes thick red siltstones with calcretes and occasional air-fall tuffs. The Gelliswick Bay Formation (locality 6) is typified by cyclically arranged intraformational conglomerates, well bedded sandstones, and red siltstones with calcretes. Air-fall tuffs are few and confined to near the base.

The Red Cliff, Albion Sands, and Lindsway Bay formations have no correlatives to the S of Milford Haven, and the Sandy Haven Formation is much thicker than its southern equivalent. Likewise, the Gelliswick Bay Formation is thicker and coarser grained than the equivalent rocks to the S.

Fossils are rare in the Milford Haven Group, but indicate the presence of Gedinnian to early Siegenian horizons (Allen & Williams 1978). From the lower part of the Sandy Haven Formation, the fish spine ?*'Onchus' wheathillensis* has been collected at two horizons, at one of which it is associated with *Lingula* sp. Although onchids occur in both the 'Downtonian' and 'Dittonian' of Shropshire (Ball & Dineley 1961; White 1961), the association with a lingulid in the light of general Lower ORS facies developments suggests a 'Downtonian' rather than a younger age for the collections. Pteraspid fish, including several specimens of *Pteraspis (Belgicaspis) crouchi* have been found at many localities in the lower part of the Gelliswick Bay Formation, thus demonstrating an early-mid 'Dittonian' (late Gedinnian) age for this portion of the unit (Ball & Dineley 1961). The higher portion is probably early Siegenian.

The Cosheston Group is a further thick sequence of distinctive formations which, occurring down-plunge in the Burton Anticline (Figs. 1, 8), succeed the Milford Haven Group without a depositional break. We use the term Cosheston Group in essentially the same sense as Strahan *et al.* (1914), who introduced it. They informally identified a lower subdivision of the Group, composed of green sandstones, associated with subordinate red sandstones, red or green siltstones and green intraformational conglomerates, all arranged in fining upward cycles. The Llanstadwell (locality 7), Burton Cliff, and Mill Bay (locality 9) formations correspond to the lower subdivision of Strahan *et al.* (1914). Their upper subdivision, represented by the Lawrenny Cliff and New Shipping (locality 8) formations, consists of sandstones and siltstones similar to those below, though frequently coarse grained and red-brown, associated with breccias and conglomerates composed of a wide variety of rock types (acid lavas and pyroclastics, acid intrusives, various sandstones, metaquartzites, and other metamorphic rocks). The total thickness of 3050 m claimed for the Cosheston Group by Strahan *et al.* (1914) is reduced by approximately one-half when account is taken of the many parasitic folds present within the Burton Anticline.

Dispersed miospores extracted from the lowermost four formations of the Cosheston Group demonstrate a mid to late Siegenian age for the beds (Thomas 1978). Two individually rich but quite different microfloral assemblages have been distinguished. The lower occurs only in the Llanstadwell Formation, but the higher ranges up to the lower part of the Lawrenny Cliff Formation. The New Shipping Formation seems to be barren.

ITINERARY

Although this excursion is arranged mainly in a stratigraphical order, it is designed to allow the user freedom to study localities individually and thus to arrange his own plans, according to geological interests, time available, size of party, and means of transport.

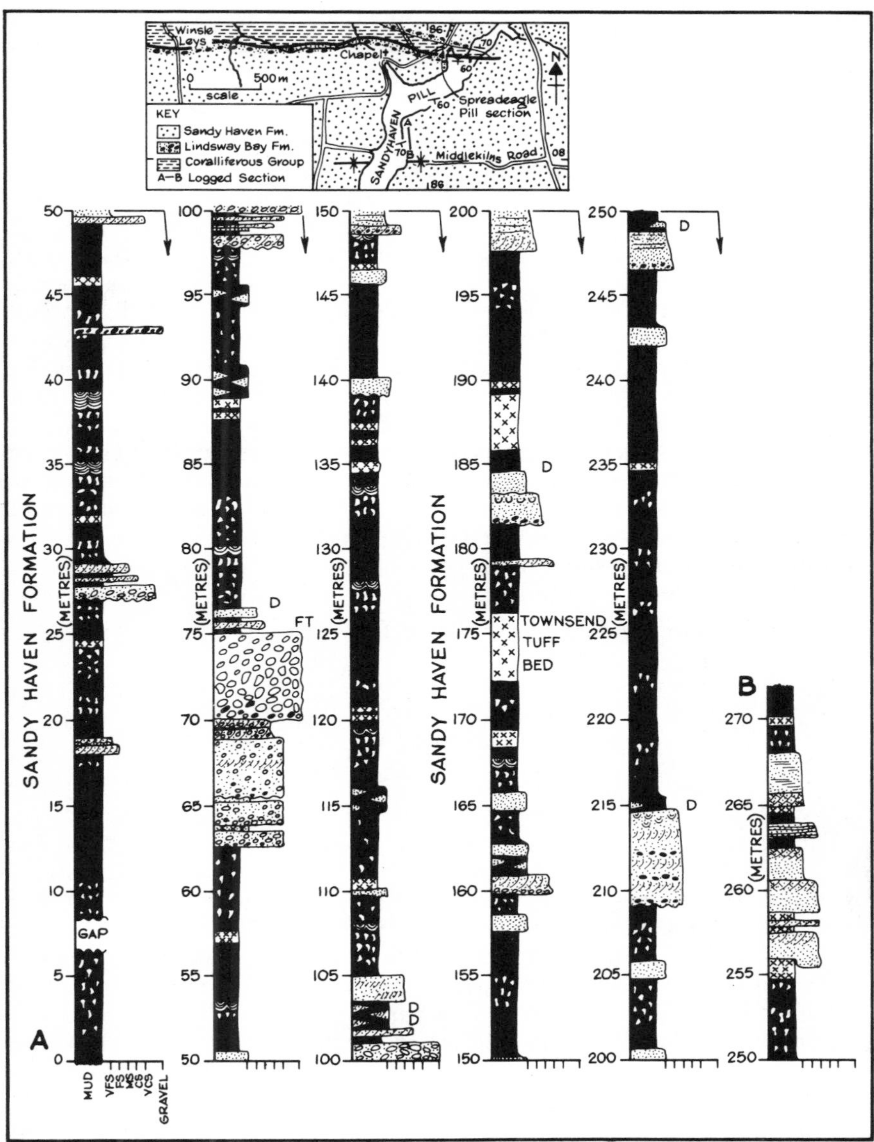

Fig. 2. The Sandy Haven Formation at Middlekilns Road. See Fig. 4 for key to symbols.

1. Middlekilns road (Sandyhaven Pill E bank). The narrow lane called Middlekilns Road leads W from the main road at Herbrandston to the foreshore on the E bank of Sandyhaven Pill (Figs. 1, 2). A few cars can be parked at the bottom of the lane, and the exposures can be worked at practically every stage of the tide.

The **section N of the bottom of Middlekilns Road** (SM 8587 0799 to 8580 0830) exposes the middle division of the Sandy Haven Formation, composed of bright red mudstones with nodular and pseudo-anticlinal calcretes, purple, brown and grey-green lithic sandstones, and occasional exotic granule to pebble grade conglomerates mainly dominated by vein quartz clasts. However, the striking feature of the division is the abundance of air-fall tuffs. These are variegated in colour — yellow, red, lilac, blue, magenta, and purple — and were called 'magenta beds' by the Geological Survey (Strahan *et al.* 1914; Cantrill *et al.* 1916) who suggested their possible volcanic origin. Twenty-two individual horizons are identifiable, varying in thickness from 0.02 to 3.86 m, and ranging in grain size from very fine, 'soapy', clay grade dust tuffs to coarse to very coarse grained crystal tuffs. Porcellanitic developments can be found, particularly in the thicker units. Most of the airfall units are relatively thin and cannot yet be correlated with other sections in the Sandy Haven Formation.

Within the middle division of the Sandy Haven Formation is a most distinctive complex of air-fall tuffs (*c.* 4 m thick) which serves as an excellent regional marker horizon and can be correlated over a wide area. This unit is called the Townsend Tuff Bed, after a locality on the W side of Dale Roads (SM 812 060). This Tuff Bed, occurring 172.5 m above the base of the section (Fig. 2), comprises three falls, the two lowest each being terminated by a tough green porcellanite, and the highest beginning with a medium grained crystal tuff on an irregular erosion surface. The sharp top of the lowest porcellanite is strewn with large oval faecal pellets.

The full logged section at this locality is 272 m thick, with part of the upper division of the Sandy Haven Formation exposed at the S end. Lithological details are shown in Fig. 2. Of the 272 m, 212.6 m are mudstones (78%), 45.8 m comprise conglomerates and lithic sandstones (17%), and 13.6 m are of air-fall tuff (5%). The mudstones are well cleaved and coarse grained. Thickness of individual units is variable but several are in excess of 6 m. One unit, occurring 215.5 m above the base of the section, is 19.5 m thick. The mudstones generally contain calcrete in the form of scattered carbonate concretions, occasionally grading up into more nodular calcrete at the top of individual profiles. Carbonate filled pseudo-anticlinal calcretes are relatively rare in this sequence, most of the pseudo-anticlinal structures seen being mud filled. The bright red colour of many mudstone units is often masked by a blue mottling which follows burrows or rootlet tubes in the mudstone. Approximately 34 beds of conglomerate and sandstone have been logged.

Well developed exotic pebble grade conglomerates are rare, but two very prominent developments are found 70.3 and 99.7 m above the base of the section (Fig. 2). Both conglomerates are mainly massive internally, with rare cross bedding.

The sandstone units include a wide variety of grain sizes and composition. Their average thickness is 1.25 m but the range is from 0.1 to 5.35 m. The coarse to very coarse grained sandstones are pink and grey-green, generally quartzitic with scattered granules of vein quartz and mud flakes. Internally they are massive or cross bedded with occasional rippled tops. The lithic sandstones are brown, purple, or red and are very fine to coarse grained. The majority of the lithic sandstones are fine to medium grained, micaceous and internally flat and cross bedded. Some of these sandstones are burrowed, calcretised or show mud-crack infills on their upper surfaces. One thick lithic sandstone (5.35 m) is purple-brown, fine to medium grained, and occurs 209.26 m above the base of the section (Fig. 2). Internally this sandstone is cross bedded with sets of <0.55 m thickness and some sediment deformation features in its upper part. The sandstone is micaceous, contains seams of mudstone clasts, and has a sharp, uneven base. It occurs 32.95 m above the top of the Townsend Tuff Bed, and correlates well with a similar sandstone on Little Castle Head (SM 855 065).

The sedimentary facies of this section are suggestive of a major alluvial floodbasin development. The thick mudstone units with calcrete profiles indicate many long periods of geomorphic stability for sites distant from the main, active river courses. This stability allowed horizonation of the pedogenic calcrete profiles in the mudstones. The coarser lithotypes — exotic conglomerates, quartzitic and lithic sandstones — suggest short-lived, sudden events of possible sheet flood type from a northern source. Distant volcanic activity, perhaps to the W of the area, gave volcanic dust showers over the floodbasin mudstone deposits. The Townsend Tuff Bed complex can be traced throughout the entire region from Skokholm Island (SM 73 04) in the W to Old Castle Head (SS 07 96) in the E, representing an event of some significance in the depositional story of the Lower Old Red Sandstone in SW Wales.

2. **Albion Sands to Gateholm Island.** Access is from the large car park at Runwayskiln Farm (SM 779 081) via the Pembrokeshire Coast Path to the cliff top (SM 7716 0774), where a path descends steeply to the beach (Figs. 1, 3). Structural details at this locality are described in excursion 12, locality 9, this volume. The Albion Sands Formation is visible at any time, but a falling tide is necessary for a complete view of the Red Cliff Formation, and for access to Gateholm Island for the lower division of the Sandy Haven Formation. A total thickness of 247.5 m has been logged through the three formations at this locality.

A magnificent section through the oldest Lower Old Red Sandstone rocks

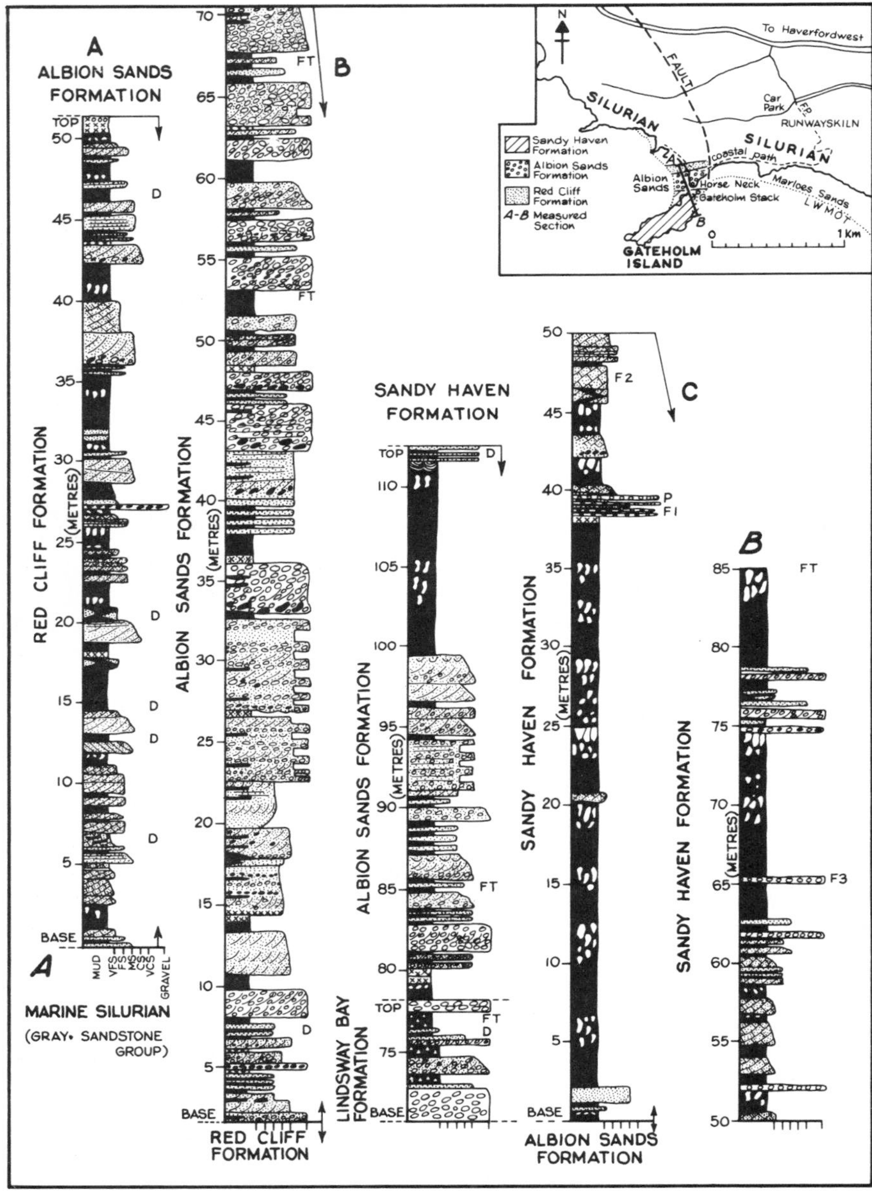

Fig. 3. The Red Cliff, Albion Sands, Lindsway Bay, and Sandy Haven formations between Albion Sands and Gateholm Island. See Fig. 4. for key to symbols.

is present on the S side of the Marloes Inlier at the **NW end of Marloes Sands** (Fig. 3). The section from the N side of Albion Sands (SM 7706 0770) to Gateholm Island (SM 7713 0722) exposes a complete sequence through the Red Cliff Formation and the Albion Sands Formation, plus an interbedded wedge of the Lindsway Bay Formation together with the lower division of the Sandy Haven Formation.

Although the Red Cliff Formation gains its name from a section at the SE end of Marloes Sands (see excursion 7, this volume), the type locality is at the **N end of Albion Sands.** On the cliffs and foreshore here the Red Cliff Formation comprises 51.6 m of steeply dipping beds (Fig. 3), made up of alternations on a scale of decimetres to metres of red to purple coarse mudstones with typically very fine to fine grained, red, purple or greyish pink sandstones. The mudstones are generally unlaminated but may include thin sandstone bands which are cross laminated and often lie on mud-cracked surfaces. Several mudstones include thin, poorly to moderately developed calcretes, in the form of layers of often vertically oriented carbonate concretions with blue haloes.

The sandstones are cross bedded, parallel- or cross laminated, and are up to 2.25 m thick. Many have sharp, down-channelling bases marked by a scattering of intraformational mudstone or calcrete clasts, sometimes accompanied by granules or small pebbles of quartz and orange-pink felsite. Many of the very fine grained sandstones-coarse mudstones show excellent bioturbation features, including the large trace fossil *Beaconites antarcticus.* A 0.95 m thick tuff is taken as the top of the Formation, and a thinner, soapy, dark red tuff occurs approximately 8 m below.

The contact between the Lower Old Red Sandstone (Milford Haven Group) and marine Silurian rocks (Gray Sandstone Group) of the Marloes Inlier is everywhere apparently structurally conformable, but whether it is transitional is open to debate (Allen & Williams 1978). The base of the Red Cliff Formation is placed at the base of a weakly scouring but laterally extensive grey-brown, fine to medium grained sandstone which overlies the locally red-stained grey and green mudstones and quartzites of the Gray Sandstone Group. Across this scoured surface there is, in our view, a major change of facies, from quartzites (flat bedded), wave- and current rippled) of marine aspect to mudstones (calcretised) and sandstones of fluvial type.

The Red Cliff Formation appears to represent near shore alluvium with representatives of both river channel and floodbasin environments. Periods of emergence are indicated by the calcretes and many mud-cracked surfaces. Occasional distant volcanic activity is evidenced by two air-fall tuff horizons.

The Albion Sands Formation also has its type section here at Albion Sands, where it conformably overlies the Red Cliff Formation. The Formation at this locality is 110.9 m thick. The Albion Sands Formation includes thick, pale yellow to buff, multistorey pebbly sandstones containing much igneous detritus. These sandstone units have sharp tops and bases, frequently containing large, often cobble grade intraformational mud clasts immediately overlying the lower erosional surface. The pebbly sandstones and conglomerates locally include beds of granule and pebble grade clasts of exotic fine grained lavas and vein quartz clasts.

Alternations of dark red, medium to coarse grained sandstones and laminated mudstones, often with mud-crack infills deflected along cleavage planes, are well seen in the Formation, particularly near the base and top of the section. Both the buff and dark red sandstone bodies are cross bedded throughout, planar and trough sets being equally abundant. Twenty one metres above the base of the Formation deformed cross bedding is seen in a 3.89 m thick conglomerate-sandstone complex. Three metres below is a channel 1.5 m deep with a steep, terraced side.

Air-fall dust and crystal tuffs occur throughout the Formation. These lithotypes are generally thinly developed, either as discrete decimetre-thick units or as alternations within a mudstone complex, but two prominent horizons are located 61 and 77 m above the base of the Formation. The lower unit is a 45 cm thick purple, medium to coarse grained tuffaceous sandstone, internally parallel laminated with scattered mud flakes. The upper unit, located on **Horse Neck** (Fig. 3) is a composite one comprisng 1m of lilac, purple, red, and yellow mottled dust tuff containing manganese and hematite nodules with scattered carbonate concretions.

The Albion Sands Formation, probably of braided stream origin, is distinguished from the Red Cliff Formation below and the overlying Sandy Haven Formation by its almost total absence of calcretes. Only two, very poorly developed horizons are seen near the top of the sequence. Elsewhere the mudstones are carbonate free. Between 69.14 m and 76.56 m above the base of the Albion Sands Formation, near Horse Neck (Fig. 3), an interbedded wedge of four exotic igneous pebble conglomerates interleaved with ill sorted granule rich mudstones is referable to the Lindsway Bay Formation, of alluvial fan origin. The top of the Albion Sands Formation is located on the **base of Gateholm Stack,** drawn above a 0.88 m thick unit of alternating coarse sandstones and mudstones, the sandstones being pebbly in their lower part. The contact is transitional with the overlying Sandy Haven Formation.

Only the lower division of the Sandy Haven Formation appears in this section between the base of the Formation on Gateholm Stack and the S tip of Gateholm Island, to a thickness somewhat in excess of 85 m (Fig. 3). The division comprises thick (up to 6m), bright red mudstone units often with blue mottles and calcretes. The calcrete are in the form of concretions, cylindroids and tubules, and some excellent profiles are seen on the E side of

Gateholm Island. The mudstones are associated with thin, sharply intercalated, green exotic conglomerates and pebbly sandstones. A quartz pebble conglomerate 38.8 m above the base of the Formation has yielded fish scales, spines referable to ?*'Onchus' wheathillensis,* and a specimen of *Lingula* sp. A second quartz pebble conglomerate, 65.5 m above the base, also yielded ?*'O'. wheathillensis.*

The exotic conglomerates comprise only 2% of the measured section, in contrast to 81% mudstone lithotypes. The conglomerate units are up to 0.75 m thick but average 0.10 m. The clast content is dominated by vein quartz, but green, ?Silurian siltstone and very fine grained sandstone clasts are present. Pink, feldspathic lava granules are also seen in some units. The conglomerates have sharp, erosional bases and tops and, internally, are locally cross bedded. The conglomerate units appear more abundant towards the top of the logged section. Red, fine to medium grained lithic or quartzitic sandstones are present in the section (Fig. 3). These sandstones are flat or ripple drift bedded and often show gradation into overlying mudstones. Cross bedding is rare and some sandstones are very fine grained and micaceous. Mudcracks and plant debris are also associated locally with some sandstones. Intraformational conglomerates and air-fall tuffs are extremely rare.

This description of the section at the NW end of Marloes Sands is applicable in broad terms to the Red Cliff and Albion Sands formations (with a wedge of the Lindsway Bay Formation) exposed at the SE end of Marloes Sands (see excursion 7, this volume, for details of location and the contact with underlying Silurian rocks).

3. Lindsway Bay. Access is from St. Ishmael's village (SM 835 073), where vehicles may be parked, via a footpath across the fields to the Pembrokeshire Coast Path, from which a descent can be made to the beach (SM 843 067) (Figs. 1, 4). Lindsway Bay exposes the Lower Old Red Sandstone and marine Silurian rocks on the northern limb of the Marloes anticlinal structure. The Red Cliff, Lindsway Bay and Sandy Haven formations are all present, but the main purpose here is to study the Lindsway Bay Formation in its type section (centre of bay to Rooks Nest Point (SM 8447 0642)).

The Red Cliff Formation appears on the **E side of Sprats Point** (SM 8423 0668), where it is complete, with 54.5% sandstone, but the thickness is a mere 16.2 m. The base, which is conformable on underlying marine Silurian rocks, is drawn beneath thick purple sandstones, apparently the same horizon as that chosen by Cantrill *et al.* (1916). The sandstones are very fine to medium grained and cross bedded or flat to ripple bedded. Interbedded mudstones, often with sandstone stripes, are blue mottled and contain rare calcrete concretions. The evidence of this section suggests that the Red Cliff Formation thins either to the E or toward the E and N.

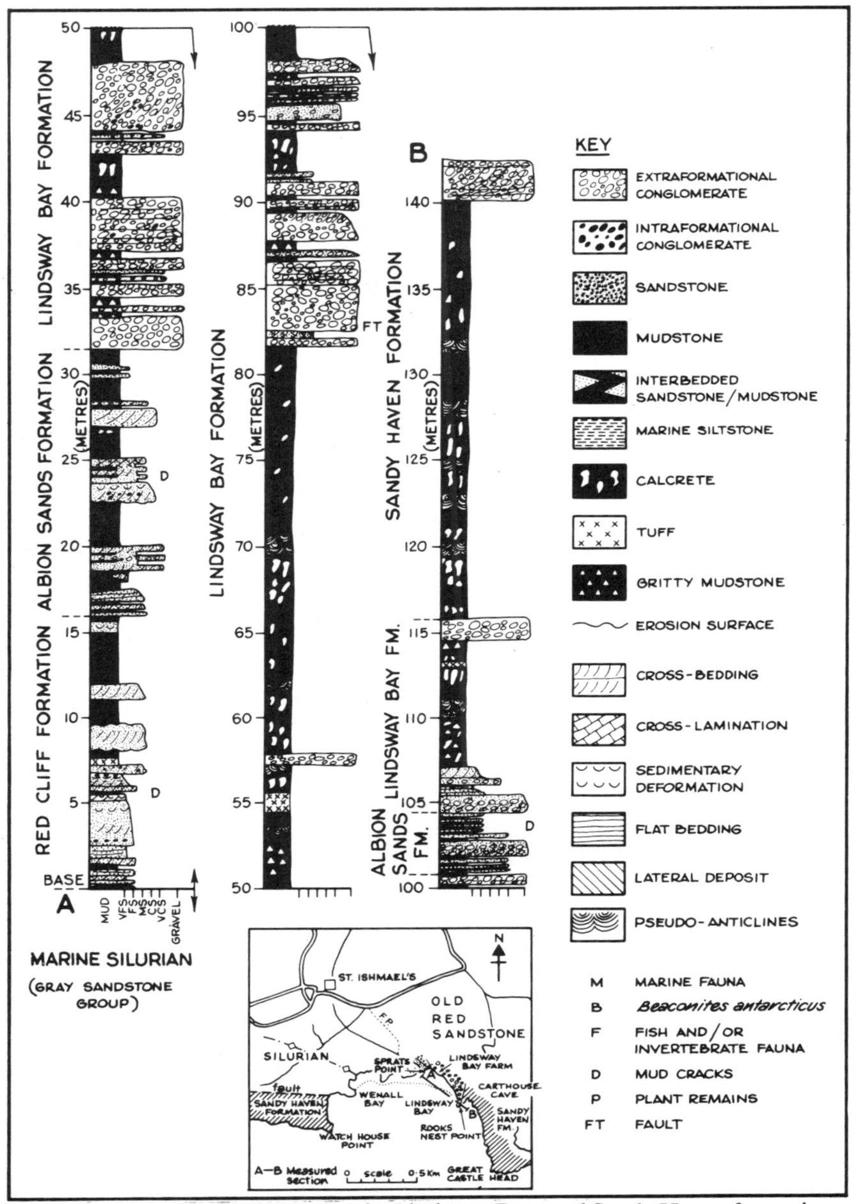

Fig. 4. The Red Cliff, Albion Sands, Lindsway Bay, and Sandy Haven formations at Lindsway Bay.

Lithologies typical of the overlying Albion Sands Formation occur in Lindsway Bay in 15.32 m and 3.67 m thick sequences occurring respectively below and above the Lindsway Bay Formation (Fig. 4). These lithologies include pebbly and quartzitic sandstones and alternating sandstone-mudstone units with mudcracks and bioturbation. The sandstones are medium to coarse grained, cross- and flat bedded, and have sharp erosional bases. The mudstones are bright red, coarse grained, and contain no calcrete profiles. The upper sequence assigned to the Albion Sands Formation includes some lithologies typical of the Lindsway Bay Formation and resembles the sequence between Horse Neck and Gateholm Stack on the Albion Sands section (locality 2). The upper sequence contains bright red mudstones, sometimes ill sorted with scattered granules of vein quartz, barren of calcrete. Interbedded units of grey-pink pebble conglomerates occur, the clasts comprising mainly vein quartz. Near the top of the upper sequence there are conspicuous pale purple quartz arenites; these are parallel laminated with rippled tops and are very similar to pale purple quartz arenites occurring towards the top of the Formation near Gateholm Stack and at Red Cliff.

The Lindsway Bay Formation attains its maximum thickness of 69.3 m at its type locality in Lindsway Bay. This Formation, essentially conglomeratic in aspect, interdigitates with the Albion Sands and Sandy Haven formations. The Formation thins westwards to Red Cliff and Albion Sands where it is 7.6 m and 7.4 m thick respectively. Pebble and cobble grade exotic conglomerates occurring in individual units up to 4.0 m thick (Fig. 4) account for more than 28% of the Formation. The conglomerates are poorly sorted, generally massive or flat bedded, with rare cross bedded sets. The clasts are dominated by igneous material, mainly lavas and acid intrusives, together with vein quartz, jasper, quartzites, epidotic rocks, and occasional mud flakes. The base of the Lindsway Bay Formation is drawn beneath the first prominent (2 m thick) conglomerate rich in igneous debris.

Another diagnostic lithology is ill sorted, granule-rich red mudstones with stringers of scattered vein quartz clasts. Other mudstones present are red or blue mottled, many of which contain calcrete in the form of nodules or tubules, or show pseudo-anticlinal structures. Some of these mudstone units reach 11 m in thickness (Fig. 4). Alternating units of sandstones and mudstones, often with sharp tops and bases, frequently show bioturbated horizons. Individual sandstone beds are rare, but those present are poorly sorted, very coarse grained, locally tuffaceous, and massive. Air-fall tuff horizons are represented by only one horizon, 1.13 m thick, occurring within the Lindsway Bay Formation proper. The Formation has many sedimentary features which indicate an alluvial fan origin. The fan sequence thins to the W and N, around the Winsle Inlier, suggesting an origin in a source area to the SE, perhaps defined by a proto-Ritec Fault.

On **Rooks Nest Point,** the interfingering of lithofacies referable to the Albion Sands, Lindsway Bay and Sandy Haven formations can be clearly demonstrated. Above the upper thin development of the Albion Sands Formation, rocks of both Lindsway Bay and Sandy Haven formation types occur. The interfingering of Lindsway Bay lithologies in the Sandy Haven Formation continues at least up to Carthouse Cave (SM 8455 0645).

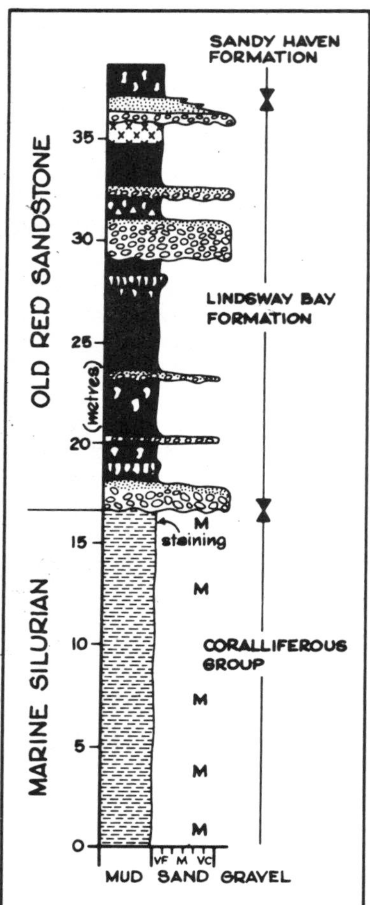

Fig.5. The marine Silurian and earliest Lower Old Red Sandstone rocks in the road cutting at Spreadeagle Pill. See Fig. 2 for location and Fig. 4 for key to symbols.

The lower division of the Sandy Haven Formation is typified on Rooks Nest Point by massive, bright red, coarse mudstone units up to 10.50 m thick and containing abundant calcrete in the form of concretions and tubules, with magnificent examples of large pseudo-anticlinal features, often mud filled (Fig. 4). These thick mudstone units, which underlie much of Rooks Nest Point, are interrupted only by sharply intercalated exotic igneous conglomerate wedges, up to 2.30 m thick, of Lindsway Bay type, the highest unit of which occurs in **Carthouse Cave.** In this lower division of the Sandy Formation some very fine to fine grained sandstone beds are present, together with some ill sorted mudstones and one air-fall tuff. The top of the logged section is in Carthouse Cave (Fig. 4), but the section continues SE through the lower division of the Sandy Haven Formation.

4. Spreadeagle Pill-Sandyhaven Pill. Minibuses and cars may be parked in the disused portion of the road at the valley bottom, and larger vehicles on the soft shoulders of the road 100-300 m to the SW. The unfossiliferous Lindsway Bay and Sandy Haven formations can be seen in relation to the richly fossiliferous Coralliferous Group in a **cutting on the NW side of the road** (SM 861 088) across the head of Spreadeagle Pill, and again in the **low**

cliffs on the NW shore of Sandyhaven Pill (SM 863 088) (Allen *et al.* 1976) (Figs. 2, 5).

Towards the **SW end of the road cutting,** red siltstones of the Sandy Haven Formation lie faulted with a gouge against the Coralliferous Group. At the partly overgrown **NE end of the cutting,** the Coralliferous Group is overlain sharply by a thin development of the Lindsway Bay Formation (Fig. 5), the Red Cliff and Albion Sands formations present to the S having been overlapped. A pink staining is developed progressively in the topmost 0.5 m of the Coralliferous Group, which nonetheless retains its lithological characteristics and richly fossiliferous nature from where it is olive-grey below. The lowest unit of the Lindsway Bay Formation is a pebble conglomerate rich in igneous debris which rests sharply, but with no evidence of faulting, on the Coralliferous Group. Sanzen-Baker's (1972, p. 149) contention that the Lindsway Bay Formation of the Winsle Inlier 'seems to continue from the Wenlock siltstones without a sedimentary break' is not supported by the evidence. The remainder of the Formation is an alternation of sharp-based, sometimes graded conglomerates with locally gritty siltstones, thin calcretes, and an air-fall dust tuff. The coarse beds may have been supplied from nearby sources to the S and E, possibly as a series of stream to debris-flow deposits. The change of facies from the Coralliferous Group to the Lindway Bay Formation is abrupt and profound.

A thicker sequence of the Coralliferous Group, including red calcareous siltstones and silty limestones, appears on the **NW shore of Sandyhaven Pill** (SM 863 088) (Fig. 2). Dips are steep to the N and NE. The S contact with the Lower Old Red Sandstone is an obvious fault associated with shattered and quartz-veined rock, to the S of which the Sandy Haven Formation forms a small anticline plunging to the ESE at a moderate angle. The N contact with the red beds is concealed beneath bushes in a stratigraphical gap of 1-2 m. It seems to involve an upward sequence, with a zone of stained siltstones and claystones, similar to that seen in the road cutting.

5. **Little Castle Head** (SM 855 065). The middle portion of the Sandy Haven Formation, including the Townsend Tuff Bed and a stratigraphically higher tuff, the Pickard Bay Tuff Bed, is here (Fig. 1) repeated four times in the limbs of mesofolds, allowing an impression to be formed of lateral variability within this part of the Old Red Sandstone succession. Access and structural details are described in excursion 12 (fig. 15) of this volume. Fig. 6 summarises the succession between the Townsend Tuff and Pickard Bay Tuff Beds on the four limbs.

The two Tuff Beds vary substantially in thickness between the four profiles but otherwise are uniform lithologically. The Townsend Tuff Bed is best seen in profiles A and C, whereas the Pickard Bay Tuff Bed (named after a locality S of Milford Haven) (excursion 9, this volume) is most readily examined in profiles B and D. The sharp, faeces-strewn top of the first fall, and the irregular erosional base of the third fall, are conspicuous features of the Townsend Tuff Bed. Interbedded dust tuffs and ripple marked crystal tuffs can be seen in the second and third falls of the Townsend Tuff Bed. The Pickard Bay Tuff Bed, although thick, is mainly of dust grade.

The four profiles (Fig. 6) reveal a complex succession of mudstones (several calcretised), sandstones, and minor air-fall tuffs. The tuffs, mudstones, and some of the calcretes are laterally persistent, but the sandstones, as befits their origin within channels and channel complexes, are very variable. Sandstone 1 thickens to the E across the Little Castle Head exposure, and is in two parts. The lower part, recognisable in all four profiles, but thinnest in profile D, consists of interbedded mudstones and often obscurely bedded sandstones, some preserving desiccation cracks below. In profile D these sandstones are considerably reduced in thickness by the erosively overlying upper sandstones, mainly purple cross bedded rocks. Sandstone 2, with prominent internal scours in profile B, thins to the E across the folds and appears to be absent from profile D. Sandstone 3 is the finest grained of all, consisting in all four profiles of interbedded mudstones and very fine grained cross laminated sandstones, some preserving desiccation cracks. This unit thins to the W, in contrast to the sandstones below.

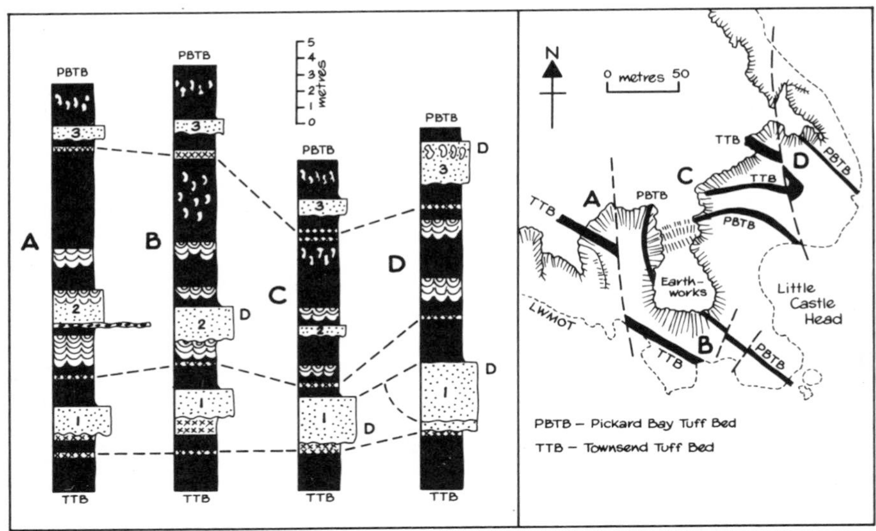

Fig. 6. Sketch map of Little Castle Head and comparative sections of the Sandy Haven Formation between the Townsend Tuff and Pickard Bay Tuff Beds. See Fig. 4 for key to symbols.

6. Little Wick (6A) and Gelliswick Bay (6B). Parking is available along the road crossing the head of Gelliswick Bay (SM 885 057) (Figs. 1, 7). Ascend the lane (joint with Pembrokeshire Coast Path) leading S and walk approximately 1.25 km to the steps leading down to the beach beneath the oil jetty at Little Wick. Skirt or climb the small rocky promontory by the slips on the W side of the inlet to gain access to the cliffs and foreshore to the W.

Coarse and fine grained facies assemblages in the lower part of the Gelliswick Bay Formation (Fig. 1) are well exposed on the **foreshore and cliffs W of Little Wick** (SM 873 054), in plunging parasitic folds which present an oblique strike section in the S limb of the Burton Anticline (Fig. 7). The Formation N of Milford Haven has a northerly and westerly provenance, in an area of mixed regional metamorphic, volcanic, and sedimentary rocks. The beds at Little Wick are divisible into coarse grade and fine grade groups which alternate on a scale generally of metres. The coarse grade groups comprise sandstones often with subordinate conglomerates (usually mixed intraformational and exotic clasts) and occasionally siltstones, and overlie laterally extensive major erosion surfaces. The fine grade groups are typified by sometimes mud-cracked siltstones with calcretes and subordinate, usually very fine grained sandstones in sharp-based, weakly graded units. Thin intra-formational conglomerates are occasionally present. The facies are fluvial in origin and the sequence compares well with other fluviatile rocks described from the Old Red Sandstone (Allen 1965*a, b,* 1970). The coarse grade groups represent zones of swiftly moving water, perhaps channels or the axial and proximal portions of sheet floods. The fine grade groups arose under calmer conditions, either of repeated submergence and emergence on floodplains or interfluvial areas, or where weak sheet floods reached only occasionally. The foreshore and cliff exposures afford an excellent opportunity to examine the lateral variability of these facies.

Now retrace the Pembrokeshire Coast Path from Little Wick as far as the **W side of Gelliswick Bay.** Keeping to the foreshore, round the point by the oil jetty on the W side, and walk W about 0.5 km to where the cliffs turn SW (SM 880 055). Traverse back to the E, ascending the succession.

This traverse, within moderately dipping beds on the long N limb of a parasitic anticline, is through approximately 245 m (Fig. 7) of the Gelliswick Bay Formation (Fig. 1). The facies are similar to those at Little Wick, but it is now possible to emphasise their vertical relationships rather than lateral variability. Ostracoderm remains, including *P. (Belgicaspis) crouchi,* occur at seven levels in the logged sequence, mainly in the conglomerates and coarser sandstones, and the large trace fossil *Beaconites antarcticus* abounds in the finer grained rocks.

From the W limit of the traverse to the first cove the sequence ascends from a coarse through a fine to a coarse grained facies assemblage. What may

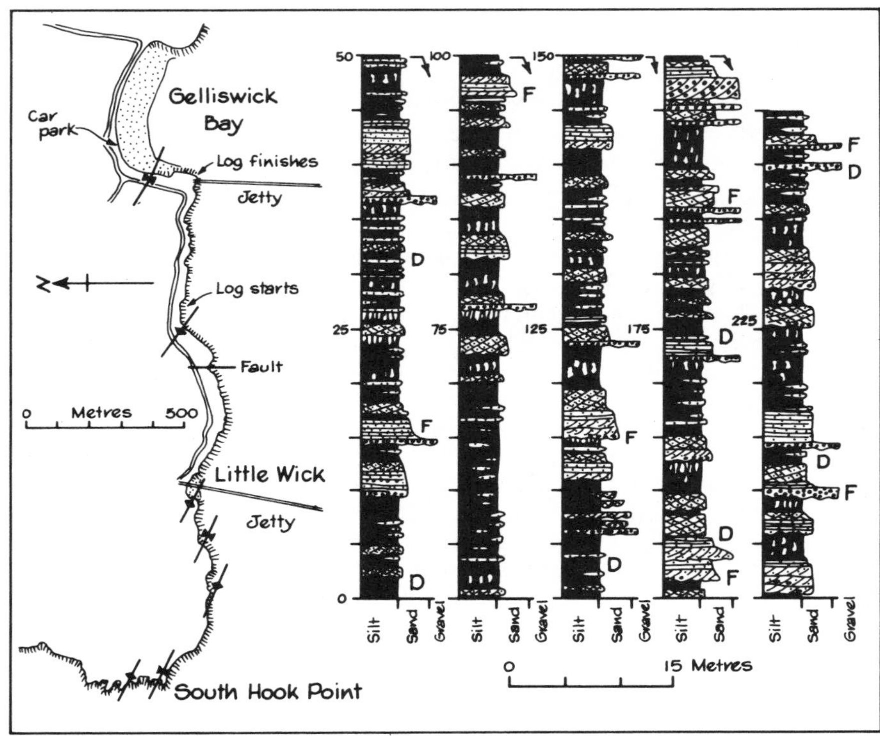

Fig. 7. The Gelliswick Bay Formation between Little Wick and Gelliswick Bay. See Fig. 4 for key to symbols.

be a lateral deposit is present near the base, and small scale channelling is conspicuous among some of the fine grade groups of beds. At the first cove another probable lateral deposit is exposed, suggesting that the streams meandered at times. A coarse grained facies assemblage is crossed between the first and second coves and persists to the end of the traverse. Approximately 50 m W of the second, an alternation of sandstones and mud-cracked siltstones cut by a sandstone-filled channel suggests a crevassed levee environment. Sandstones and conglomerates on the W side of the second cove are particulary rich in disarticulated pteraspid remains. A prominent bedding surface beneath the oil jetty near the E end of the traverse shows a good example of a set of conglomerate filled erosional grooves on one of the major erosion surfaces (Nagtegaal 1966).

7. Muscle Bridge Quarry (SM 9565 0558). Ample parking space is available on the quarry floor (Fig. 1). This quarry, on the N side of the B4325 Waterston-Neyland road, exposes 60 m of beds belonging to the basal

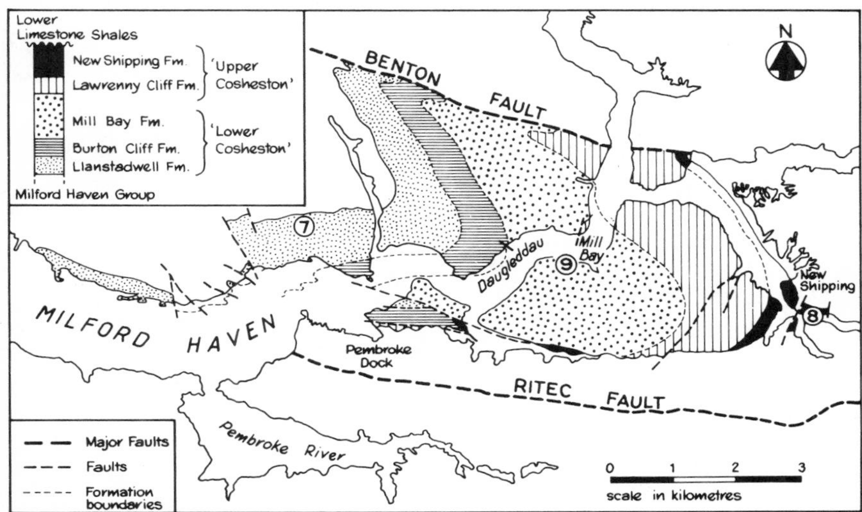

Fig. 8. General distribution of formations in the Cosheston Group.

one-third of the Llanstadwell Formation (Figs. 8, 9), and is the largest publicly accessible inland exposure of the Cosheston Group. The beds in the quarry are affected by two parasitic folds whose axial traces intersect the W and E quarry faces.

Lithologically, the sequence consists of fining upward cycles of variable thickness, complexity, and completeness, made up of intraformational conglomerates, medium to very fine grained sandstones, and siltstones. The conglomerates and sandstones are for the most part green, whereas the siltstones are mainly red.

The intraformational conglomerates are 0.01 to 1.0 m thick, and overlie erosion surfaces of irregular (0.1 - 0.10 m) relief; their upper boundaries may be erosional or transitional. They are massive or crudely flat to low-angle parallel, or sometimes planar cross bedded, and contain poorly sorted, disc or blade shaped siltstone and sandstone intraclasts. Plant fragments and occasional rolled subspherical calcareous or limonitic nodules up to 0.15 m diameter are also present. The conglomerate matrices are medium to fine grained litharenites and clast : matrix ratios vary considerably. The medium to fine grained coarse member sandstones are texturally immature to submature litharenites with garnet-dominated (60-80%) heavy mineral fractions. The sandstones are typified by horizontal to low-angle parallel laminations with subordinate large scale planar cross lamination and mixed parallel lamination and ripple cross-lamination, and infrequent large scale trough cross lamination. Large and small scale soft sediment deformation is

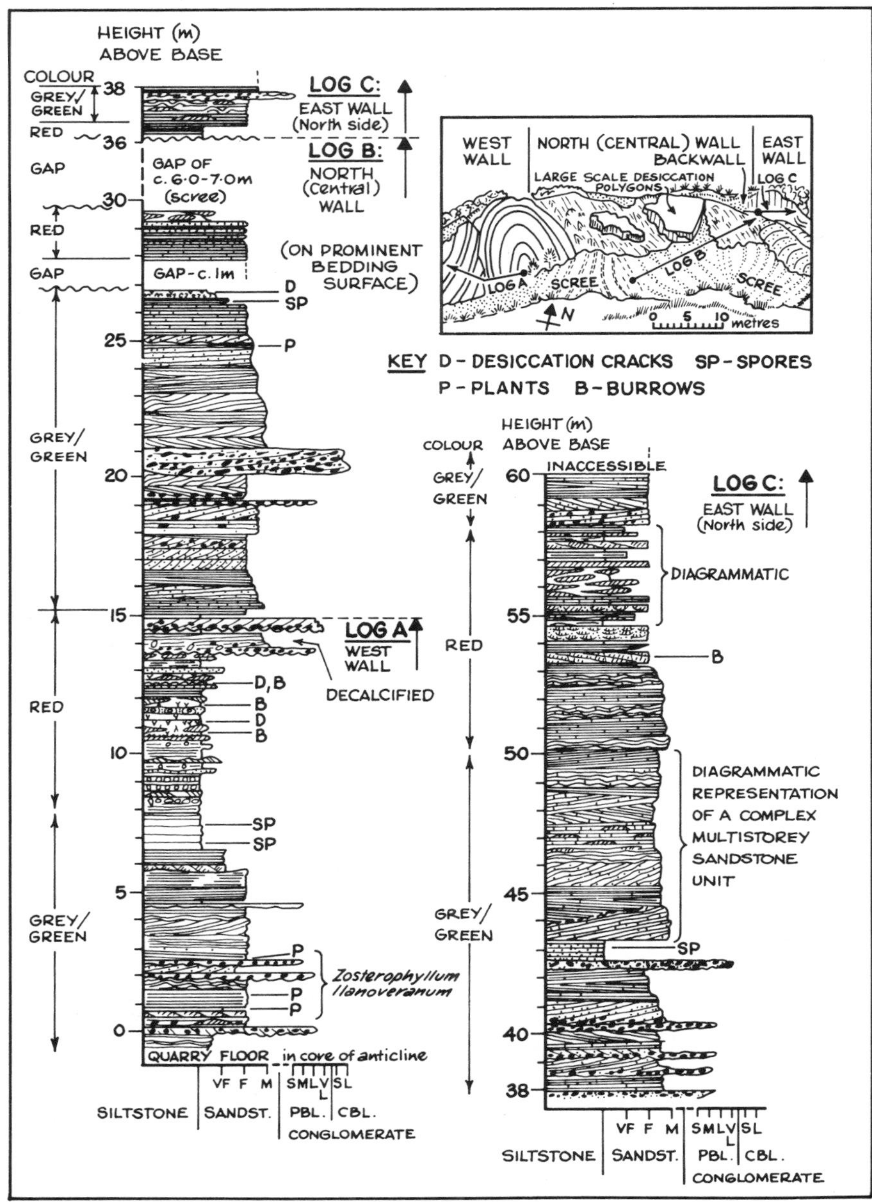

Fig. 9. The Llanstadwell Formation at Muscle Bridge Quarry. See Fig. 4 for key to symbols.

common. Mica lamination is the most abundant type, followed by grain size and heavy mineral lamination. Fragmentary plant remains occur at several horizons (Fig. 9), including *Zosterophyllum llanoveranum, Prototaxites, ?Psilophyton* sp., and *Pachytheca.*

Fine member sandstones are either parallel laminated or ripple cross laminated. Small scale ball and pillow structures are common. Siltstones are non bedded or flat laminated, and several green silts have yielded spore assemblages (Fig. 9). A few red siltstones contain poorly developed calcretes represented by scattered subspherical calcite nodules. Burrow structures and mudcrack infills are common within the fine members, and an excellent example of the latter, with polygons of 1 m diameter, occurs at 26.64 m above the base of the log (Fig. 9).

Channel lag, channel bar, bar top, splay, and overbank deposits can be recognised at Muscle Bridge. However, due mainly to the preponderance of horizontal to low angle parallel lamination, and paucity of large scale planar and trough cross strata in the fining upward cycles, they cannot be matched in detail with those predicted by published models of meandering, braided, and ephemeral stream deposition (reviewed by Allen 1965*a, b,* 1970; Cant & Walker 1976; Picard & High 1973). Similar cycles exist in the Senni Beds and Brownstones sequences of the Brecon Beacons, and in the Woodbank Group of the Clee Hills (Allen 1974, fig. 30).

These Llanstadwell Formation cycles are thought to have been deposited by braided-meandering streams somewhat similar to the Cimarron River (Shelton & Noble 1974). The palaeocurrent directions indicated by parting lineations and avalanche foresets in both Muscle Bridge and Mill Bay (locality 9) lie almost at right angles to one another, a relationship also reported from the Cimarron River deposits (Shelton *et al.* 1974).

8. New Shipping. This locality (Figs. 1, 10) is suitable only for small parties but the rocks are accessible for 3.5 - 4.5 hours either side of low water. **Permission to park and visit** the exposures should be obtained from New Shipping Farm.

Here in its type section (Fig. 10), the New Shipping Formation (Fig. 8) is exposed in low cliffs and platforms along the **N shore of the Carew River,** between New Shipping Point (SN 0335 0463) and a point 200 m SSW of New Shipping Farm (SN 0388 0410). For most of its length, New Shipping presents a dip or oblique dip section, and the beds within it incline S or SE at angles of 15-55°. It is affected by two main faults whose senses and amounts of displacement are uncertain. Because of this, and the general discontinuity of exposure, the thickness of the New Shipping Formation is uncertain. Also unknown is the exact nature of its relationship to the underlying Lawrenny Cliff Formation, its original depositional thickness, and its subsurface (downplunge) extent. However, an unconformable contact with the overlying Lower Limestone Shales can be seen.

In terms of lithofacies and petrographic composition the New Shipping Formation is the simplest and most complex respectively of the five formations of the Cosheston Group. It consists of unfossiliferous granule, small-, medium-, and occasionally large-pebble extraformational conglomerates, pebbly and pebble-free very coarse to fine grained sandstones, and very fine sandstones/siltstones, all of which are usually red or, infrequently, green. The green colour is due to reduction and leaching, some of which is comparatively recent. These lithologies are arranged in 1 to 10 m thick fining-upward cycles, in combination with a lesser number of coarsening-upward cycles to 7 m in thickness.

The conglomerates are dominated by exotic clasts, and the rock types recorded include: red, brown, orange, pink, yellow, green and white, flow banded and non-flow banded, porphyritic and non-porphyritic, rhyolitic and latitic lavas; crystal lithic tuffs and varieties of ignimbrite; white and orange microgranite and microgranophyre; meta-microgranite; pink, white, red and black metaquartzite, semi-schists and psammites; quartz-mica schist; brown, red, grey and green very fine to very coarse grained lithic arenites; pink and white vein quartz; jasper and radiolarian chert. Intraformational clasts consist of red or green siltstones or very fine grained sandstones. The usually abundant matrix is a fine to very coarse grained sandstone. Individual conglomerates may coarsen or fine upwards, and often possess more and less conglomeratic layers, or even sandstone or siltstone lenses or interbeds. They overlie erosion surfaces of irregular relief, and are obscurely or crudely flat, low angle or large scale planar cross bedded.

The coarse member sandstones are either massive or crudely to well flat-, low angle, or large scale planar or trough cross bedded. The fine to very fine grained sandstones and siltstones are usually thinly flat bedded or flat laminated, and have planar or irregular (erosional) tops and bottoms. They contain some garnet and muscovite, whilst the heavy mineral fractions of the coarse member sandstones are dominated by zircon and tourmaline. Desiccation cracks and bioturbation are rare in the fine members and there are no calcretes.

The lack of lateral control hinders environmental interpretation, and palaeocurrent evidence is sparse, but the sequence is regarded as a braided stream deposit in which deposition occurred upon longitudinal and transverse bars and in abandoned channels. it contains four of the eight facies included by Cant & Walker (1976) in their model of a sandy braided stream.

9. Mill Bay (SN 002 049). Limited parking space (ask farm manager for permission) is available beyond Home Farm (Fig. 11) and the locality is

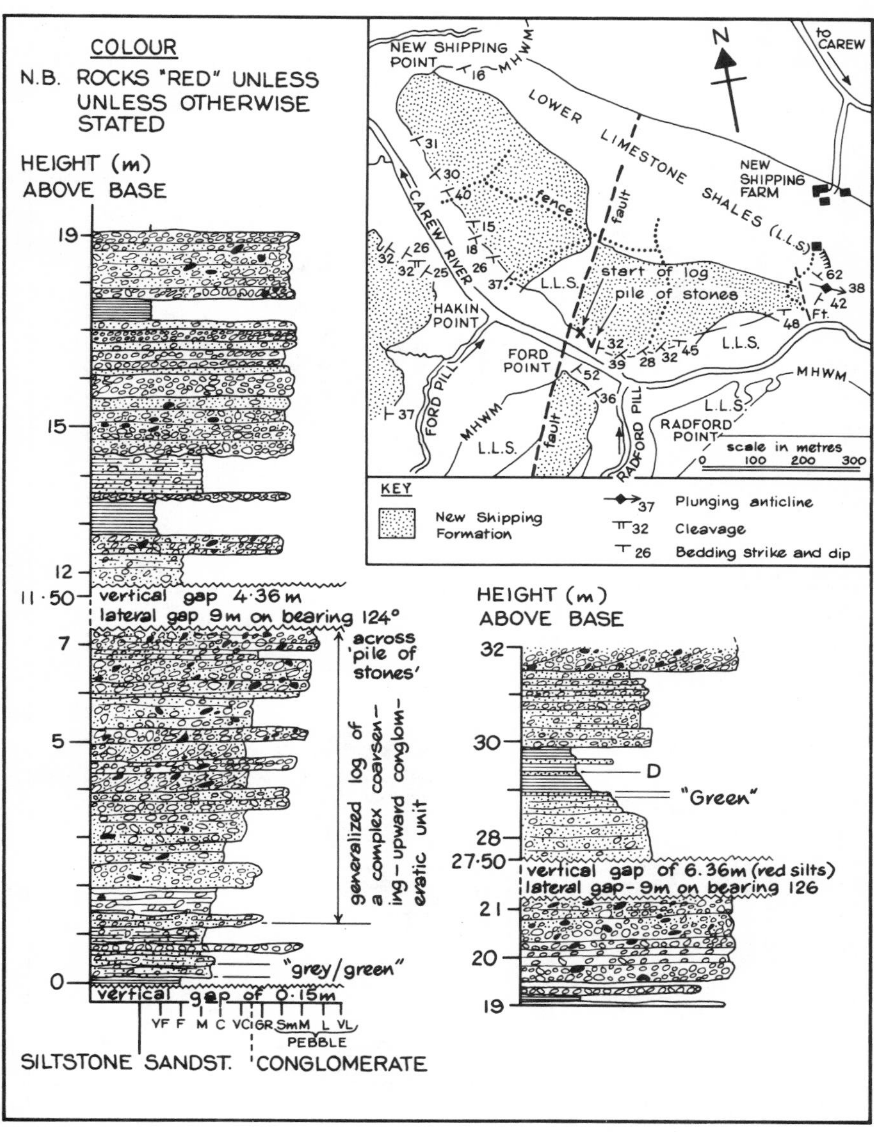

Fig. 10. The New Shipping Formation at New Shipping. See Fig. 4 for key to symbols.

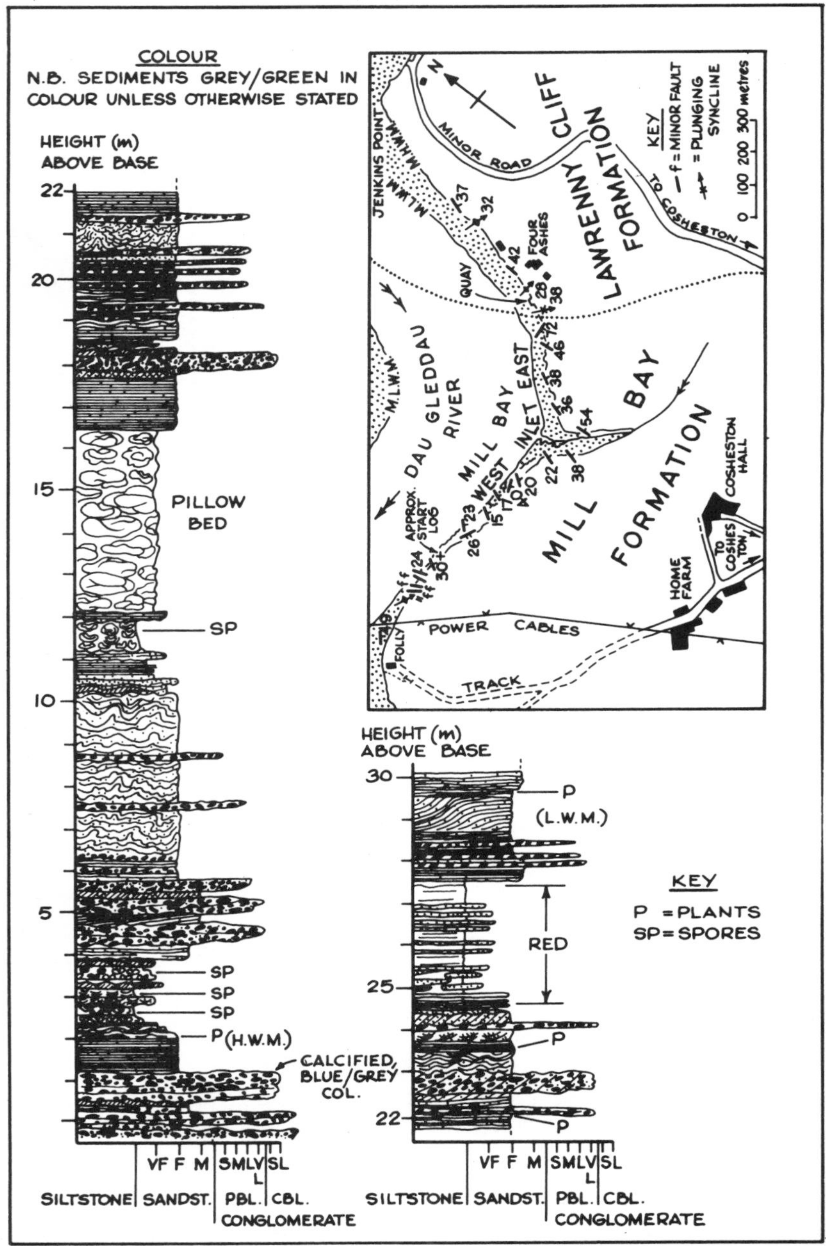

Fig. 11. The Mill Bay Formation (representative log) at Mill Bay, Dau Gleddau River. See Fig. 4 for key to symbols.

suitable only for parties of small or moderate size. The exposure is accessible for 3.0 - 3.5 hours either side of low water.

The Mill Bay Formation (Fig. 8) is the thickest and best exposed of the Cosheston Group. In Mill Bay, a sequence of 425 m is displayed in the virtually continuous oblique dip and strike section, together with 45 m of the overlying Lawrenny Cliff Formation. The log (Fig. 11) is representative of the rocks in the W part of Mill Bay.

Although the Mill Bay Formation contains all the lithologies and lithofacies associations recorded at Muscle Bridge (plus several others), they are arranged in generally thicker, more complex, and more frequently interrupted fining upward cycles. The Formation is dominantly grey/green in colour but red fine members, half of which contain calcretes (identical in type to those at Muscle Bridge), are present. Intraformational conglomerates are extremely common in Mill Bay. Several are calcified (see base of log) and a number form transverse-bar, or delta-like, wedge shaped, large scale planar cross bedded sets. Evidence of small to medium scale isolated or (repeatedly) superimposed channelling is abundant, and channel widths and depths of up to 9.2 m and 1.7 m respectively have been recorded.

Most coarse member sandstones are fine grained micaceous litharenites, but subordinate amounts of medium and coarse grained sandstone also occur. Subarkoses are common immediately N of the inlet and sublitharenites are present above and below the Lawrenny Cliff Formation junction. All these sandstones have garnet dominated heavy mineral fractions and are usually mica laminated. Their dominant stratification type is low angle to horizontal parallel lamination (*cf.* Muscle Bridge), cosets of which attain thicknesses of 4.5 m. Some sets may represent overbank flood deposits similar to those from Bijou Creek (McKee *et al.* 1967). Others resemble the low angle cross stratification of ephemeral stream 'point bars' (Picard & High 1973, p. 168), and a number are interpreted as products of sand wave deposition (see Smith 1971). Fragments of *Psilophyton* sp. are common in the sandstones in the W part of Mill Bay. Alternations of red or green, fine to very fine cross laminated sandstones and flat laminated siltstones on scales from 0.001 - 0.10 m dominate the fine members, which also contain mudcrack infills and bioturbation features. Silt drapes are common in channel and bar-top sequences.

The Mill Bay Formation is remarkable for the abundance and diversity of soft-sediment deformation structures it contains, most of which have resulted from vertical (and not lateral) movements of water (escape) and sediment (founder). Structures include load casts, small scale ball and pillow structures, convolute lamination and piled loaded ripples, plus spectacular large scale founder folding and up to 4.42 m thick pillow beds. The latter consist of interbedded and interlaminated green, very fine grained sandstones and siltstones which may represent abandoned channel fills or other types of fluvio-lacustrine deposits. Seismic activity may have triggered their formation. Rapid deposition and high water table conditions are indicated by the western Mill Bay sequences. Channel lag, channel fill, transverse and 'point' bar, bar top, crevasse splay, ?levee and various overbank deposits have been recognised in the Formation as a whole. As at Muscle Bridge, a braided-meandering stream depositional environment seems plausible.

REFERENCES

ALLEN, J. R. L. 1965*a*. Fining-upward cycles in alluvial successions. *Geol. J.* **4,** 229-246.

ALLEN, J. R. L. 1965*b*. A review of the origin and characteristics of recent alluvial sediments. *Sedimentology,* **5,** 89-191.

ALLEN, J. R. L. 1965*c*. Upper Old Red Sandstone (Farlovian) palaeogeography in South Wales and the Welsh Borderland. *J. sedim. Petrol.* **35,** 167-195.

ALLEN, J. R. L. 1970. Studies in fluviatile sedimentation: a comparison of fining-upward cyclothems, with special reference to coarse-member composition and interpretation. *J. sedim. Petrol.* **40,** 298-323.

ALLEN, J. R. L. 1974. Sedimentology of the Old Red Sandstone (Siluro-Devonian) in the Clee Hills area, Shropshire, England. *Sedim. Geol.* **12,** 73-167.

ALLEN, J. R. L. & WILLIAMS, B. P. J. 1978. The sequence of the earlier Lower Old Red Sandstone (Siluro-Devonian), north of Milford Haven, south-west Dyfed (Wales). *Geol. J.* **13,** 113-136.

ALLEN, J. R. L. & WILLIAMS, B. P. J. 1979*a*. Old Red Sandstone facies and Wenlock stratigraphy and palaeogeography in Wales and the Welsh Borderland. *Proc. Geol. Ass.* **90,** 229-231.

ALLEN, J. R. L. & WILLIAMS, B. P. J. 1979*b*. Interfluvial drainage on Siluro-Devonian alluvial plains in Wales and the Welsh Borders. *J. geol. Soc. Lond.* **136,** 361-366.

ALLEN, J. R. L. & WILLIAMS, B. P. J. 1981. Sedimentology and stratigraphy of the Townsend Tuff Bed (Lower Old Red Sandstone) in South Wales and the Welsh Borders. *J. geol. Soc. Lond.* **138,** 15-29.

ALLEN, J. R. L., BASSETT, M. G., HANCOCK, P. L., WALMSLEY, V. G. & WILLIAMS, B. P. J. 1976. Stratigraphy and structure of the Winsle Inlier, southwest Dyfed, Wales. *Proc. Geol. Ass.* **87,** 221-229.

BALL, H. W. & DINELEY, D. L. 1961. The Old Red Sandstone of Brown Clee Hill and the adjacent area. I. Stratigraphy. *Bull. Br. Mus. nat. Hist.* **A5,** 177-242.

CANT, D. J. & WALKER, R. G. 1976. Development of a braided-fluvial facies model for the Devonian Battery Point Sandstone, Quebec. *Can. J. Earth Sci.* **13,** 102-119.

CANTRILL, T. C., DIXON, E. E. L., THOMAS, H. H. & JONES, O. T. 1916. The geology of the South Wales Coalfield. Part XII. The country around Milford. *Mem. geol. Surv. U.K.* 185 pp.

DIXON, E. E. L. 1921. The geology of the South Wales Coalfield. Part XIII. The country around Pembroke and Tenby. *Mem. geol. Surv. U.K.* 220 pp.

HURST, J. M., HANCOCK, N. J. & McKERROW, W. S. 1978. Wenlock stratigraphy and palaeogeography of Wales and the Welsh Borderland. *Proc. Geol. Ass.* **89,** 197-226.

McKEE, E. D., CROSBY, E. J. & BERRYHILL, H. L. Jr. 1967. Flood deposits, Bijou Creek, Colorado, June 1965. *J. sedim. Petrol.* **37,** 829-851.

NAGTEGAAL, P. J. C. 1966. Scour-and-fill structures from a fluvial piedmont environment. *Geologie Mijnb.* **45,** 342-354.

PICARD, M. D. & HIGH, L. R. Jr. 1973. Sedimentary structures of ephemeral streams. *Devs. Sedimentol.* **17,** 223 pp.

SANZEN-BAKER, I. 1972. Stratigraphical relationships and sedimentary environments of the Silurian-early Old Red Sandstone of Pembrokeshire. *Proc. Geol. Ass.* **83,** 139-164.

SHELTON, J. W., BURMAN, H. R. & NOBLE, R. L. 1974. Directional features in braided-meandering stream deposits, Cimarron River, north-central Oklahoma. *J. sedim. petrol.* **44,** 1114-1117.

SHELTON, J. W. & NOBLE, R. L. 1974. Depositional features of braided-meandering stream. *Bull. Am. Ass. Petrol. Geol.* **58,** 742-752.

SMITH, N. D. 1971. Pseudo-planar stratification produced by very low amplitude sand waves. *J. sedim. Petrol.* **41,** 69-73.

STRAHAN, A., CANTRILL, T. C., DIXON, E. E. L., THOMAS, H. H. & JONES, O. T. 1914. The geology of the South Wales Coalfield. Part XI. The country around Haverfordwest. *Mem. geol. Surv. U.K.*, 262 pp.

THOMAS, R. G. 1978. *The stratigraphy, palynology and sedimentology of the lower Old Red Sandstone Cosheston Group, S. W. Dyfed, Wales.* Unpublished Ph.D Thesis, University of Bristol.

WALMSLEY, V. G. & BASSETT, M. G. 1976. Biostratigraphy and correlation of the Coralliferous Group and Gray Sandstone Group (Silurian) of Pembrokeshire, Wales. *Proc. Geol. Ass.* **87,** 191-220.

WHITE, E. I. 1961. The Old Red Sandstone of Brown Clee Hill and the adjacent area. II. Palaeontology. *Bull. Br. Mus. nat. Hist.* **A5,** 243-310.

Note added in proof:

Since the manuscript was submitted for publication recent work relevant to the area north of Milford Haven has been published. The controversial nature and age of the contact between the Gray Sandstone Group and Red Cliff Formation has been debated by Hurst, Hancock & McKerrow (1978) and Allen & Williams (1979*a*).

Aspects of the sedimentation of the intraformational conglomerates and their environmental significance on alluvial plains have been outlined for the Milford Haven Group (Allen & Williams 1979*b*).

The nature and origin of the Townsend Tuff Bed and its immense value as a regional marker horizon has been detailed by Allen & Williams (1981). The Tuff Bed originated in distant and powerful Plinian eruptions and was spread over extensive and virtually featureless coastal mud flats. The stratigraphic position of the Townsend Tuff Bed, within a barren interval of the Lower Old Red Sandstone of the Anglo-Welsh area, has been assessed. The base of the Devonian System in South Wales and the Welsh Borders has been accordingly defined as occurring at a regionally uniform lithological contact with the Townsend Tuff Bed (Allen & Williams 1981, p. 26-27).

9

OLD RED SANDSTONE FACIES OF THE PEMBROKE PENINSULA, SOUTH OF THE RITEC FAULT

by B. P. J. WILLIAMS, J. R. L. ALLEN, *and* J. D. MARSHALL

Maps	*Topographical:*	1 : 50 000	Sheets 157 St David's and Haverfordwest, 158 Tenby
		1 : 25 000	Sheets SM80, SR89, SR99 SS09, SS19
	Geological:	1 : 50 000	Sheets 226/227 Milford Haven, 244/245 Pembroke and Linney Head

THE Old Red Sandstone (ORS) rocks of the Pembroke peninsula range in age from late Silurian to early Carboniferous (Fig. 1). The Lower ORS (Upper Silurian-Lower Devonian) comprises a fine example of a post-orogenic molasse sequence, the dominantly continental style of sedimentation following the main phase of the Caledonian Orogeny. The Lower ORS is divided customarily into the Downtonian, Dittonian and Breconian stages (Fig. 1) but as yet stratotypes have not been defined. The Upper Old Red Sandstone is attributed to a single Stage, the Farlovian.

Apart from the thin, basal conglomerates of the Old Red Sandstone in the Pembroke peninsula, mudstones are dominant in the Downtonian where they represent deposits of marginal marine and distal fluvial environments (Allen & Williams 1978 and MS; Williams 1978). Associated lithotypes in the Downtonian include rare, sharply intercalated coarse grained sandstones, intraformational conglomerates, air-fall tuffs, and pedogenic limestones (calcretes). Sandstones and fine conglomerates become more conspicuous and common upwards through the Dittonian and coarse, extraformational conglomerates are particularly abundant in the Breconian as a consequence of a more proximal style of fluvial sedimentation (Williams 1971, 1978). Thus, in broad terms, the Lower ORS of the Pembroke peninsula is a progressively upward-coarsening sequence.

Everywhere in the Pembroke peninsula an unconformity (disconformity) separates the Lower from the Upper ORS, the Middle division probably being unrepresented anywhere in the area. The sparsely fossiliferous Upper ORS Farlovian Stage (Upper Devonian — Lower Carboniferous) (Fig. 1)

[pp. 151-174 *In* BASSETT, M. G. (ed.). 1982. Geological excursions in Dyfed, south-west Wales.]

consists essentially of fluvial conglomerates and sandstones, giving way to shallow marine mudstones, limestones and thin sandstones followed by marine Carboniferous beds. This conformable sequence comprises a fine example of a major transgressive event.

Due to the paucity of palaeontological and palynological evidence some stratigraphical problems still exist in the ORS of SW Dyfed. ORS sequences N and S of the Ritec Fault differ in many important aspects (Fig. 1). However, new work in the area has shown that broad stratigraphical correlations can be made based largely on sedimentary facies, regionally important pedogenic limestones and air-fall tuffs, and the scattered occurrences of vertebrate and plant remains and spores. One major stratigraphical problem remains: the age of the Ridgeway Conglomerate Formation. A disconformity appears to separate the Formation from the underlying Lower ORS rocks, while it is overstepped by the Upper ORS which accounts for its attenuation at Skrinkle Haven and absence on Caldey Island. The Formation has been ascribed a Middle Devonian age by Allen (1965, 1974*a*, 1977), a Lower-Middle Devonian age by Allen *et al.* (1967) and Williams (1971), and Lower Devonian age by Dixon (1921), Williams (1978), Thomas (1978) and Allen (1979). The age and correlation problems of the Formation will not be resolved until palynological evidence becomes available.

The purpose of this excursion is to examine the ORS succession, displayed in magnificent coastal sections, and its sedimentary facies as seen in vertical profiles. By virtue of the late Carboniferous-early Permian Variscan Orogeny, the ORS sequence of the Pembroke peninsula is repeated by folding and crops out in three major belts (Fig. 2). These outcrops, south of the Ritec Fault, are contained in Hancock's (1973) structural Zone Ia, the southern ORS outcrops being separated by the compound Castlemartin Corse-Orielton Anticline, while the northern (Ridgeway) outcrop is situated on the northern limb of the complementary Pembroke Syncline (Fig. 2). The Pembroke peninsula has also become a classic example of the relationship between folds, thrust and wrench faults (Hancock 1973), and examples of such fractures can be seen at several of the localities described in the excursion.

The Pembroke peninsula is a classic area for the study of Upper Palaeozoic rocks in Wales. This is due largely to the outstanding work of Dixon (1921, 1933 *a, b*) whose memoir still serves as a sound basis for any new research in the area. Dixon (1921) made a thorough investigation of the ORS rocks of the peninsula, while recently Allen & Williams (1978 and MS) and Marshall (1978*a*) have refined the lithostratigraphy and made a detailed appraisal of the sedimentology of the ORS sequence. Dixon (1921) ascribed most of the Lower ORS to the 'Red Marls' and divided this sequence into four units. The

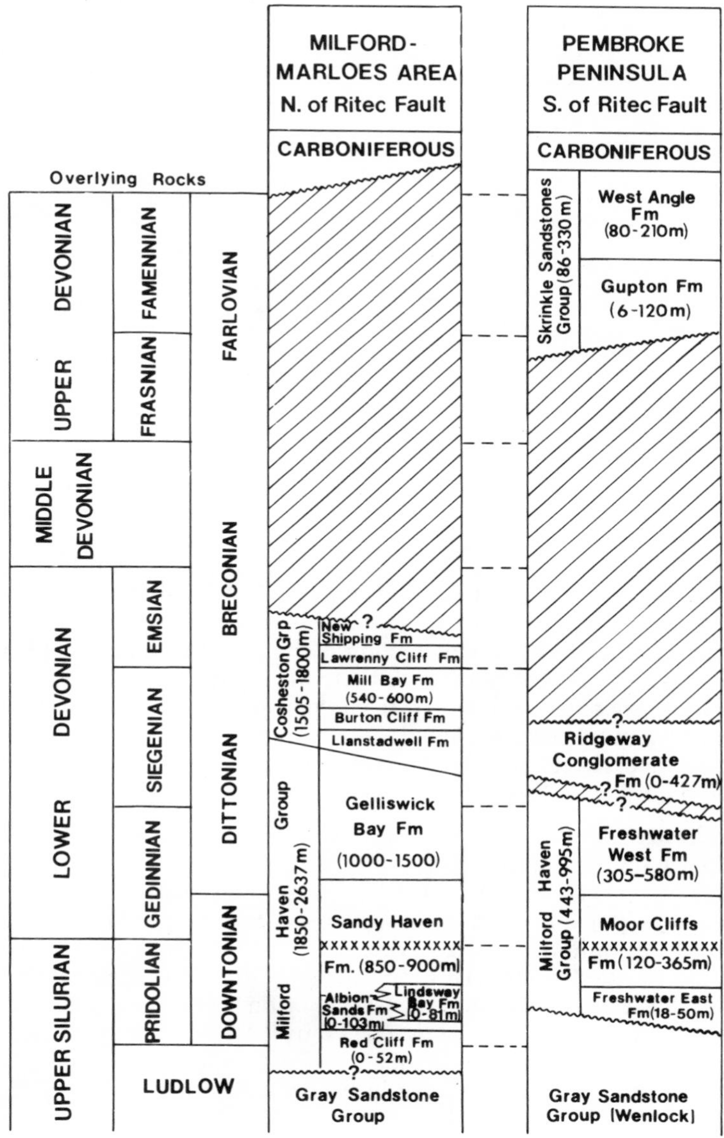

Fig. 1. Old Red Sandstone stratigraphy of the Pembroke peninsula and its correlation N of the Ritec Fault. New stratigraphical information from Allen & Williams 1978; Marshall 1978*a*; Thomas 1978; Williams 1978.

remainder of the ORS in the peninsula was grouped by Dixon (1921) into the Ridgeway Conglomerate and the Upper Devonian Skrinkle Sandstones. Dixon's (1921) subdivisions and the refined lithostratigraphy of Allen & Williams (MS), Williams (1978) and Marshall (1978*a*) are given below for comparative purposes:

DIXON		WILLIAMS, ALLEN & MARSHALL		*thickness at Freshwater West*
	Skrinkle Sandstones	Skrinkle Sandstones Group	West Angle Formation	210 m
	u/c		Gupton Formation	120 m
		u/c		
	Ridgeway Conglomerate	Ridgeway Conglomerate Formation		115 m
		u/c		
Red Marls	Upper Marls	Milford Haven Group	Rat Island Mudstone Member[1]	81 m
	Sandstone & Marls		Conigar Pit Sandstone Member[1]	265 m
	Lower Marls		Moor Cliffs Fm	120 m
	Basement Beds		Freshwater East Fm	18 m

[1]These two members comprise the Freshwater West Formation

This guide to the succession is based on the joint work (largely unpublished) of Allen & Williams and on the unpublished doctoral study of Marshall (1978*a*).

ITINERARY

The itinerary commences at the classic section of Freshwater West where most of the sedimentary facies and depositional features of the Old Red Sandstone can be studied. This section is described in some detail. Other localities (Fig. 2) are described in order to highlight variations in rock types and sedimentary phenomena away from the main Freshwater West section. The numbers attached to the localities correspond to these shown in Fig. 2. The letters, in brackets, indicate the exposures at individual localities and are noted on the relevant figures.

1. Freshwater West, 26 km W of Tenby, is reached via the A4139 road to Pembroke and then the B4319 through Castlemartin (Fig. 2). The Middle to Upper Palaeozoic sequence exposed at Freshwater West comprises one of the most accessible and continuous sections in the whole of Dyfed. Wenlock to Lower Carboniferous rocks crop out on the foreshore between the headlands of Little Furzenip (SR 885 994) and Great Furzenip (SR 887 987). Over half the section lies within the Castlemartin Tank Range and, although firing is concentrated SE of Frainslake Sands (SR 88 96), **permission to visit this part of the section** must be obtained beforehand from the Commandant, Merrion Camp, Castlemartin. A mid to low tide affords full access to the section exposed in the rock platform. Structural details at this locality are described in excursion 12, locality 3, this volume.

(A). From the B4319 above Little Furzenip there is a magnificent view of the steeply dipping sequence younging to the S, exposed in a rock platform cut through the S limb of the Castlemartin Corse Anticline (Hancock 1973).

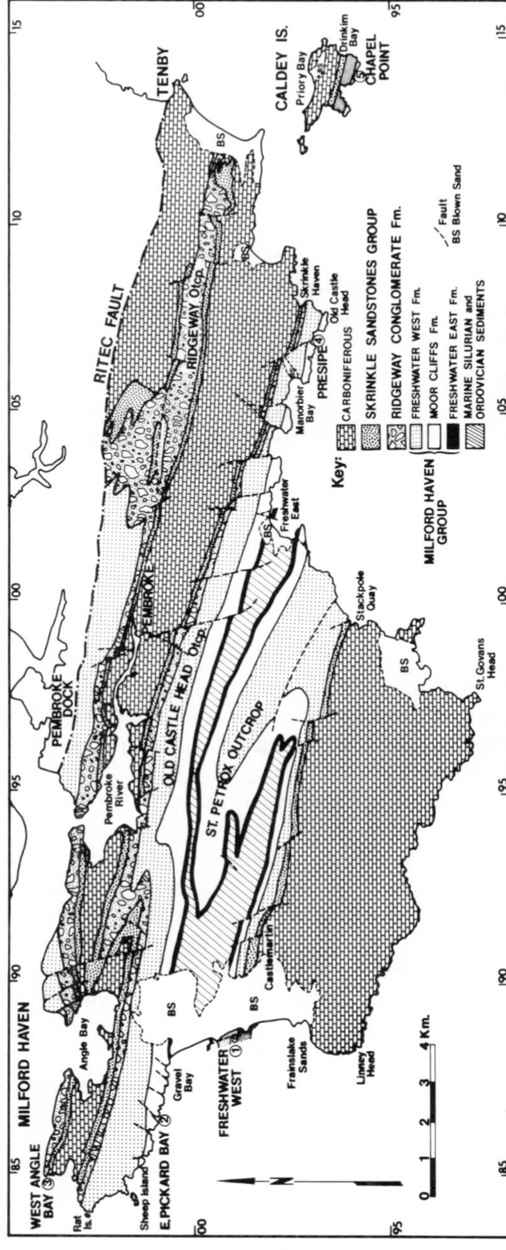

Fig. 2. Geological map of the Pembroke peninsula with emphasis on the Old Red Sandstone outcrops (based on Dixon 1921, and Allen & Williams MS). Positions of localities described in the text are shown.

The ORS succession comprises the bulk of the section (Fig. 3), the outcrops at first being confined to the foreshore from a point some 150 m N of Little Furzenip stack to SR 8872 9900, but southwards beyond this locality the Ridgeway Conglomerate Formation and Skrinkle Sandstones Group give rise to cliffs about 35 m high. From the roadside view-point the trace of the Flimston Bay Fault, a Variscan dextral wrench fault, which bisects the entire succession with a displacement of about 120 m in the middle of the section, can be seen. The fault isolates Little Furzenip stack from the headland and also gives rise to a shatter zone on Great Furzenip (SR 887 987). In Gravel Bay (SM 878 006) (Fig. 2), on the N limb of the Castlemartin Corse Anticline, the Flimston Bay Fault is no longer detectable, having terminated in a myriad of small splay faults which disrupt the foreshore sequence both to the N and in the vicinity of Little Furzenip (Fig. 3).

(B). Proceed to **beach level at the N end of the section** (SR 884 996) where the ORS unconformably overlies marine Silurian rocks of Wenlock age (Bassett 1974; Allen & Williams, 1979a). These rocks are part of the Gray Sandstone Group (Walmsley & Bassett 1976) and comprise an 11 m sequence of pebble grade conglomerates, green fine to medium grained sandstones, thin limestones and dark mudstones. The sandstones are locally pebbly and are associated with brown-weathering calcarenites crowded with rhynchonellid and chonetid brachiopods, indeterminate gastropods and bivalves (Bassett 1971).

The basal ORS division — the Freshwater East Formation — totals 18.45 m in thickness at Freshwater West and lies unconformably, with a basal scoured and channelled surface on the underlying Wenlock sequence. The contact is best seen on the seaward side of the main fault splay (Fig. 3). The lower part of the Formation is characterised by thick, green to dark grey, cobble and pebble grade conglomerates interbedded with fine to medium grained sandstones and grey-green mudstone (Fig. 4-Log A). The conglomerates are framework-supported and include clasts, up to 450 mm in size, of quartzitic and lithic sandstones, vein quartz, and olive-green mudstones, in a coarse sandstone matrix. Some of the clasts appear to match lithotypes in the underlying marine Silurian. The conglomerates are massive or possess internal fabric, overlie erosion surfaces, and commonly display internal scour features. These conglomerates, which dominate the lower part of the Freshwater East Formation, were derived locally and are only found at this locality, Gravel Bay and Freshwater East (Fig. 2). The upper, finer grained portion of the Formation, not fully represented at Freshwater West, has yielded lingulids, plant remains, spores, arthropod tracks, *Pachytheca,* and ostracoderms (Dixon 1921; Richardson & Lister 1969; Edwards 1979; Allen & Williams MS), demonstrating its Downtonian age (Allen & Williams 1979*a*) and closely resembling the lower division of the Sandy Haven Formation, N of Milford Haven (Allen & Williams 1978) (Fig. 1).

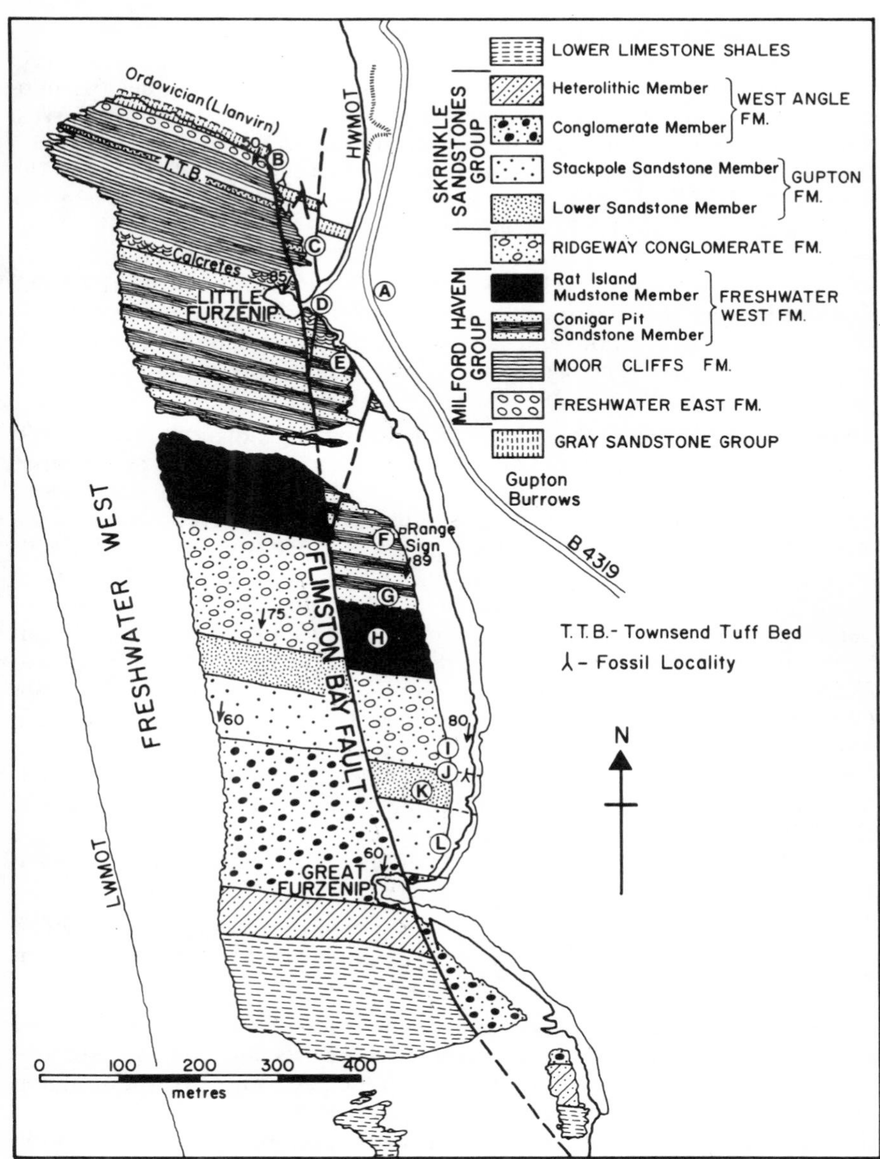

Fig. 3. Geological map of Freshwater West (after Dixon 1921; Marshall 1978; Allen & Williams MS). Circled letters indicate outcrops referred to in the text.

(C). Walking S towards Little Furzenip the finer grained facies, typical of the Moor Cliffs Formation, is traversed. The Moor Cliffs Formation is dominated by thick, red and green mudstones, rich in pedogenic calcrete concretions and tubules, plus large mud- and carbonate-filled pseudo-anticlinal structures. The Formation is 119.56 m thick at Freshwater West and contains surbordinate lithologies of very fine to fine grained sandstone, air-fall tuff, and rare exotic and intraformational conglomerate. The Townsend Tuff Bed (2.81 m thick) crops out on the **foreshore N of Little Furzenip** (Fig. 3) at SR 8847 9946. Here the Bed is only 19.44 m above the base of the Moor Cliffs Formation (Allen & Williams 1981) and a mere 37.89 m above the base of the Old Red Sandstone. Some 56 m above the Townsend Tuff Bed a very prominent rib of medium to very coarse grained sandstone crops out on the foreshore and can be correlated across the faults into Little Furzenip headland. The sandstone is a litharenite with a sharp, erosional base and is internally cross bedded with 4 to 6 tabular sets.

(D). In the E wall of the **gully of Little Furzenip** headland (SR 8851 9939) the highest beds of the Moor Cliffs Formation can be studied. The sequence here is dominated by red mudstones, up to 5.70 m thick, containing much pedogenic carbonate. These calcretes display large concretions and rods, locally showing a preferred orientation parallel to cleavage (Hancock 1965), or are arranged in festoons or pseudoanticlines. The latter have been attributed (Allen 1973) to seasonal deep soil wettings in the earlier stages of pedogenesis producing pattern-forming compressions. Furthermore, it has been suggested that complete calcrete profiles may have taken 10^4 years to form (Allen 1974*b*). As such the multiple profiles at the top of the Moor Cliffs Formation, as seen at Freshwater West (Fig. 3) are of regional importance and this horizon can be traced throughout the Pembroke peninsula. It has been named the Chapel Point Calcretes (Allen & Williams MS) after a magnificent section through these beds on Caldey Island (Locality 5 - Fig. 8). The Calcretes are thought to be mid Gedinnian in age (Allen 1974*a*), referable to the horizon of the '*Psammosteus*' Limestone and mark the Downtonian-Dittonian boundary (Fig. 1).

Although the Moor Cliffs Formation is thin at Freshwater West it can be correlated with the thicker middle and upper divisions of the Sandy Haven Formation, N of Milford Haven (Allen & Williams 1978).

(E). The contact between the Moor Cliffs and Freshwater West formations is well exposed on the **S tip of Little Furzenip** headland (SR 8851 9938) (Fig. 3). The sedimentary features of the Freshwater West Formation (345.78 m thick) are displayed in a wave polished foreshore section between the headland and the base of the Ridgeway Conglomerate Formation (Williams 1971). A clear division can be made into a lower sandstone dominated sequence (265.02 m) — the Conigar Pit Sandstone Member — and an upper mudstone sequence (80.76 m) — the Rat Island Mudstone

Member (Allen & Williams MS).

The Conigar Pit Sandstone Member comprises intraformational conglomerates, medium to very fine grained sandstones, and calcrete-bearing mudstones commonly arranged in upward fining cycles averaging 3 m in thickness (Allen 1963). The conglomerates are typically of fine pebble grade, composed of calcrete and mudstone clasts and overlie erosion surfaces of relatively low relief. The conglomerates, together with the coarser sandstones, yield fish plates, spines and scales of pteraspids, onchids, and traquairaspids — four such horizons have been identified at Freshwater West.

(F). Near the **range warning sign** (SR 8857 9917) an excellent wave polished section through a typical facies association in the Conigar Pit Sandstone Member of the Freshwater West Formation may be studied in detail (Fig. 4 - Log B). The sandstones are mainly fine grained, red or green in colour, some containing plant debris. Internally the sandstones are flat or cross bedded, grading upwards to ripple drift bedded units. Some of the sandstones and intraformational conglomerates are arranged in thick complexes formed by lateral accretion in a meandering river. These 'lateral deposits' commonly display epsilon cross bedding. Many of the sandstones are bioturbated; large burrows of *Beaconites antarcticus* abound in the finer grained sandstones and mudstones and have been identified in some thirty horizons of the lower member of the Freshwater West Formation. A particularly fine example occurs 123.29 m above the base (Fig. 4 - Log B).

The mudstones may be laminated or massive, are frequently blue mottled, and contain small burrows. Some very fine grained sandstone/mudstone complexes display mudcracks and arthropod tracks. Occasional soft sediment deformation features of sand balls in mudstone are present. Many mudstones contain calcrete, commonly as nodules or tubules but some good examples of massive, vein and pseudo-anticlinal calcretes occur. Near the top of the Member grey mudstones crop out which contain plant fragments and *Pachytheca.*

(G). Only one extraformational conglomerate has been identified in the Freshwater West Formation (SR 8858 9912). The unit occurs 260 m above the base of the Formation, is 0.26 m thick, and comprises granule grade vein quartz, felsite and microgranophyre clasts. The top of the Conigar Pit Sandstone Member is drawn above the highest, major green sandstone complex (5.18 m thick), a complex which has the extraformational conglomerate at its base.

(H). The Rat Island Mudstone Member is dominated by thick, red mudstones which are often blue mottled, laminated, and contain calcretes in the form of nodules or pseudo-anticlinal structures. Some massive calcrete beds are present. None of the subordinate sandstone lithologies present are

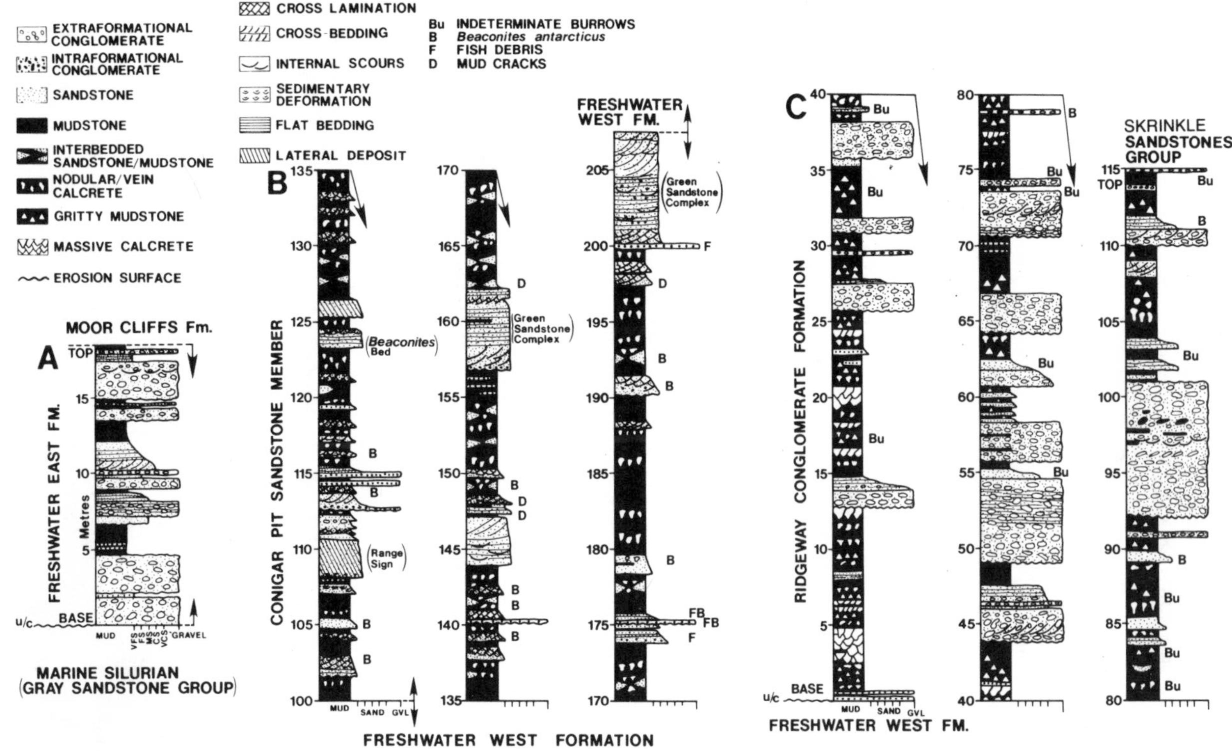

Fig. 4. Representative sedimentological logs of the Old Red Sandstone at Freshwater West. *A*, Complete log through the Freshwater East Formation (outcrop B, Fig. 3). *B*, Partial log through the Conigar Pit Sandstone Member of the Freshwater West Formation commencing 100 m above the base of the Formation (between Outcrops F and G, Fig. 3). *C*, Complete log through the Ridgeway Conglomerate Formation (through Outcrop I, Fig. 3).

coarser than very fine grained. The sandstones are mainly ripple drift bedded and six horizons of *B. antarcticus* have been recorded. Very prominent in this Member is the occurrence of thick (2.05 m), fine to coarse pebble intraformational conglomerates containing burrows and fish scales. One good example crops out 316. 27 m above the base of the Formation.

The Freshwater West Formation, which crops out extensively in the Pembroke peninsula, is clearly similar to, but rather finer grained and thinner than the Gelliswick Bay Formation, N of Milford Haven (Fig. 1) (see also excursion 8, this volume). The Freshwater West Formation (?mid Gedinnian to lower Siegenian) was deposited in a high sinuosity fluvial regime.

(I). The disconformable contact of the Freshwater West Formation with the overlying Ridgeway Conglomerate Formation is drawn beneath an intraformational conglomerate/mudstone complex. The complex comprises a marked facies change in that the mudstones are bright red and ill sorted, with scattered granules of vein quartz and carbonate, and represent a mudflow deposit.

The Ridgeway Conglomerate Formation (Williams 1971) comprises 115 m of coarse, polymictic, exotic conglomerates, coarse to fine grained sandstones, and mudstones, some of which contain calcrete (Fig. 4 - Log C). Eleven major conglomerates are present in the section at Freshwater West. The conglomerates, which total 30 m thickness in the section, vary in bed thickness from 0.6 to 9 m. The beds are internally massive or show poorly developed flat or cross bedding with some clast imbrication. One thick (9 m) complex, occurring 14 m below the top of the Formation, contains boulders of vein quartz up to 300 mm in size — the largest clasts present anywhere within the Formation (Owen *et. al.* 1971). The Ridgeway Conglomerate Formation is best studied in the upper half of its outcrop between SR 8871 9898 and SR 8873 9891. The conglomerates are mainly framework-supported, the clasts lying generally within the 4-64 mm size grade. The clasts mainly comprise protoquartzite, lithic greywacke, siltstone, and vein quartz, with a marked input of phyllite debris in the upper conglomeratic units. The clasts are held in a coarse, lithic sandstone matrix. A carbonate cement is rarely present. The conglomerates have sharp, erosional bases and the tops are either sharp or gradational. The conglomerates are poorly sorted but some display imbrication. Pebble filled scour pockets of conglomerate within sandstone beds occur in the section.

Other lithologies present in the Formation include coarse, lithic sandstones (some are phyllarenites) which tend to be massive, flat or cross bedded, and occasionally burrowed. The mudstones are thick, bright red and ill sorted. They contain scattered granules and seams of vein quartz, carbonate debris, and exotic detritus of granule grade. Calcretes, where developed, are nodular, cylindrical, massive or of the vein type (Fig. 4 - Log C).

The lithofacies association indicates deposition of the Ridgeway Conglomerate Formation as an alluvial fan. A study of cross bedding, clast imbrication, bed thickness, and particle size suggests a southerly derivation for the conglomerates from sedimentary/metasedimentary source rocks of Lower Palaeozoic - ?Precambrian age.

The age of the Ridgeway Conglomerate Formation remains enigmatic. No stratigraphically definitive body fossils have been found although fish fragments, of crossopterygian affinity, and some plant debris have been discovered and are suggestive of a Lower Devonian age.

(J). Overlying the Ridgeway Conglomerate Formation, with no angular discordance but with marked unconformity is the Upper Devonian-Lower Carboniferous Skrinkle Sandstones Group. An abrupt facies change at the contact is well exposed in **the cliff and on the foreshore** at SR 8873 9891. Dixon (1921) obtained scales of *Holoptychius* sp. from a very fine grained sandstone in the cliff immediately above the contact, referring these rocks to the Upper Old Red Sandstone (Farlovian) (Fig. 1).

More recently, detailed work by Marshall (1978*a*) has shown the Skrinkle Sandstones Group to extend through the Famennian into the Courceyan Stage of the Dinantian. Marshall divides the Skrinkle Sandstones into two formations — a lower Gupton Formation and an upper West Angle Formation (Fig. 3). Both formations, and their constituent members, are well exposed at Freshwater West.

(K). At SR 8876 9885 the Lower Sandstone Member of the Gupton Formation crops out in **the cliffs and on the foreshore** (Fig. 3). This member only occurs at Freshwater West where Marshall (1978*a*) has recognised an overall coarsening and thickening upward trend through its constituent 55 m thickness. This trend is discernible through an increase in the number of thick, lenticular and tabular sandstone and pebbly sandstone horizons until the Member is capped by a contact with mudstones of the overlying Stackpole Sandstone Member. The Lower Sandstone Member is considered to be wholly fluvial in origin, with southeasterly palaeocurrents, and may be best understood in terms of three component divisions: a basal braided stream association, a minor channel association at SR 8874 9883, and an upper major channel association (Marshall 1978*a*).

(L). Approaching the headland of **Great Furzenip,** at SR 8875 9878, the cliff and foreshore section comprises some 65 m of the Stackpole Sandstone Member of the Gupton Formation. This Member overlaps its predecessor, and is marked by a basal pebble layer throughout the Pembroke peninsula (Marshall 1978*a*). The Member comprises a lower, mudstone dominated division which includes a laminated facies of thinly bedded sandstones and mudstones passing up into fining upward couplets of rippled sandstones and mudstones characteristic of a rippled sheet facies. This coarsening upwards trend within the lower mudstone association is one of the principal arguments used by Marshall (1978*a*) for interpretation of the lower mudstone dominated division as a lacustrine delta fill.

The Member also includes an upper sandstone dominated division comprising pale yellow-white quartzarenites arranged in wedging and mutally erosive units. Parallel lamination is ubiquitous, as are scour and fill structures, within the quartzarenites. These features are attributed to bar development and channel switching in a braided stream complex (Marshall 1978*a*).

The white sandstones of the Stackpole Sandstone Member pass up to red sandstones and mudstones of the West Angle Formation as the ground rises to meet the headland of Great Furzenip. Two exotic conglomerates near the base of the West Angle Formation are just visible **near the cliff top.** Although the West Angle Formation crops out around Great Furzenip headland (Fig. 3), it is strongly advised that because it lies close to an active firing area of the range, it should be studied at its type locality at West Angle Bay (Locality 3).

2. Proceed N on the B4319 to the car park at Broomhill Burrows (SM 884 004) where access can be gained via a path through the sand dunes to the rock platform section of **Gravel Bay** (SM 878 006) (Fig. 2). The ORS sequence is here exposed on the N side of Freshwater West, on the N limb of the Castlemartin Corse Anticline, the rocks dipping N at 50° - 60° into the cliff (Fig. 5).

(A). On the **E side of Gravel Bay,** low on the foreshore between two sinistral wrench faults, a 30 m section of rock platform exposes a sequence through the marine Silurian Gray Sandstone Group of Wenlock age (Walmsley & Bassett 1976). This sequence is overlain by 3.25 m of grey-green extraformational conglomerates and 1.45 m of coarse to medium grained pebbly sandstones (SM 8798 0058). These lithotypes are the only representatives of the Freshwater East Formation exposed in the Gravel Bay area.

Westwards into Gravel Bay (Fig. 5), a section through the lower part of the Moor Cliffs Formation is well exposed. Thick, bright red, cleaved mudstones with calcretes and pseudoanticlines are prominent, interbedded with grey-green, coarse to medium grained, cross bedded sandstones locally displaying sedimentary deformation features. Some of these sandstones form complexes up to 3.5 m thick. In Gravel Bay a superb, polished rock platform section includes thick mudstones with a variety of calcrete developments and occasional calcretised tuffs. On the **W headland of Gravel Bay** (SM 8761 0066) thick mudstones, containing strongly developed pseudoanticlines, crop out. Several sandstone units are present, the lowest of which preserves dune forms, with wavelengths between 0.5 and 4 m, on its upper surface. A higher, purple medium to fine grained sandstone exhibits downclimbing cross bed sets in its lower part.

(B). Following the **cliff path** between Gravel Bay and Black Cave (SM 8708 0082) (Fig. 5) the sequence of Moor Cliffs Formation can be traversed along the strike, across the faults which have only minor offsets. Mudstones with calcretes are dominant, but several sandstone bundles are exposed. The sandstones provide the marker horizons in calculating the offsets across the faults. At SM 8726 0070 a prominent 2.5 m thick purple sandstone complex crops out. The sandstone is cross bedded to flat bedded, and displays magnificent sedimentary founder folds and diapirs with a separation along strike of *c.* 1 m.

(C). In the vicinity of **Black Cave** (Fig. 5) a stratigraphical sequence of some 150 m through the Moor Cliffs Formation is exposed. Bright red to dark, bioturbated mudstones with well developed calcretes and pseudoanticlines, often mud filled, predominate. Four prominent green sandstone complexes, up to 3.6 m thick, occur below a major sandstone complex which crops out between the W side of Black Cave (SM 8702 0081) and the headland to the E of East Pickard Bay at SM 8652 0090. This impressive, grey-green sandstone development comprises a 4.06 m thick complex overlying a sharp, erosional base. The complex has a basal, fine pebble grade quartz conglomerate passing up into interleaved cross and flat bedded sandstones, with locally developed dune forms. In addition to the green sandstones several red to purple very fine to fine grained, micaceous sandstones, up to 1 m thick, are present. These sandstones are internally flat or cross bedded, passing up into ripple cross lamination and tend to wedge out laterally over 25-50 m.

(D). Proceed along the cliff path, which in this area is one of the most spectacular yet underused parts of the Pembrokeshire Coast Path, to **East Pickard Bay** where a descent can be made to the **rock platform on the W headland** (SM 8631 0095). This is an important locality in that the main tephra developments within the Moor Cliffs Formation can be studied in detail in wave polished sections. The tephras include the Townsend Tuff Bed (3.38 m thick) and the type section of the Pickard Bay Tuff Bed (1.70 m thick), two regionally important air-fall complexes which comprise basal Devonian marker horizons in the Anglo-Welsh ORS outcrop (Allen & Williams 1981).

In East Pickard Bay the Townsend Tuff Bed is well exposed on the E side of the sinistral wrench fault which transects the bay (Fig. 5). Here, at SM 8648 0101, the bed, although cleaved, is seen to comprise three graded air fall units of crystal-lithic tuff to dust tuff. The dust tuff at the top of Fall A and B is

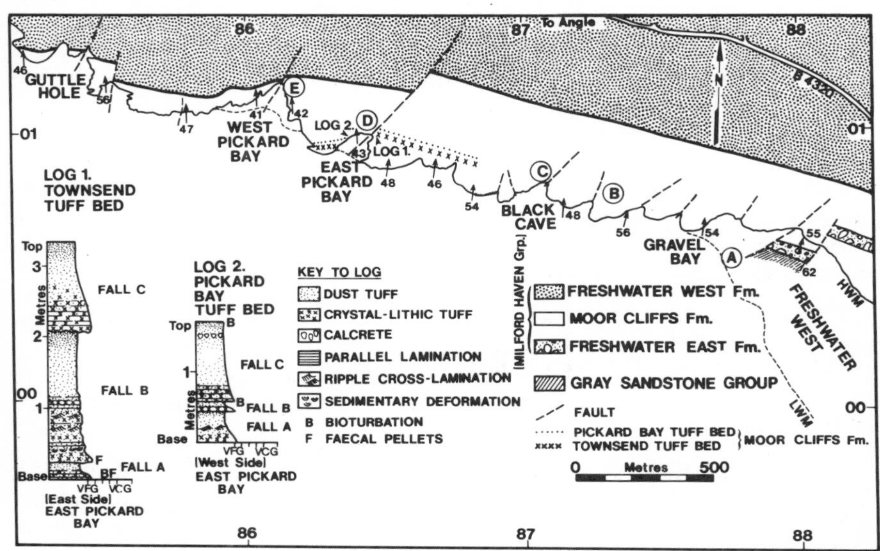

Fig. 5. Geological map of the Gravel Bay — Pickard Bays area with logged sections through the Townsend Tuff Bed and Pickard Bay Tuff Bed. Circled letters indicate outcrops referred to in the text.

silicified and forms prominent porcellanitic ribs. Fall A sharply overlies a mudstone bedding surface which has several large infilled pipes emerging from it, shallow 'trumpet-like' depressions, and some faecal debris all of biogenic origin. The silicified top of Fall A (Fig. 5 - Log 1) also preserves many clusters of oval faecal pellets. Fall B has a sharp base overlain by fine to medium grained crystal-lithic tuff grading up into rippled horizons with small sedimentary founder folds. The Fall is capped by a very prominent (0.78 m) rib of tough, silicified dust tuff (porcellanite) (Fig. 5 - Log 1). Fall C has a sharp erosional base overlain by medium grained crystal-lithic tuff grading through parallel laminated lithic tuff to a dust tuff (Allen & Williams 1981).

Return to the **W headland of the Bay** to study the Pickard Bay Tuff Bed at SM 8635 0099. The succession between the two tuff beds here totals 17.05 m of mudstone containing variable amounts of calcrete. A spectacular, 1.94 m thick, calcretised mudstone occurs 6.50 m above the top of the Townsend Tuff Bed. It comprises a mud filled boxwork calcrete with well developed pseudoanticlines. Five, thin dust tuffs are also present within this section. The Pickard Bay Tuff Bed (Fig. 5 - Log 2) includes 1.70 m of tuff arranged in three graded air-fall units of very fine grained lithic tuff to dust tuff. The former are parallel laminated with locally preserved flaser structures. The dust tuffs are intensely bioturbated, locally calcretised and preserve large *Beaconites* burrows on the upper surface of the Bed.

(E). In the **NW corner of West Pickard Bay** (SM 8610 0120), immediately W of the sinstral wrench fault (Fig. 5), the contact between the Moor Cliffs Formation and Freshwater West Formation is exposed. The contact is drawn above a 20 m sequence of thick, red and purple calcretes and beneath a grey, fine grained, micaceous sandstone with a thick intraformational conglomerate at its base. Above this basal bed are five upward fining sequences of intraformational conglomerate-fine grained sandstone-mudstone typical of the lower part of the Freshwater West Formation (Conigar Pit Sandstone Member). The contact between the formations in West Pickard Bay occurs 218.50 m above the top of the Townsend Tuff Bed.

3. From Broomhill Burrows, travel W on the B4320 through Angle village, turning left at SM 861 030 to the car park at **West Angle Bay** (SM 854 032). Take the cliff path, over the N headland, to a point (SM 8499 0387) where access can be gained to the rocky foreshore via a steep, but safe, track (Fig. 6 - A).

(A). This section, which is well exposed and may be fully traversed only at low tide, includes the Ridgeway Conglomerate Formation and Skrinkle Sandstones Group contained in the N limb of the Angle Syncline (Dixon 1921; Williams 1971). The section, from SM 8499 0387 to SM 8492 0379, comprises a steeply dipping, 130 m thickness of Skrinkle Sandstones Group which displays a much reduced Gupton Formation, a proximal (pebbly) development of the West Angle Formation, and a complex of red and grey interbeds just below the Lower Limestone Shales (Dinantian). The section was described in detail by Dixon (1921, p. 53), who recorded a 'Devonian' fauna from the uppermost grey beds, and was sampled by Dolby (1970) and Bassett & Jenkins (1977) for spores and conodonts, to determine the Devonian-Carboniferous boundary. Recently the lithostratigraphy has been revised and the sedimentology detailed by Marshall (1978 *a, b*), who noted that the succession through the Group represents the northward transgression of the Carboniferous sea recorded by a transition from red bed alluvial plain sediments (Conglomerate Member), through lagoon and coastal (Heterolithic Member), into carbonate marine sediments (Lower Limestone Shales).

(B). At this locality (Fig. 6) the Gupton Formation, which consists of 6 m of thinly bedded quartzose sandstones, overlies red mudstones and a green sandstone of the Ridgeway Conglomerate Formation. The quartzose sandstones are ripple cross laminated, passing up into parallel laminated and cross bedded units, and are the sole representatives of the Stackpole Sandstone member in this section.

(C). the Conglomerate Member of the West Angle Formation (Fig. 6 - Log) is red coloured and comprises numerous conglomerate and sandstone based sequences capped by calcretes (Marshall 1978*b*). The conglomerates contain a varied assemblage of exotic clasts including vein quartz, acid igneous debris, mylonites, purple quartzites, and intraformational mud flakes. Three excellent examples of lateral accretion sets are exposed in the Member between SM 8502 0389 and SM 8493 0386 (C on Fig. 6). The sets are associated with various calcrete profiles and lenses of intraformational conglomerate. The Conglomerate Member is thought to have resulted from fluvial sedimentation on a semi arid flood plain, with a south-westerly dispersal direction and source areas in the Carmarthen or N Pembrokeshire region (Marshall 1978*a*).

(D). The Heterolithic Member of the West Angle Formation begins at a malachitic horizon (Fig. 6-D) originally noted by Dixon (1921 p. 55). It is initially red, with locally grey coloured upward fining sequences, macerated plant remains, and mottled mudstones with rare calcrete horizons, largely of fluvial origin but finer grained than before.

(E). At this deep cleft, between the cliff and a seastack, are patchy accumulations of grey mudstone and coarse sandstone directly overlying a green calcrete. The beds contain phosphatised fragments, plants, fish teeth, and bivalves, and mark the onset of true grey-red interbedding.

(F). Six metres to the S and across a sinistral wrench fault (Fig. 6) the beds contain a coal, root traces, *Planolites,* calcretes, and a shelly limestone, which has been interpreted as a clastic, lagoonal infill (Marshall 1978*a*). Dixon (1921) recovered *Orthoceras* sp. from the top red siltstones, while Dolby (1970) and Bassett & Jenkins (1977) obtained an Upper Devonian PL spore zone age from two spore horizons at this locality.

(G). The top of the Heterolithic Member is best seen on the **sea stack** at SM 8493 0379, where thin dolomitic sandstones interbed with grey shales. Fish remains, a sparse brachiopod-gastropod fauna, and the trace fossil *Chondrites* can be found in these beds, which have been spore dated as Carboniferous (Courceyan) VI subzone, and interpreted as a back-barrier lagoonal deposit (Marshall 1978*a*).

(H). On the seaward, **S side of the stack,** the top of the Skrinkle Sandstones Group is marked by thick, yellow weathering calcareous sandstones which are sharp based, internally parallel laminated, and cross bedded. A lag horizon of quartz pebbles and bryozoan fronds occurs about a metre above the base. These rocks have been interpreted as a transgressive barrier-beach sequence. They are overlain by a sharp, irregular surface followed by grey mudstones and calcareous sandstones of the Lower Limestone Shales, the lower part of which displays, at SM 8491 0362, spectacular sedimentary slump folds (Kelling & Williams 1966; Williams 1971).

4. Return to Pembroke via the B4320 and take the **A4139 and B4585** roads to **Manorbier.** At SS 066 977 turn right on the beach road and park at the

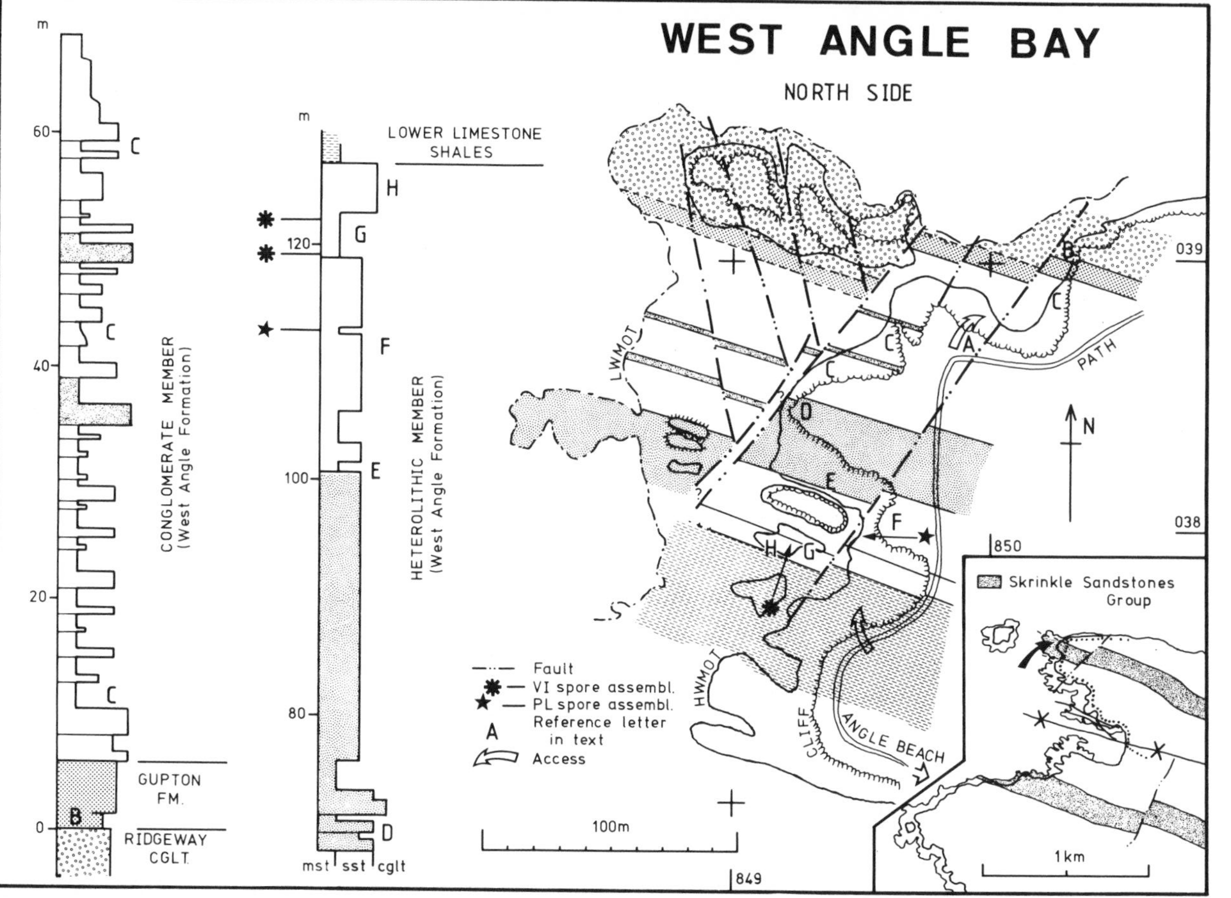

Fig. 6. Geological sketch map of the Skrinkle Sandstones Group outcrop on the N side of West Angle Bay, together with a log through the West Angle Formation (after Marshall 1978*a*). Letters indicate outcrops referred to in the text.

large car park near the castle. Proceed across the beach to join the cliff path, noting en route the upward fining cycles of the lower member of the Freshwater West Formation, exposed in the low southern cliffs of Manorbier Bay. Ascend the cliff path, where at **King's Quoit** (SS 0596 9733) a pronounced indentation of the cliff marks the boundary of the Moor Cliffs and Freshwater West formations, the former possessing thick purple calcretes at its top.

(A). In the vicinity of **Priest's Nose** (SS 059 972) a low angle, bevelled cliff platform provides an excellent section through part of the Moor Cliffs Formation (Fig. 7). The sequence dips steeply N and is through that part of the Formation rich in air-fall tuffs. The succession here is dominated by thick red mudstones with calcretes, air-fall tuffs of variable thickness and rare fine to medium grained sandstones. On the **S side of the platform** a prominent, 0.68 m thick tuff — the Rook's Cave Tuff — crops out. This tuff can be followed for a few hundred metres along strike to **Rook's Cave** (SS 0623 9706) across a number of sinistral wrench faults with small offsets. In this strike section the Tuff is seen to be of variable thickness due to original deposition in ponds or channels, and inter-pond areas. The lower surface of the Tuff preserves a magnificent array of trace fossils — groove and brush marks, burrows, and faecal pellet clusters **[PLEASE DO NOT HAMMER]** — which are abundant in the thicker channel areas but absent from the inter-channel regions.

In the **Priest's Nose section,** 54.98 m above the Rook's Cave Tuff, is a magnificent massive calcrete (2.95 m thick) which can be correlated through East Moor Cliff (SS 047 976) to the W side of Swanlake Bay on West Moor Cliff (SS 035 978). The calcrete contains an abundance of large carbonate concretions with a mudstone boxwork in its lower half and large pseudoanticlines above. Between the calcrete and the Rook's Cave Tuff two marker sandstone beds, in the thick mudstone sequence, can be traced along the strike from Priest's Nose to Rook's Cave. The sandstones are medium to fine grained, micaceous and purple (upper) and green (lower). They are 1.28 m and 1.40 m thick respectively, and cross bedded throughout in several sets.

The Townsend Tuff Bed (2.44 m) and the Pickard Bay Tuff Bed (1.02 m) occur 92.79 m and 108.62 m respectively above the Rook's Cave Tuff. They are best studied, at low tide, at the **foot of the cliffs** where they are found in deep recesses formed by sea erosion. Some of the tuffs have been eroded out up to 200 m into the cliffs and thus form dangerous near-vertical clefts on the headland of Priest's Nose (Fig. 7).

(B). Rejoin the Pembrokeshire Coast Path and proceed E past Coomb (SS 0661 9703) to **Presipe,** where access can be gained to the beach near the major dextral wrench fault at SS 0690 9707 (Fig. 7). Here, an impressive, mudstone dominated section through the Moor Cliffs Formation crops out in the **W cliff of the bay** (Fig. 7 - Log). The mudstones occur below the level of the Rook's Cave Tuff which can be seen high up in the **NW corner of the bay** 5.85 m below a prominent cross bedded, fine to medium grained sandstone. The logged section (Fig. 7) serves to illustrate the mudstones and pseudoanticlinal calcretes with their associated intraformational conglomerates (Allen & Williams 1979*b*, Plate 1A). The dextral wrench fault brings the lower member of the Freshwater West Formation into the bay between Presipe and Conigar Pit. The rock section in the **central area of the bay,** which is difficult of access after mid tide, displays bedding surfaces preserving a variety of trace fossils, including arthropod tracks and large scour marks, *Beaconites* burrows, mud filled polygons, and ripple marks. The rocks are commonly arranged in upward fining cycles, and excellent examples of soft sediment deformation features occur in some of the sandstone units.

(C). Access to **Conigar Pit** (SS 0724 9696) may also be gained from the cliff path via the small valley of Water Come-on (SS 0717 9704) (Fig. 7). The **E cliff of Conigar Pit** exposes the magnificent type section through the Conigar Pit Sandstone Member of the Freshwater West Formation. The rocks dip steeply N and the section can be examined from the NE corner of the bay (SS 0725 9695) to low water mark where the contact of the Member with the Moor Cliffs Formation crops out (SS 0722 9680). The sequence here is mainly arranged in upward fining cycles of fine pebble intraformational conglomerates-sandstones-mudstones with calcretes. The conglomerates may be massive or cross bedded, and five horizons bearing ostracoderm debris have been noted. The sandstones are mainly fine to very fine grained, and display much ripple drift bedding, *Beaconites* burrows, and mud cracks. The mudstones contain carbonate concretions and tubules, with weak pseudoanticlinal developments.

The most notable feature of the section is the occurrence of eleven sandstone-mudstone complexes arranged as lateral accretion deposits. These deposits vary in thickness from 0.70 m to 3.09 m, the lateral accretion surfaces (epsilon cross bedding) being magnificently displayed and showing closure mainly in a southerly direction. However, northerly and westerly closing sets are also present. The Conigar Pit Sandstone Member is seen to overlie a minimum thickness of 11.20 m of a grey purple development of the Chapel Point Calcretes at the top of the Moor Cliffs Formation.

5. Return to Tenby via the A4139. There are frequent sailings during the summer season from Tenby Harbour to **Caldey Island** where passengers are landed at Priory Bay (SS 136 968). Walk from the landing stage past the monastery to the lighthouse above **Chapel Point** (SS 1435 9576).

The contact between the Moor Cliffs Formation and Freshwater West Formation is well exposed in strike section across **the rock platform from**

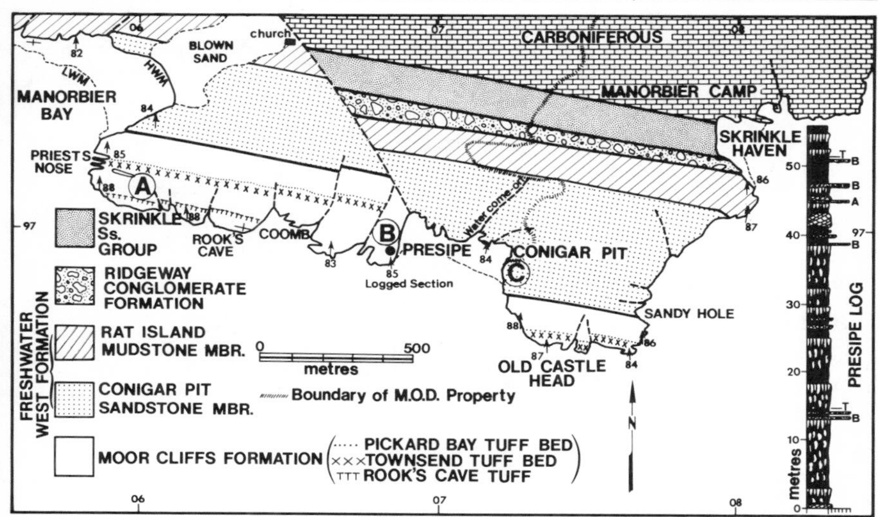

Fig. 7. Geological map of the Manorbier Bay — Old Castle Head area with a representative sedimentological log through part of the Moor Cliffs Formation at Presipe. Circled letters indicate outcrops referred to in the text. For key to log see Fig. 8.

Chapel Point to The Flats (Fig. 8). The basal unit of the Freshwater West Formation is marked by grey-green, medium to coarse grained sandstones, which are pebbly at the base and internally flat or cross bedded. This basal complex is 1.55 m thick and contains plant debris, fish fragments and malachitic horizons. Wave ripples are also present locally.

The top of the Moor Cliffs Formation is marked by a thick (+30 m) sequence of mudstones with spectacular calcrete developments and interbedded intraformational conglomerates (Fig. 8 - Log). This is the type section of the Chapel Point Calcretes which can be traced throughout the entire Pembroke peninsula (*cf.* Freshwater West). The calcretes may be massive, or contain tubules and large concretions often arranged orthogonally to pseudoanticlinal surfaces.

Two types of intraformational conglomerate are distinguished (Allen & Williams 1979*b*). Type A are associated with relatively thick quartzose channel sandstones and include a matrix of quartzose sand, whereas Type B (Fig. 8 - Log) are frequently found interbedded with mudstones and pebbly mudstones, lack a quartz sand matrix, and consist wholly of calcrete and mudstone debris. It has been suggested (Allen & Williams 1979*b*) that Type A conglomerates are related to streams that entered from distant uplands and drained across the Lower ORS alluvial plains. However, Type B conglomerates formed within the bounds of the depositional basin and

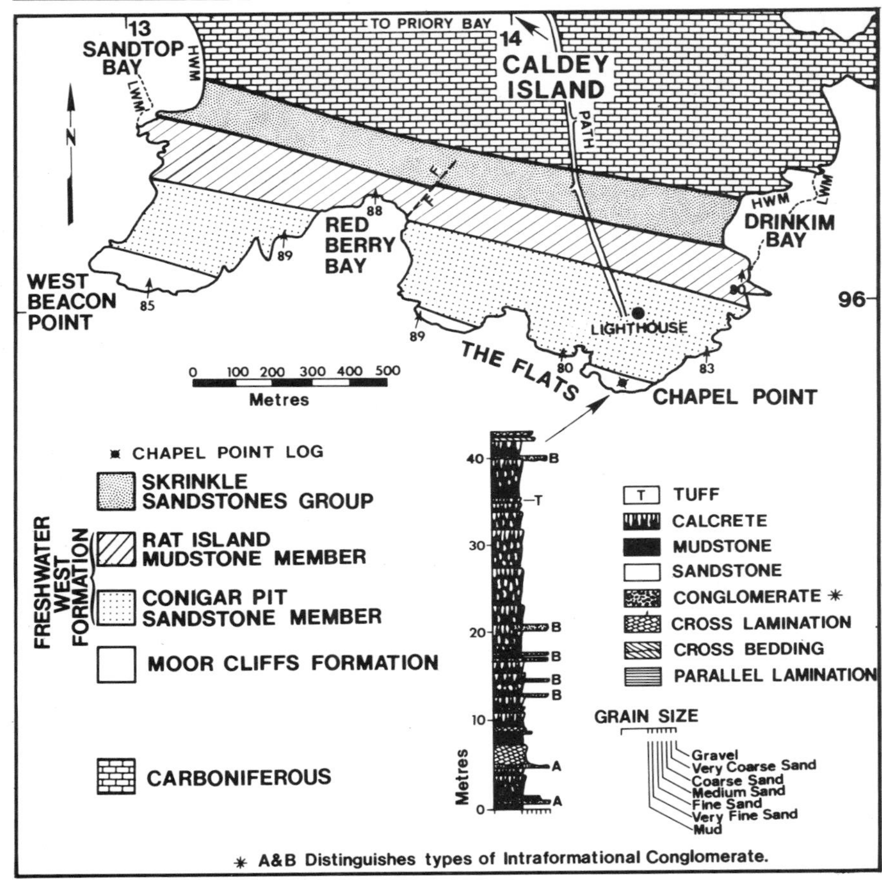

Fig. 8. Geological map of the southern half of Caldey Island with a sedimentological log through the Chapel Point Calcretes at the top of the Moor Cliffs Formation.

represent minor systems of ephemeral drainage that developed from time to time on slightly elevated interfluves between the envalleyed prinicpal rivers.

Acknowledgements.
We thank Miss Toni Shaffer and Mr. John Wright (Geology Department, West Virginia University, U.S.A.) for respectively typing the manuscript and draughting the figures.

REFERENCES

ALLEN, J. R. L. 1963. Depositional features of Dittonian rocks: Pembrokeshire compared with the Welsh Borderland. *Geol. Mag.* **100**, 385-400.

ALLEN, J. R. L. 1965. Upper Old Red Sandstone (Farlovian) palaeogeography in South Wales and the Welsh Borderland. *J. sedim. Petrol.* **35**, 167-195.

ALLEN, J. R. L. 1973. Compressional structures (patterned ground) in Devonian pedogenic limestones. *Nature phys. Sci.* **243**, 84-86.

ALLEN, J. R. L. 1974*a*. The Devonian rocks of Wales and the Welsh Borderland. pp. 47-84 *In* OWEN, T. R. (ed.), *The Upper Palaeozoic and Post Palaeozoic rocks of Wales*. viii + 426 pp., Univ. Wales Press, Cardiff.

ALLEN J. R. L. 1974*b*. Studies in fluviatile sedimentation: implications of pedogenic carbonate units, Lower Old Red Sandstone, Anglo-Welsh outcrop. *Geol. J.* **9**, 181-208.

ALLEN, J. R. L. 1977. Wales and the Welsh Borders. pp. 40-54 *In* HOUSE, M. R. *et al.* A correlation of Devonian rocks of the British Isles. *Spec. Rep. geol. Soc. Lond.* No. 8, 110 pp.

ALLEN, J. R. L. 1979. Old Red Sandstone facies in external basins, with particular reference to Southern Britain. *In* HOUSE, M. R., SCRUTTON, C. T., & BASSETT, M. G. (eds.), The Devonian System, *Spec. Pap. Palaeont.*, No. 23, 65-80.

ALLEN, J. R. L., DINELEY, D. L., & FRIEND, P. F. 1967. Old Red Sandstone basins of North America and Northwest Europe. *Proc. Int. Symp. Devonian System, Alberta Assoc. Petrol. Geol.* **1**, 69-98.

ALLEN, J. R. L. & WILLIAMS, B. P. J. 1978. The sequence of the earlier Lower Old Red Sandstone (Siluro-Devonian), north of Milford Haven, south-west Dyfed (Wales). *Geol. J.* **13**, 113-136.

ALLEN, J. R. L. & WILLIAMS, B. P. J. 1979*a*. Old Red Sandstone facies and Wenlock stratigraphy and palaeogeography in Wales and the Welsh Borderland. *Proc. Geol. Ass.* **90**, 229-231.

ALLEN, J. R. L. & WILLIAMS, B. P. J. 1979*b*. Interfluvial drainage on Siluro-Devonian alluvial plains in Wales and the Welsh Borders. *J. geol. Soc. Lond.* **136**, 361-366.

ALLEN, J. R. L. & WILLIAMS, B. P. J. 1981. Sedimentology and stratigraphy of the Townsend Tuff Bed (Lower Old Red Sandstone) in South Wales and the Welsh Borders. *J. geol. Soc. Lond.* **138**, 15-29.

ALLEN, J. R. L. & WILLIAMS, B. P. J. MS. The sequence of the earlier Lower Old Red Sandstone (Siluro-Devonian), south of Milford Haven, southwest Dyfed (Wales).

BASSETT, M. G. 1971. Silurian rocks of the south Pembrokeshire coast. pp. 206-221 *In* BASSETT D. A. & BASSETT M. G., (eds.), *Geological Excursions in South Wales and the Forest of Dean*. 267 pp. Geol. Ass., South Wales Group, Cardiff.

BASSETT, M. G. 1974. Review of the stratigraphy of the Wenlock Series in the Welsh Borderland and South Wales. *Palaeontology,* **17**, 745-777.

BASSETT, M. G. & JENKINS, T. B. H. 1977. Tournaisian conodont and spore data from the uppermost Skrinkle Sandstones of Pembrokeshire, South Wales. *Geologica Palaeont.* **11**, 121-134.

DIXON, E. E. L. 1921. Geology of the South Wales Coalfield. Part XIII. The country around Pembroke and Tenby. *Mem. Geol. Surv. UK*. 220 pp.

DIXON, E. E. L. 1933*a*. Some recent stratigraphical work and its bearing on south Pembrokeshire problems. *Proc. Geol. Ass.* **44**, 217-225.

DIXON, E. E. L. 1933*b*. Notes on the geological succession in south Pembrokeshire.

Proc. Geol. Ass. **44,** 402-411.

DOLBY, G. 1970. Spore assemblages from the Devonian-Carboniferous transition measures in Southwest Britain and Southern Eire. *Colloque sur la stratigraphie du Carbonifere. Congres et Colloques, Univ. Liege,* **55,** 267-274.

EDWARDS, D. 1979. A late Silurian flora from the Lower Old Red Sandstone of southwest Dyfed. *Palaeontology,* **22,** 23-52.

HANCOCK, P. L. 1965. Axial-trace-fractures and deformed concretionary rods in south Pembrókeshire. *Geol. Mag.* **102,** 143-163.

HANCOCK, P. L. 1973. Structural zones in Variscan Pembrokeshire. *Proc. Ussher Soc.* **2,** 509-520.

KELLING, G. & WILLIAMS, B. P. J. 1966. Deformation structures of sedimentary origin in the Lower Limestone Shales (basal Carboniferous) of south Pembrokeshire, Wales. *J. sedim Petrol.* **36,** 927-939.

MARSHALL, J. D. 1978*a*. *Sedimentology of the Skrinkle Sandstones Group (Devonian-Carboniferous), South West Dyfed.* Unpublished Ph.D. thesis, Univ. of Bristol, 371 pp.

MARSHALL, J. D. 1978*b*. West Angle Bay, Dyfed. pp. 99-101 *In* FRIEND, P. F. & WILLIAMS, B. P. J. (eds.), *A field guide to the Devonian of Scotland, the Welsh Borderland and South Wales.* ii + 106 pp. Palaeontological Association, London.

OWEN, T. R., BLOXAM, T. W., JONES, D. G., WALMSLEY, V. G. & WILLIAMS, B. P. J. 1971. Summer (1968) Field Meeting in Pembrokeshire, South Wales. *Proc. Geol. Ass.* **82,** 17-60.

RICHARDSON, J. B. & LISTER, T. R. 1969. Upper Silurian and Lower Devonian spore assemblages from the Welsh Borderland and South Wales. *Palaeontology,* **12,** 201-252.

THOMAS, R. G. 1978. *The Stratigraphy, Palynology and Sedimentology of the Lower Old Red Sandstone Cosheston Group, S. W. Dyfed, Wales.* Unpublished Ph.D. thesis, Univ. of Bristol, 552 pp.

WALMSLEY, V. G. & BASSETT, M. G. 1976. Biostratigraphy and correlation of the Coralliferous Group and Gray Sandstone Group (Silurian) of Pembrokeshire, Wales. *Proc. Geol. Ass.* **87,** 191-220.

WILLIAMS, B. P. J. 1971. Sedimentary features of the Old Red Sandstone and Lower Limestone Shales of south Pembrokeshire, south of the Ritec Fault. pp. 222-239 *In* BASSETT, D. A. & BASSETT, M. G. (eds.), *Geological Excursions in South Wales and the Forest of Dean.* 267 pp. Geol. Ass., South Wales Group, Cardiff.

WILLIAMS, B. P. J. 1978. The Old Red Sandstone of the Welsh Borderland and South Wales. pp. 55-106 *In* FRIEND, P. F. & WILLIAMS, B. P. J. (eds.), *A field guide to the Devonian of Scotland, the Welsh Borderland and South Wales.* ii + 106 pp. Palaeontological Association, London.

10
STRATIGRAPHY AND SEDIMENTOLOGY OF UPPER CARBONIFEROUS SEQUENCES IN THE COALFIELD OF SOUTH-WEST DYFED

by G. T. GEORGE *and* G. KELLING

Maps	*Topographical:*	1 : 50 000	Sheets 157 St David's and Haverfordwest, 158 Tenby
		1 : 25 000	Sheets SM81, SN10, SN20
	Geological:	1 : 50 000	Sheets 226/227 Milford, 228 Haverfordwest, 229 Carmarthen, 224/245 Pembroke and Linney Head

THE Upper Carboniferous strata of the coalfield in south-west Dyfed [Pembrokeshire Coalfield] include some of the most intensely deformed rocks of this age in Britain. Tectonic deformation has resulted in the compression of the ESE-WNW trending Coalfield syncline to about one third of the width of its counterpart in the main basin of South Wales. The southern limb of the syncline is intricately folded and foreshortened by thrusts, reverse faults, and wrench faults of considerable magnitude, some of which are fold-limb replacements and appear to have formed contemporaneously with folding. The scale of these dislocations is best appreciated to the N of Milford Haven where the E-W Johnston thrust carries Precambrian rocks N onto Coal Measures. Further to the SE the Ritec Fault carries the Pembroke and St Florence synclines for at least 1 km onto the Sageston anticline (see geological map sheets). Along the N crop of the coalfield the effects of the Hercynian orogeny are less pronounced.

Despite the complexity of the structure it is possible to examine nearly complete stratigraphical sequences of Namurian and Westphalian strata in various parts of the coalfield (Fig. 1). The Namurian succession is broadly comparable with that in the main South Wales Coalfield basin. In the latter area the Millstone Grit was originally subdivided into three lithological units (Basal Grit, Middle Shales, and Farewell Rock) and this classification was later adopted throughout South Wales. Unfortunately, these units,

[pp. 175-201 *In* BASSETT, M. G. (ed.). 1982. Geological excursions in Dyfed, south-west Wales.]

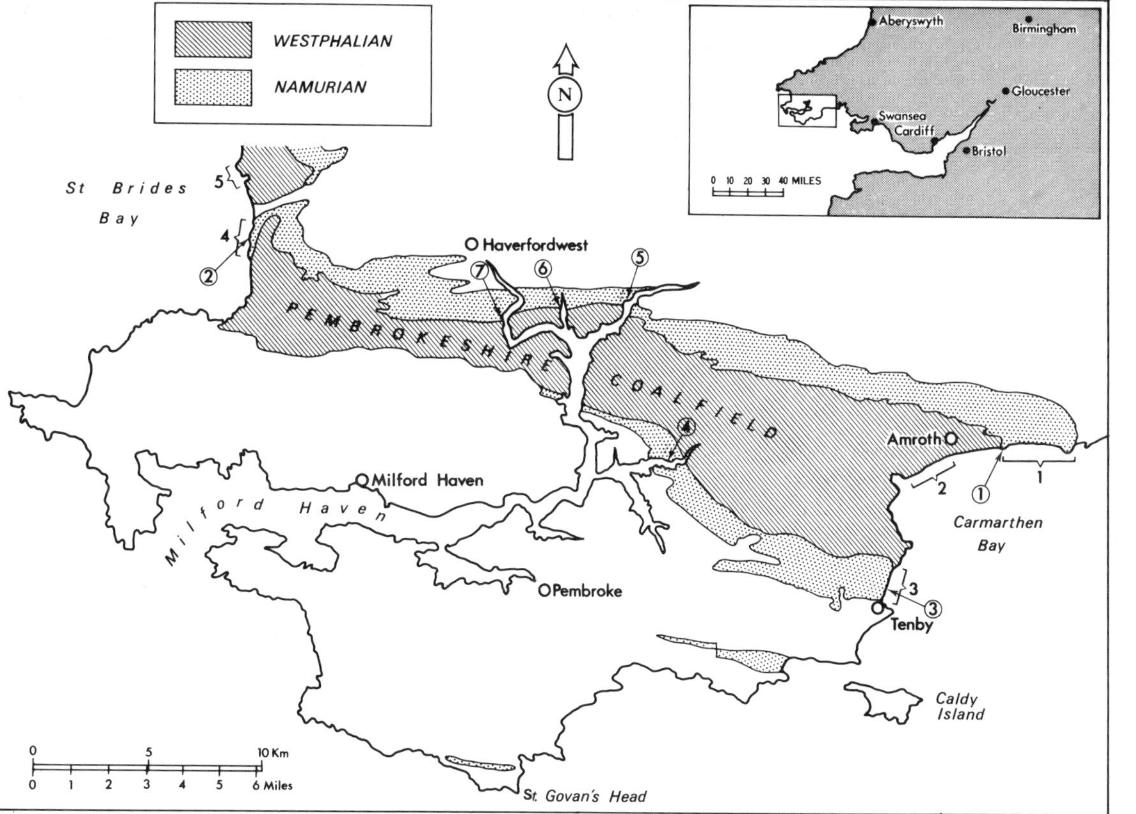

Fig. 1. Geological map showing the distribution of Namurian and Westphalian strata in SW Dyfed. Coastal sections: 1, Ragwen Point to Amroth; 2, Amroth to Wiseman's Bridge; 3, Tenby Harbour to Waterwynch Bay; 4, Settling Nose to Broad Haven; 5, Nolton Haven:
Localities for excursion 11 circled: 1 Telpyn Point; 2 Settling Nose; 3 Tenby, First Point; 4 Cresswell Quay; 5

particularly the Farewell Rock, can be shown to be diachronous when related to goniatite marker bands. In fact the name Farewell Rock has been applied to a number of sandstones ranging in age from Namurian to Westphalian A (see Jenkins 1962; Archer 1965; Jones 1974). Most of these authors agree that this term, at least, should be abandoned because it has no stratigraphical significance. In the Pembrokeshire Coalfield the problem of subdivision is not so acute because the various lithogical units are well defined, synchronous, and restricted to the Namurian Series. Thus it is suggested that in this area the term Farewell Rock should be replaced by the Upper Sandstone Group. The proposed subdivision is:

(3) UPPER SANDSTONE GROUP (G_1) — one major fining-upward sequence; basal sandstone member erosional on Middle Shale Group, upper argillaceous member overlain by the *G. subcrenatum* marine band. (30-42 m).

(2) MIDDLE SHALE GROUP (R_2 - G_1) — two or more coarsening-upward sequences; *G. cancellatum* marine band well developed; top truncated by overlying group. (90-120 m).

(1) BASAL GRIT GROUP (E_1 - R_2) — quartz arenites interbedded with carbonaceous and marine shales; base generally erosional on Carboniferous Limestone, top marked by *R. superbilinque* marine band. (0-45 m).

Summaries of the stratigraphy and correlation of Namurian sequences in SW Dyfed appear in Archer (1965), Jones (1969, 1974), and in Fig. 2. Jenkins (1962) has produced the most comprehensive work on the stratigraphy and correlation of the Coal Measures in the area. Marine bands including the *G. subcrenatum, A. vanderbeckei* (Amman) and *A. aegiranum* (Cefn Coed or Picton Point) have been recognised (Fig. 2), as well as distinctive non-marine bivalve faunas. Westphalian A and B strata, consisting of mudstones and shales with thin anthracite coals and lenticular sandstones, occur in a series of fault blocks in the core of the coalfield syncline between Little Haven and Amroth. Younger strata, assigned to the Westphalian C and D stages, are more arenaceous and occur in the detached part of the coalfield between Nolton Haven and Newgale (Fig. 1).

ITINERARY

This itinerary is intended to provide an introduction to the stratigraphy and sedimentology of the Upper Carboniferous rocks of SW Dyfed. Although the main localities are described in broadly stratigraphical order, it may be more practical to combine certain localities out of their descriptive sequence to achieve economy of travel and time. Time is of particular relevance since all the localities are coastal outcrops and are therefore subject, in varying degrees, to tidal conditions. Tidal ranges of 9-12 m (30-40 ft) are common in

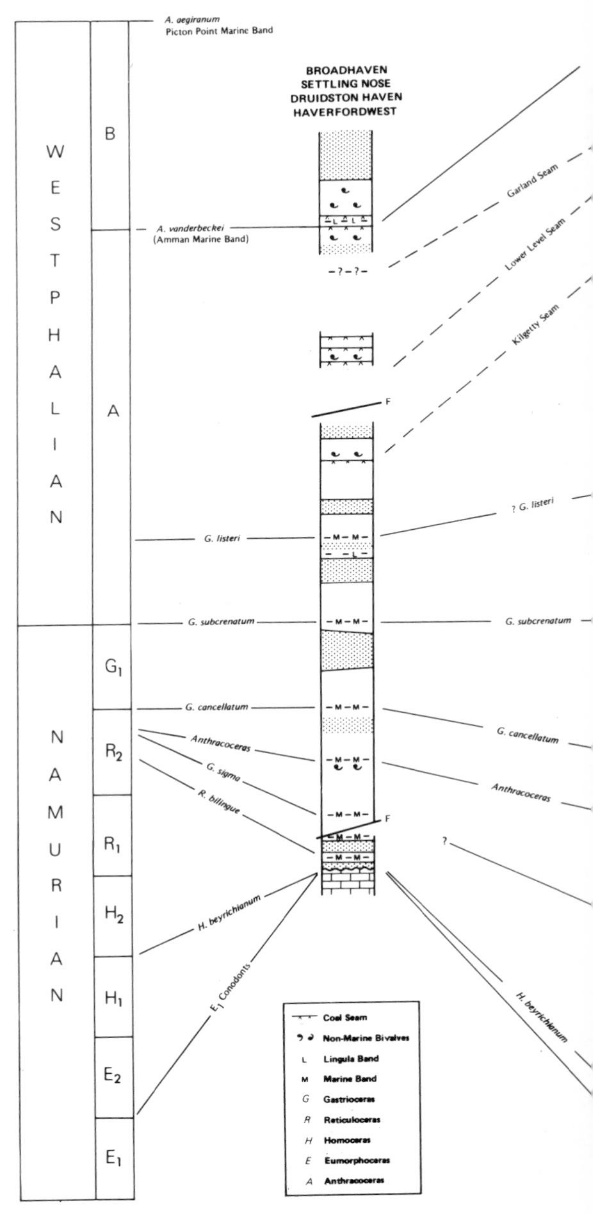

A. aegiranum
Picton Point Marine Band
BROADHAVEN
SETTLING NOSE
DRUIDSTON HAVEN
HAVERFORDWEST
W E S T P H A L I A N
B
A
A. vanderbeckei
(Amman Marine Band)
Garland Seam
Lower Level Seam
Kilgetty Seam
F
G. listeri
? G. listeri
G. subcrenatum
N A M U R I A N
G1
R2
R1
H2
H1
E2
E1
G. cancellatum
Anthracoceras
G. sigma
R. billingue
H. beyrichianum
E1 Conodonts
Coal Seam
Non-Marine Bivalves
Lingula Band
Marine Band
Gastrioceras
Reticuloceras
Homoceras
Eumorphoceras
Anthracoceras

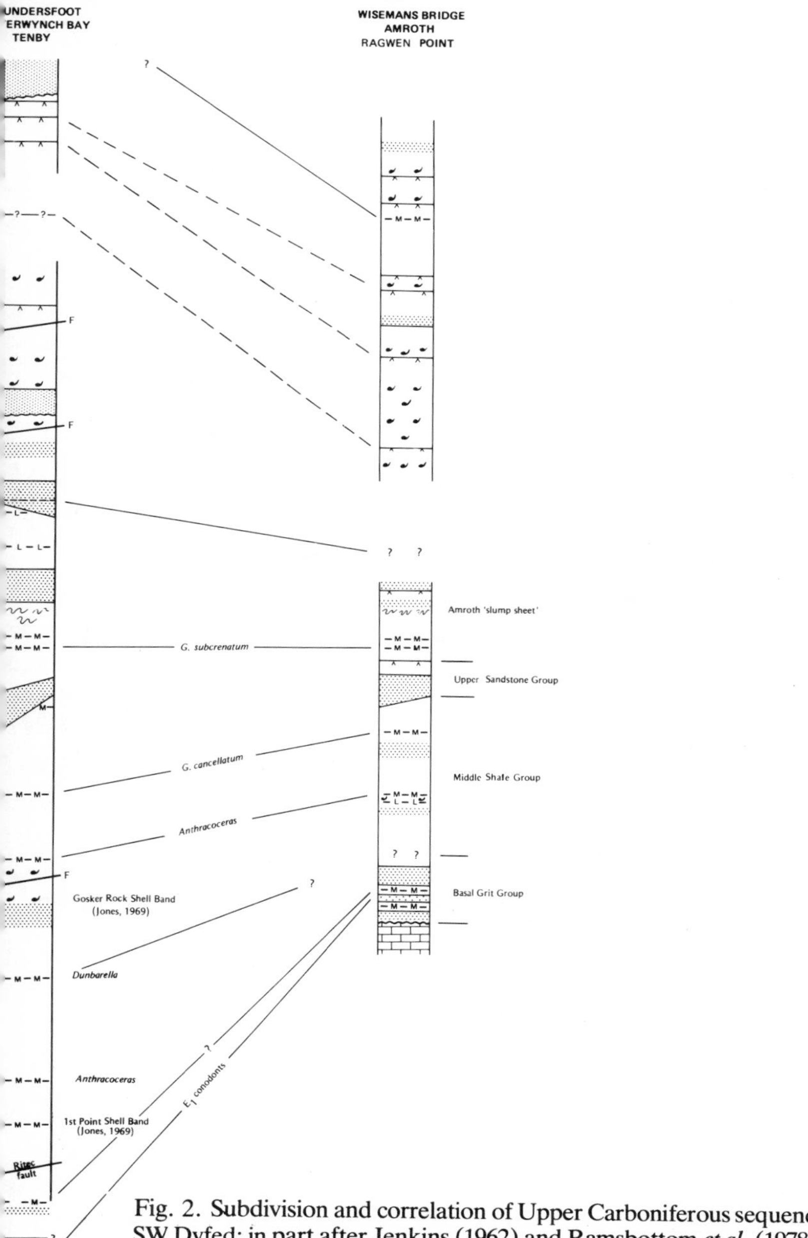

Fig. 2. Subdivision and correlation of Upper Carboniferous sequences in SW Dyfed; in part after Jenkins (1962) and Ramsbottom *et al.* (1978).

Carmarthen Bay and it is essential that tide tables are consulted when planning an excursion. It is also recommended that safety helmets are worn when working at the foot of cliff sections.

1. Ragwen Point to Amroth. This magnificent coastal section in Namurian and basal Westphalian strata extends from Ragwen Point (SN 220 071) across Marros Sands to Telpyn Point (SN 185 072) and ends at the storm beach to the E of Amroth (SN 175 073). **Ragwen Point** can be reached by walking S down a track leading off the Pendine-Amroth road, 200 m to the SE of Pendine Church (SN 2291 0865). If possible the transport should proceed to the New Inn, Amroth where the traverse ends. Some additional details of the structure around Amroth are described in excursion 12, locality 11, this volume. The complete itinerary requires a full day, and with good tides the traverse should be timed to commence about two hours after high tide.

Towards the S end of Ragwen Point (SN 2210 0715) the erosional contact between the Basal Grit Group and the Carboniferous Limestone can be examined. The limestones at this locality are in the upper part of the *Dibunophyllum* Zone (D_2 - D_3) and are interbedded with calcareous shales. Good brachiopod faunas and large burrows *(Thalassinoides)* are conspicuous on some bedding planes. The absence of fossils of zonal value from the overlying 'grits' led to the tentative assignment of this sequence to the Kinderscoutian (R_1) Stage (Archer 1965). However, conodonts, incuding *Gnathodus bilineatus, G. girtyi simplex, G. girtyi subspindit,* and *G. commutatus commutatus,* recovered from septarian nodules at 11.7 m and 19.8 m in the section (Fig. 3) suggest a much older Pendleian (E_1) age (George 1970). Thus the magnitude of the sub-Namurian unconformity at this locality does not appear to be as great as previously thought. The succession at Ragwen Point consists of a variety of quartz arenite facies, erosive on and interbedded with argillaceous facies (Fig. 3).

The environmental interpretation of the Basal Grit Group is one of the remaining major problems in the study of the sedimentology of the Upper Carboniferous of South Wales. The stratigraphical position of the group, between Visean shelf limestones and younger Namurian shelf and fluvio-deltaic clastics, and the association of mineralogically mature quartz arenites and marine shales both suggest a littoral origin. Conversely, the low textural maturity of some of the arenites, the abundance of palaeosol horizons, and southerly directed palaeocurrents off St George's Land, are indicative of more continental conditions. In the past the quartz arenite facies have been interpreted as the deposits of braided delta-distributaries, and their associated argillaceous facies as inter-distributary bay deposits (George 1970; Kelling & George 1971; Kelling 1974). Recent work on the Basal Grits also seems to substantiate this deltaic model. Lithofacies and palaeocurrent studies strongly suggest that the arenites are syntectonic in origin and were

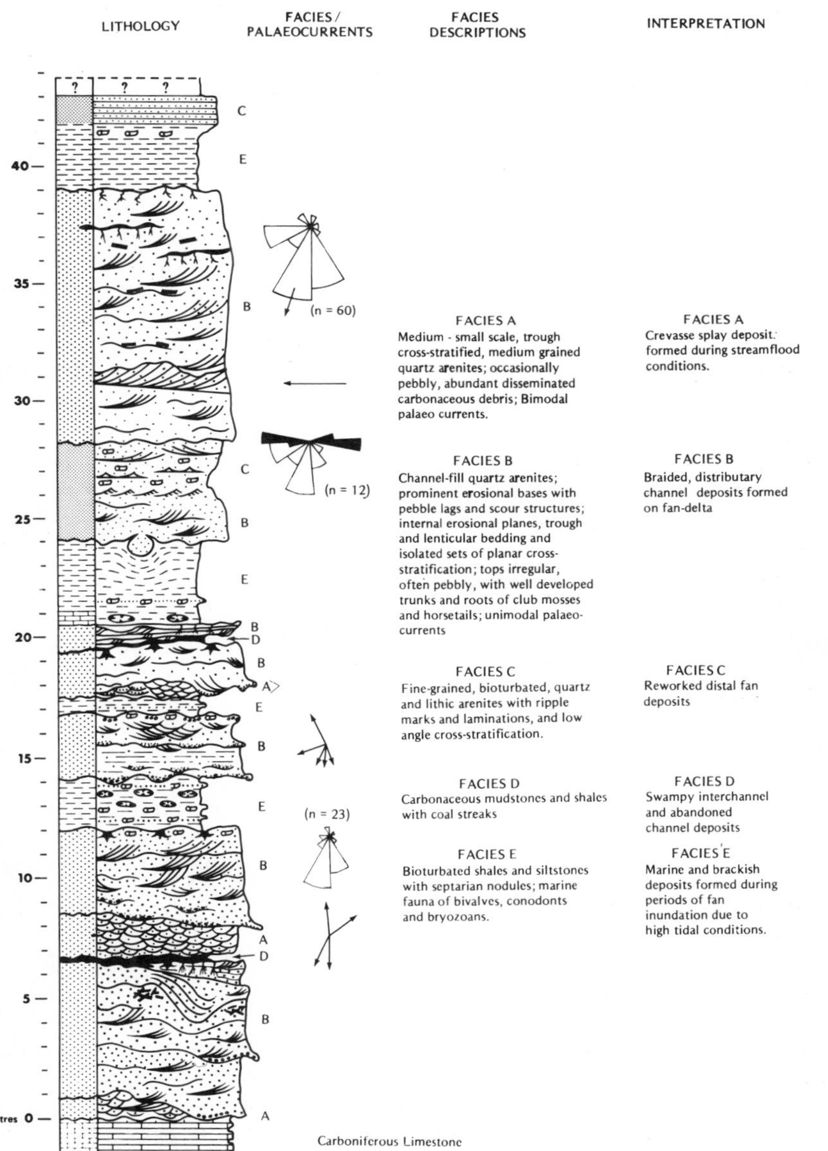

Fig. 3. Vertical sequence of facies and palaeocurrents, Basal Grit Group, Ragwen Point.

derived from predominantly Old Red Sandstone source rocks exposed as a result of uplift along positive features such as the Usk and Towy anticlines and the Carreg Cennen and Neath disturbances (Owen-Roberts pers. comm.). These and other structural elements appear to have influenced sedimentation in South Wales throughout the Upper Palaeozoic (see discussion in Owen 1971, 1974).

Probably the best depositional model for the Basal Grit Group is the fan-delta. Fan-deltas form where alluvial fans or short-headed streams prograde into standing bodies of water. In the present example the fans were fed by short-headed streams that prograded into a marine embayment. In such a model Facies B (Fig. 3) would represent the sediments deposited in braided distributary channels during high discharge conditions on the fan. A large volume of this sediment would have been deposited as a result of the downstream migration of dunes with lee-side scours, which would produce trough and lenticular bedding. The isolated set of planar cross stratification (Fig. 3, 31 m) was deposited in the lee of a transverse bar. Emergence, due to channel abandonment and/or the growth of mid-channel bars, is indicated by palaeosol horizons with roots and trunks of giant club mosses (Fig. 3, 12 m and 19.5 m) and delicate rootlets of horsetails (Fig. 3, 6 m and 20 m). The undulating, pebbly tops of many of the broad channel units suggest rapid abandonment during high stage.

Facies A is interpreted as crevasse splay deposits formed during stream-flood conditions. These deposits often show bimodal palaeocurrents and evidence of laterally waning current velocities, and are truncated by the overlying channel deposits (Fig. 4).

The thin carbonaceous shales and mudstones (Facies D) that drape the channel facies (Fig. 3, 6.5 m and 19.5 m) were deposited in swampy interchannel troughs, while the thicker marine and brackish marine sediments (Facies E) were deposited when the fan was inundated as a result of high tidal conditions in the bay. Facies C (Fig. 3, 26-28 m and 42-43 m) probably represents the deposits of a destructive phase when the fan was reworked by marine agencies. Excellent examples of palaeosol horizons, flutes and scour structures and load casts can be examined within the sequence.

Although the cliff section is interrupted for 2 km along **Marros Sands,** the low dips result in only 10-15 m of the Namurian succession being concealed. These concealed beds possibly contain the *R. bilinque* and *R. superbilinque* marine horizons that are strongly developed within the Basal Grit Group in other parts of the north crop.

Before the next cliff section to the W is reached some well preserved trunks and root systems of trees, belonging to the post-glacial submerged forest, can

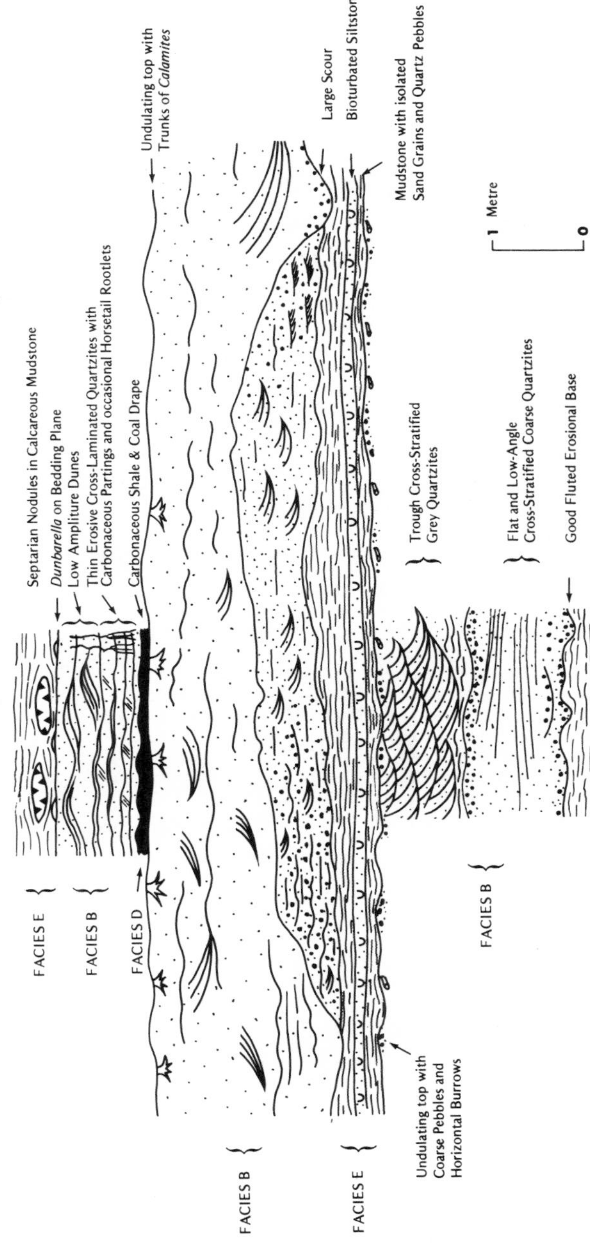

Fig. 4. Field sketch showing the details of vertical and lateral facies relationships between 14 - 21 m (Fig. 3) Basal Grit Group, Ragwen Point.

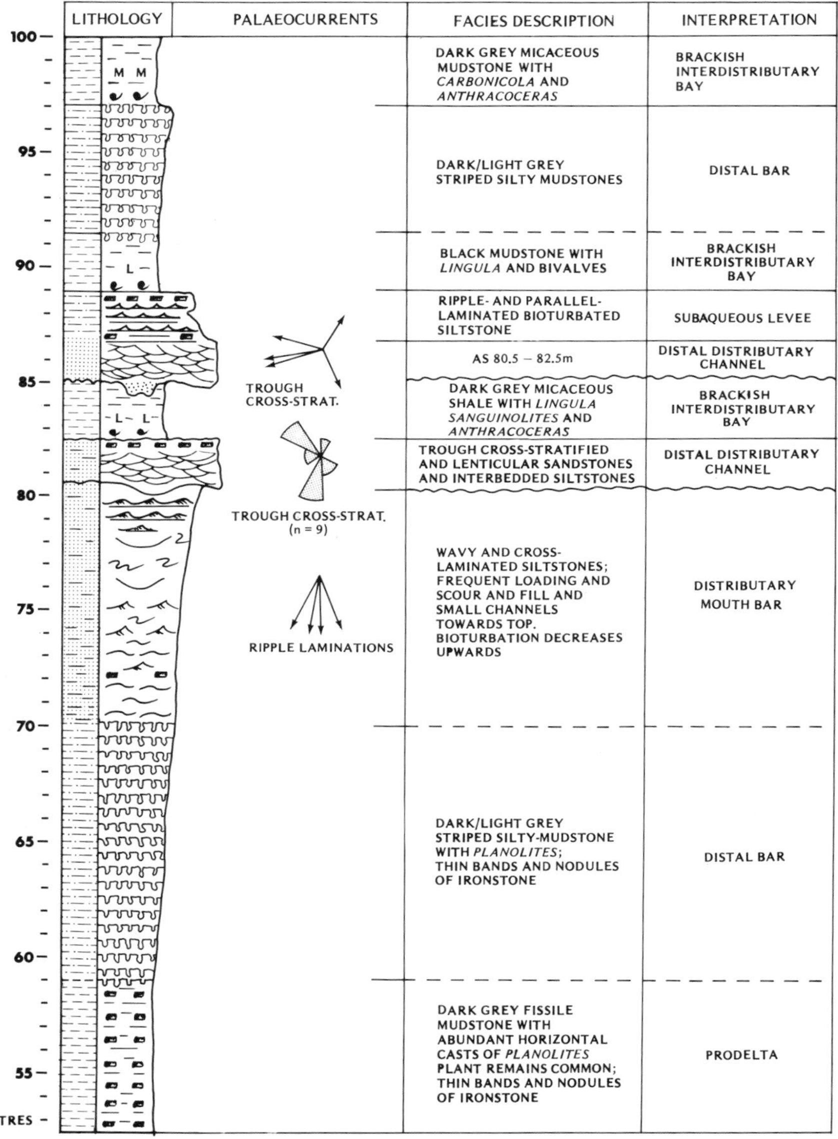

Fig. 5. Vertical sequence of facies and palaeocurrents, Middle Shale Group (53 - 100 m). Marros Sands.

be examined on the beach (SN 199 075). Well formed ice-crack polygons can occasionally be seen in the low drift-cliffs **in front of Marros Mill.**

The Middle Shale Group strata exposed in the cliffs between SN 198 076 and a small stream at SN 193 075, represent an excellent example of a coarsening-upward deltaic sequence (Fig. 5). Within this cycle there is a complete record of prodelta (53-59 m), distal bar (59-70 m), distributary mouth bar (70-80 m), and distributary channel (80-83 m) deposition (see also Elliott 1978, fig. 6.40). In the distal bar to mouth bar facies the upward increase in grain size is associated with a change in sedimentary structures from regular parallel laminations (striped beds) to wavy, lenticular and cross-laminations. Scour and fill, channel, and penecontemporaneous deformation structures occur in the upper part of the sequence. Many of these structures are identical with those described by Coleman & Gagliano (1965) from similar environments in the Mississippi delta.

At 81 m (Fig. 5) the mouth bar sediments are truncated by lenticular and trough cross-bedded fine sandstones with silty-mudstone drapes and interbeds. The latter are often highly bioturbated and commonly contain streaks and pellets of bright coal. Penecontemporaneous load structures and syneresis cracks are also common. This erosional facies is interpreted as the deposits of a distributary channel. Polymodal palaeocurrents and the relatively thin sequence suggest that the distributary channel was located in a distal position where it was beginning to flare out over the mouth bar. High in the cliffs 400 m to the E of the stream, the same sequence is much thicker and occupies a well defined, symmetrical channel. This channel probably marks a more proximal and/or axial region within the distributary channel-mouth bar system.

The abandonment of this distributary channel is recorded by the bioturbated horizon at 82.5 m and the overlying brackish-marine interdistributary bay deposits containing *Lingula* and *Sanguinolites.* The sudden diversion of a further distributary into this bay is marked by the channel deposits and possible reworked subaqueous levee deposits between 85-89 m. Delta abandonment is again indicated by a bioturbated horizon and brackish-marine mudstones (Fig. 5, 89-92 m).

The succeeding cycle (SN 191 075 — SN 187 073) represents a second major advance of a fluvially dominated delta (Fig. 6, 100-134 m). In this cycle the ripple laminated sandstones, well exposed on the most easterly promontory of **Telpyn Point,** are interpreted as shoal-water, mouth bar deposits. Some reworking by marine currents is suggested by the NW-directed palaeocurrents. Lateral migration of the distributary channel feeder is suggested by the overlying delta plain and wave-reworked subaqueous levee deposits between 131-134 m.

A very interesting sequence of transgressive/regressive marine deposits crops out in the bay **between the two promontories forming Telpyn Point** (SN

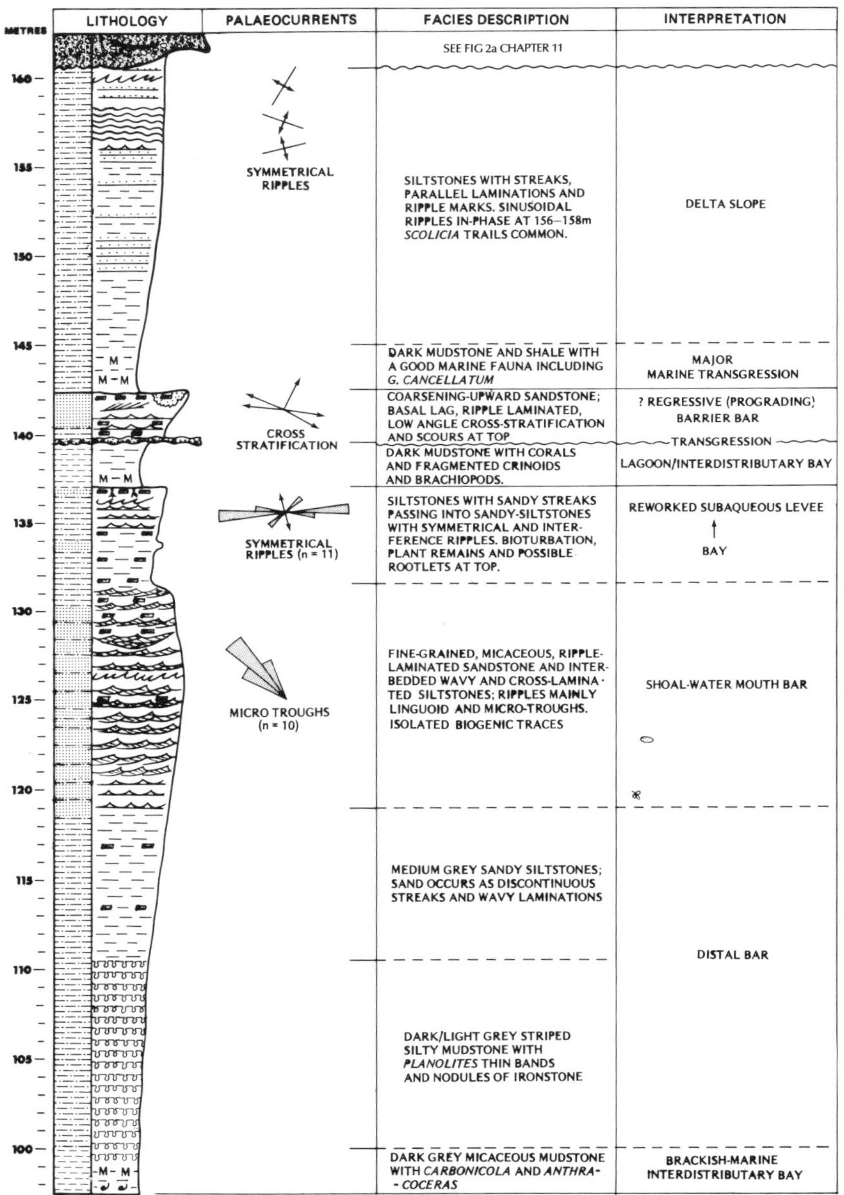

Fig. 6. Vertical sequence of facies and palaeocurrents, Middle Shale Group (98 - 160 m), Marros Sands to Telpyn Point.

187 073). The sequence (Fig. 6, 136-145 m.) consists of four units:

(4) Dark mudstones with a good fauna of thick-shelled goniatites including *G. cancellatum.*

(3) Thin, coarsening-upward silty sandstone unit with ripple laminations and low angle cross-stratification and highly bioturbated top.

(2) Basal lag deposit with quartz clasts and mudstone and phosphorite pebbles.

(1) Dark mudstones with a ?displaced fauna of solitary corals, crinoid debris and fragmented brachiopods.

Sequences of this type are deposited during delta destructive phases when delta top sediments are reworked by marine agencies to form barrier bars and/or linear sand ridges. Intense bioturbation at the top of unit 3 and the succeeding *G. cancellatum* horizon (unit 4) represents the main transgressive event. The thin basal lag deposit (unit 2) may be the only record of an earlier, and higher energy, transgression over lagoonal sediments (unit 1). The coarsening-upward sandstone (unit 3) would then represent a period of barrier bar, shoreface progradation that occurred between the two transgressive phases. Alternatively, the complete sequence may record the formation and abandonment of an isolated sand ridge during a single transgressive phase. In this case the coarsening-upward unit can be attributed to winnowing of fines from the bar crest, while the lag was formed as a result of scouring in the adjacent trough (see discussion in Johnson 1978, pp. 224-229).

The *G. cancellatum* transgression initiated a phase of deeper water sedimentation throughout SW Dyfed. Parallel-laminated and graded siltstones, with biogenic tracks and trails of *Scolicia* on their bases, characterise the sequence above this marine band. In the cliffs just below the erosive base of the Upper Sandstone Group (SN 1860 0724) a 2 m unit of sinusoidal ripples-in-phase forms a very prominent feature. These ripples have dome shaped crests, although some are elongate, sinuous, and some bifurcate laterally. Wave lengths of 40 cm are common and the amplitude of the ripples increases to a maximum of 6 cm.

A large proportion of this sequence was deposited by suspension fall-out from low density turbidity currents flowing down a relatively steep delta slope. This interpretation is discussed more fully below under locality 3.

To the **W of Telpyn Point** (SN 186 072 — SN 183 073) the Upper Sandstone Group is completely exposed and forms an excellent example of a fining-upward, fluvially dominated distributary channel sequence. This sequence is described in detail in excursion 11 of this volume.

The *G. subcrenatum* marine band, which marks the base of the Westphalian and terminates the Upper Sandstone Group cycle, is exposed at

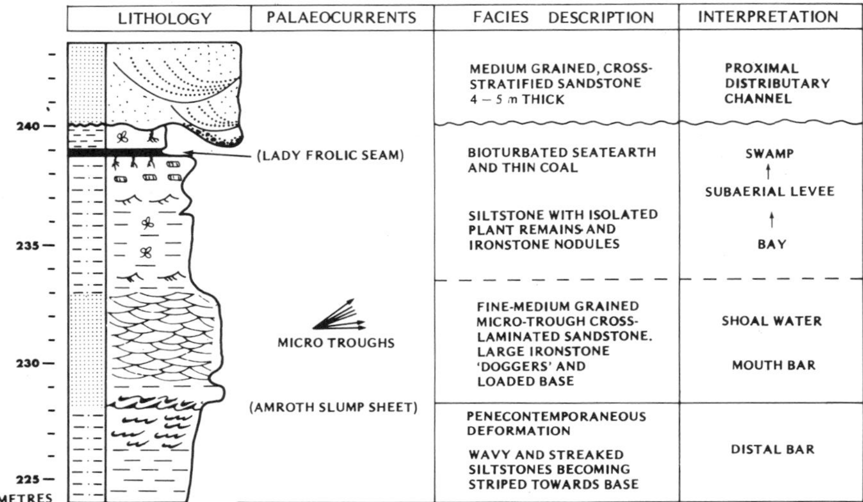

Fig. 7. Vertical sequence of facies and palaeocurrents. Westphalian A, Amroth.

SN 1815 0726. From this point to the **storm beach at the E end of Amroth** (SN 175 073) the cliffs are occupied by another coarsening-upward deltaic sequence approximately 50 m thick. Two lines of detached slump balls occur in the distal mouth bar sediments, and the Amroth 'slump sheet' (Kuenen 1948) occurs at the base of the ripple-laminated proximal mouth bar sediments (Fig. 7). Slumping appears to be an integral part of mouth bar progradation in the Mississippi delta (see Elliott 1978).

Although the distributary channel sandstone present at the top of the sequence is rather inaccessible, it can be observed in the **cliffs along the foreshore.** It displays a strongly erosive base and at one point it almost 'washes-out' the Lady Frolic coal seam. Further E (SN 1795 0735) a normal fault downthrows the sandstone 10-12 m to the E.

2. Amroth to Wiseman's Bridge. Magnificent cliff and foreshore exposures in this stretch of coastline reveal a sequence within the *communis, modiolaris* and *similis-pulchra* zones of the Lower and Middle Coal Measures.

For some 120 m S of the S end of the **promenade at Amroth** the sequence is strongly folded and cut by at least four thrust zones (Fig. 8) (see also excursion 12, locality 11, this volume). These repeat a 12 m succession involving the Kilgetty Vein coal with its overlying shale and a group of cross-bedded and ripple-laminated sandstones. The roof shale of the Kilgetty coal yields abundant fish scales, and a mudstone band approximately 5 m above the coal, carries *Carbonicola pseudorobusta.* South of this thrust zone the rocks are disposed in a broad anticline, the faulted core of which occurs at SN 1591 0683. The southern limb of this anticline reveals the 200 m sequence

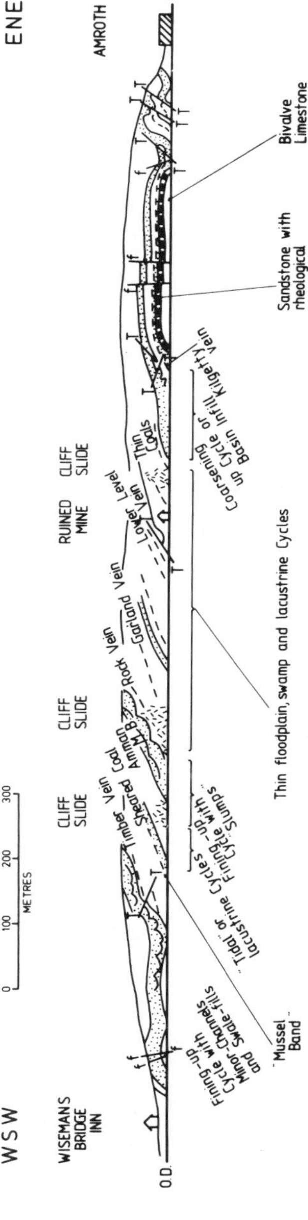

Fig. 8. Section showing the structure and sequence of Westphalian A and B strata between Amroth and Wiseman's Bridge.

indicated in Fig. 8, and these rocks form the **coast almost as far as the Inn at Wiseman's Bridge** (SN 1475 0626), dipping gently to the S and with only a few minor faults to interrupt the succession.

The basal bed of this sequence, the Amroth freshwater limestone, is a buff-weathering, laminated ankeritic siltstone with abundant shells of the non-marine bivalve *Anthracosia regularis*. The overlying 105 m, extending **S to the headland** at SN 1525 0650, comprises repetitions of underclay-coal-interbed associations and involves at least eleven coal seams (including the Lower Level, Fiddlers, Garland, and Rock) and nine mussel bands (Jenkins 1962; Williams 1968, fig. 21). This sequence represents a succession of floodplain deposits accumulating in the swamps and freshwater lakes of a coastal plain environment, which may have been advancing to the N and W with time (Williams 1966, pp. 109, 110).

The Rock Vein coal is poorly exposed **in the cliff** at SN 1526 0652 and is succeeded erosively by a prominent lag breccia which floors a 12 m sequence of contiguous minor channels. Each of the channels displays a fining-upward fill, and the upper, silty portions of the fill contain numerous excellent examples of synsedimentary deformation features, including basal loading, hydroplastic folds, and pseudonodules (Williams 1969, p. 411). This complex of contiguous channels forms the lower, substratum member of a major fining-upwards cycle, some 22 m thick overall, which is capped by a poorly exposed silty underclay with conspicuous sphaerosiderite nodules and a thin coal. This cycle evidently represents the advance of a major river system into this area; cross bedding in the channel sandstones indicates a consistent westerly flow (Williams 1968, p. 356).

The capping coal is overlain by the Amman Marine Band, a 30 cm thick goniatite/brachiopod bearing mudstone. This band is obscured on the foreshore by a recent cliff slip, but it can be seen in the **upper part of the accessible cliff face.** Southwards for the next 110 m the sequence is continued by three coarsening-upward cycles (respectively 10 , 7 m, and 9.5 m thick), each capped by an underclay and coal. The silty or sandy upper member of each cycle is characterised by abundant symmetrical ripple lamination and bioturbation, indicative of shallow, wave-agitated conditions, probably in a freshwater lake. The thin, sheared coal and overlying planty mussel band, which caps the third of these cycles, is exposed in a **low cliff on the SW side of the sandstone reef** at SN 1507 0636. The succeeding oscillatory and bioturbated silt-mud alternations are poorly exposed **on the foreshore** and there is then a small gap in the exposure caused by another cliff fall.

South of this gap a thin coal (Timber Vein) crops out **high in the cliff.** This is succeeded erosively by a thick lag breccia, rich in ironstone and coal clasts, and a cross bedded sandstone. Together these represent the erosive base of a fining-upward fluvial cycle (25 m thick in total), which continues upwards in a set of contiguous minor channels, displaying spectacular cross-cutting relationships. The fill of each minor channel exhibits a fining-upward sequence, grading from sandstone into silt/mud alternations. Cross bedding and channel orientations in this sequence indicate consistently westwards transport (Williams 1968, fig. 26). The succeeding top stratum member is represented by siltstones (with thin erosional sandstones of crevasse-splay aspect) which grade upwards into mudstones capped by a thin coal. In the cliff this sequence is terminated prematurely by a group of high angle faults at a point (SN 1484 0624) **130 m SE of the Inn at Wiseman's Bridge.**

The sequence thus traversed indicates that, following upon the marine transgression represented by the Amman Marine Band, there was prolonged accumulation of sediments in a coastal plain environment, including swamps, freshwater, and brackish lakes. Ultimately, this phase of marine regression was completed by the advance of alluvial sediments, deposited in a westerly flowing river system (Williams 1968, p. 358).

Between the high angle faults and the **N end of the beach** at Wiseman's Bridge, there is a tectonically disturbed sequence of beds some 17 m thick and including a thin coal overlain by channelled sandstones. This sequence may be a faulted repetition of the Timber Vein and the overlying fluvial cycle.

3. Tenby Harbour to Waterwynch Bay. At Tenby the Namurian succession has been intensely deformed as a result of Variscan earth movements. Much of the folding and thrusting is associated with the Ritec fault, which at Tenby consists of three southerly dipping splays. The details of the structure and correlation of these strata have been discussed by Dixon (1921), Jones (1969), Owen *et. al.* (1971), and Kelling & George (1971); details are also described in excursion 12, localities 14 and 15, this volume. Broadly, the structure comprises three down-faulted blocks that young towards the N (Fig. 9).

There are few exposures between Tenby Harbour and the North Sands, especially since the completion of the new sea defences along North Cliff. However, a very profitable hour can be spent examining the **reefs adjacent to Barrel-Post Rock and Gosker Rock** for way-up structures (load casts, scour and fill etc.) and minor fold axes (see Kelling & George 1971).

Excellent sedimentary sequences of upper Marsdenian and Yeadonian age can be examined in the cliff section **between First Point and Waterwynch Bay.** To study this section in detail, good tidal conditions (e.g. low tide around noon; height at low tide < 1.0 m) are essential. Such tides give a working time of up to four hours between First Point and Waterwynch Bay.

The oldest sediments in the section occur in the core of the anticline in Second Bay (Fig. 9) and are silty mudstones containing *Anthracoceras* and bivalves. These marine beds are overlain by a 35 m, coarsening-upward sequence which develops into the sandstone that forms **Second Point and Bowman's Point** (Fig. 9). Between these points the sandstone displays quite marked lateral facies changes. At Second Point the sequence consists of 4 m

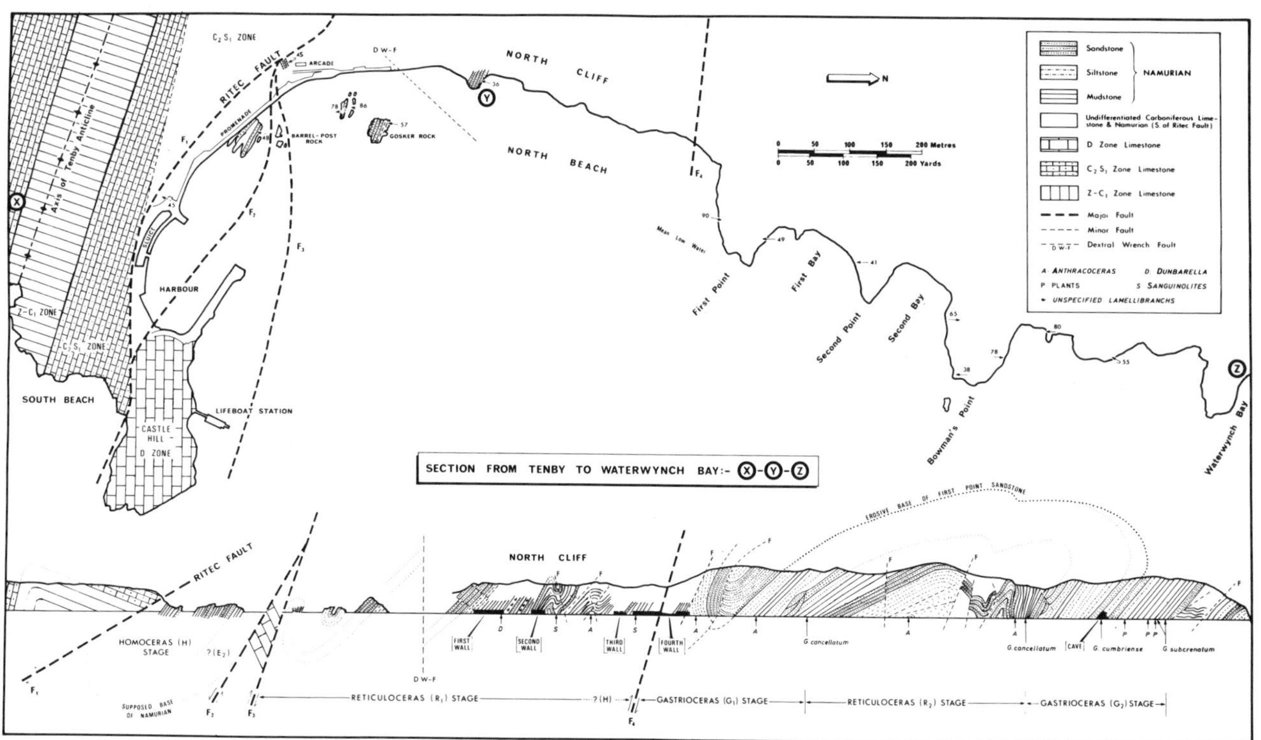

Fig. 9. Section showing the structure and sequence of Namurian strata between Tenby and Waterwynch Bay; in part after Dixon (1921) and Sullivan (1964).

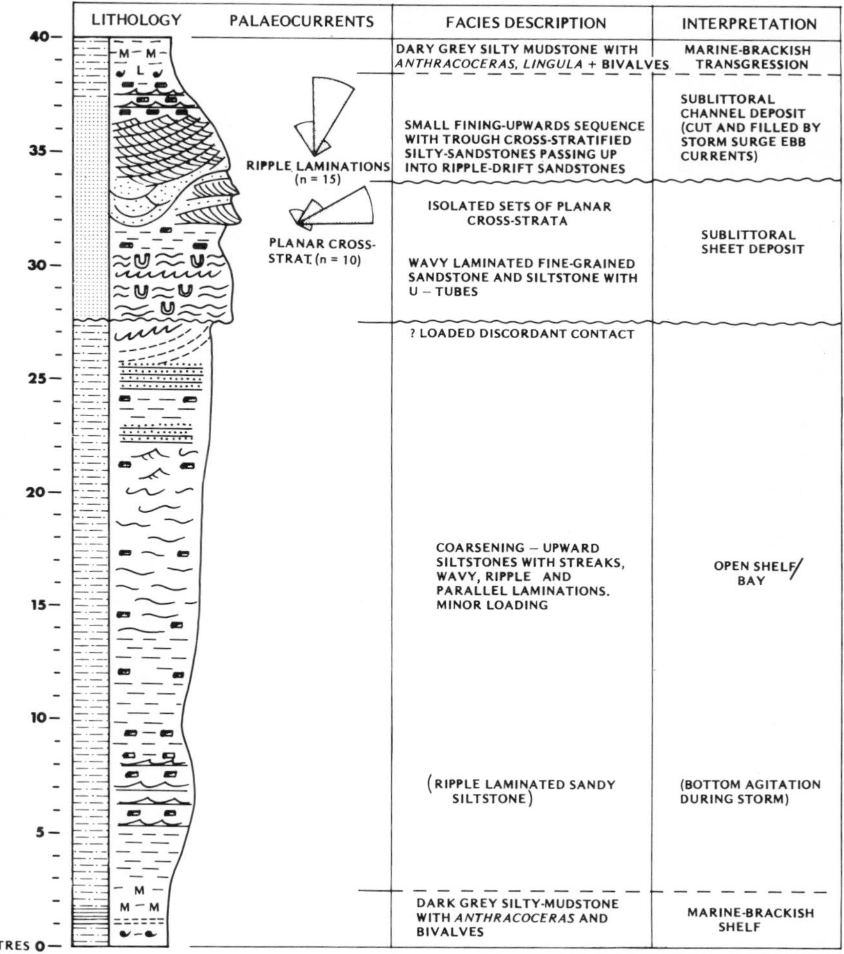

Fig. 10. Vertical sequence of facies and palaeocurrents, Middle Shale Group, Bowman's Point.

of wavy and ripple-laminated silty sandstones with abundant U-tube biogenic structures, overlain by a small, fining-upward, channel fill sequence (Fig. 10). Towards the **E end of the Point** isolated sets of planar cross-strata appear in the bioturbated facies, and palaeocurrent measurements indicate transport to the E. This facies displays many of the characteristic features of shallow marine deposits (e.g. Heterolithic Facies (H) of Johnson 1978, p. 233). The complete coarsening-upward sequence would appear to represent progradation of sublittoral facies in a fairly open, shallow shelf environment. Decreasing water depth is indicated by the small channel unit at the top of the sequence. Unimodal palaeocurrents from individual facies (Fig. 10) suggest that tidal activity was negligible during their formation. This cycle represents the lateral equivalent of the sub-*cancellatum* prograding barrier bar sequence at Telpyn Point.

The overlying succession, exposed in **First Bay and to the N of Bowman's Point,** also displays a number of interesting vertical and lateral facies changes (Fig. 11). Above the *G. cancellatum* marine band, barren silty mudstones gradually pass upwards into distal turbidites with biogenic tracks of *Scolicia.* At SN 1360 0172, N of Bowman's Point, two thicker graded units, the lower one bearing delicate, elongate flute casts, suggest a more proximal origin. In First Bay these beds are truncated by pebbly sandstones that occupy at least four individual channels. These channels have erosional bases and sharp irregular tops and are filled with massive, rheologically deformed and cross-stratified pebbly sandstones. Some of the larger channels carry large mudstone and ironstone clasts in the upper part of the fill, while the top portions of other channel fills are finer-grained and display well developed linguoid ripples. The interchannel facies consist of bioturbated sandy siltstones with linguoid ripples that pass into silty mudstones with impoverished ripples. North of Bowman's Point only one composite channel is present.

The above association represents an excellent example of a small turbidite fan deposited on the distal slopes of a prograding delta front. The terminology used to describe depositional environments on modern deep-sea fans (see Kelling & Stanley 1976; Rupke 1978) can be applied satisfactorily to this relatively shallow water fan. The channel-fill sandstones and related ripple-laminated facies represent fan channels and their related levee deposits, that prograded over proximal and distal turbidites deposited on mid and outer fan areas. Palaeocurrents indicate that flow within the channels was to the S, and in this direction the single, composite channel seen to the N of Bowman's Point, splits into a number of discrete braid channels (Fig. 11). Channel aggradation occurred as a result of both traction and mass flow processes, while deposition on the mid and outer fan was largely the result of turbidity currents flowing down the delta slope.

A period of slow deposition or deterioration of the delta slope is recorded by the second *Anthracoceras* horizon (Fig. 11). The overlying coarsening-upward sequence consists predominantly of siltstones and fine sandstones characterised by parallel and graded bedded units with *Scolicia,* wave and current induced ripples, polygonal interference ripples, and frequent slumped horizons. Catenary ripples in-phase, some showing slight lateral drift, are common sedimentary structures. This thick sequence is terminated N of Bowman's Point by a 4.5 m coarsening-upward sandstone. In the

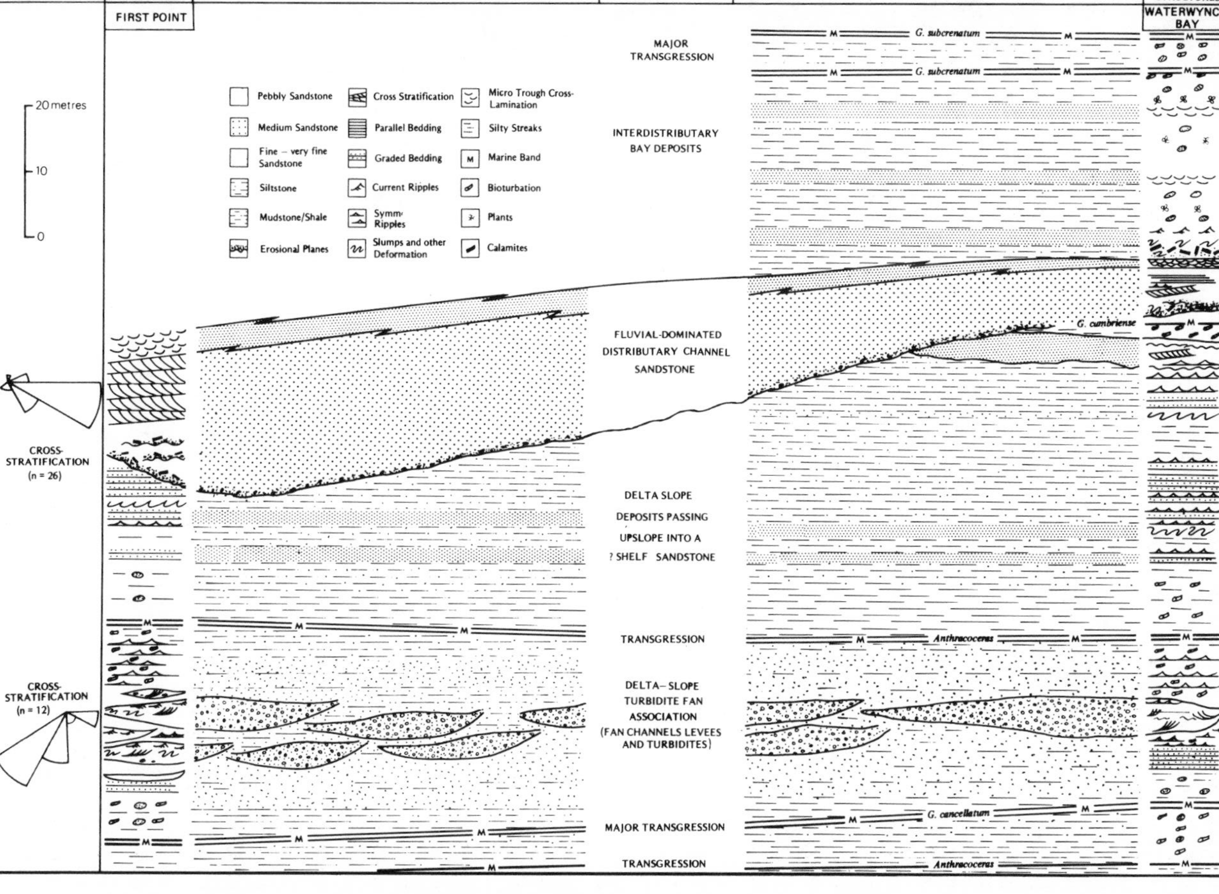

Fig. 11. Vertical and lateral facies relationships with Namurian (G_1) strata between First Point and Waterwynch Bay, Tenby.

overlying silty mudstones Jones (1969) has recorded *Gastrioceras cumbriense*.

Within this delta slope sequence the formation of current induced sedimentary structures, such as graded and parallel bedding and current ripples, is attributed to high suspension fall-out from low density turbidity currents. Sinusoidal ripples, similar to those seen at Telpyn Point, have also been attributed to such processes (Jopling & Walker 1968). Interaction between density underflow and backflow currents (and possibly contour-following currents) is believed to be responsible for the formation of the variety of symmetrical and interference ripples observed in the sequence. Catenary ripples in-phase have been described from a Pleistocene esker delta sequence in Finland (Aario 1972), and they have also been observed in a similar kame delta sequence at Mullock Bridge, near Dale (Dyfed). In the former case the ripples appear to have formed in the zone of zero velocity between the forward and reverse components of flow at the base of the delta slope.

Frequent slumped horizons within the succession point to periodic oversteepening of the delta slope. Some of the slumped horizons are up to 1.5 m thick and die out laterally.

At the **S end of the cliff section,** to the N of First Point, the greater part of the previously described cycle is cut out by a deeply entrenched distributary channel sandstone (Upper Sandstone Group), which has an erosional relief of approximately 40 m between First Point and Waterwynch Bay (Fig. 11). This observation helps to explain the past controversy over the correlation of the Farewell Rock (Upper Sandstone Group) (see discussion in Owen *et. al.* 1965, 1971). The sedimentology of the Upper Sandstone Group is described in detail in excursion 11 of this volume.

4. Waterwynch Bay. Access to Waterwynch Bay (SN 137 020) may be obtained from the private sign-posted road which leads E off the A478 (SN 128 033), about 2 km N of Tenby. The Bay can also be reached by walking along the coast path from Tenby. The coast from Waterwynch N to Monkstone Point exposes a sequence of basal Coal Measure sediments disposed in a number of broad folds and in part disrupted or repeated by shallow thrusts (see also excursion 12, localities 13 and 14, this volume).

The **cliffs on the N side of Waterwynch Bay** (1370 0205) display part of the coarsening-upwards deltaic regression cycle, some 47 m thick, which overlies the *G. subcrenatum* marine band. The alternating siltstone-mudstone sequence contains numerous examples of the synsedimentary deformational structures described as 'slumps' by Kuenen (1948). Williams (1966, 1969) has demonstrated that most of these rheologic features may be ascribed to vertical and minor lateral adjustments of mobilised sediment. Structures of this type are widely developed at this stratigraphical level in the area and a regional study of their orientation suggests that the south-dipping palaeoslope that prevailed at this time exerted some control on the lateral movement of mobilised sediment (Williams 1969, p. 409).

The *G. subcrenatum* marine band crops out in the **headland forming the S side of the first cove N of Waterwynch** (SN 138 032). The band comprises some 10 m of dark, blocky mudstone carrying a rich goniatite/brachiopod fauna, especially near the base and top of the unit. On the **N side of this inlet** a shallow thrust brings a thin coal from the sequence below *G. subcrenatum* northwards, to overlie beds of the regressive cycle previously seen in Waterwynch Bay. The **next headland to the N** is formed by a thick arenite which has an erosional contact with the underlying laminated siltstones. This thick sandstone (which can also be seen forming the upper cliff on the S side of Waterwynch Bay) represents one of a series of fining-upward, fluvial channel-fill cycles that include thin brackish-marine horizons (M_1 and M_2 bands of Leitch *et. al.* 1958).

5. Settling Nose to Broad Haven. Access to the Settling Nose (SM 858 157) and Black Point (SM 859 153) part of this rugged coastal section is not easy; unless the tide is very favourable it entails scrambling down the grassy and rocky slopes of the inlet (SM 860 156) between Settling Nose and Haroldstone Bridge (Fig. 12). However, most of the sequence can be examined by walking N across the rocky foreshore for about 1 km from the N end of Broad Haven (SM 860 141). Structures around Broad Haven are described in excursion 12, locality 18, this volume.

Settling Nose and Haroldstone Bridge are composed largely of sandstone belonging to the Upper Sandstone Group (Namurian G_1). These sandstones, which form part of a strongly erosive, distributary channel sequence, are described fully in excursion 11, this volume.

To the **S of Settling Nose** the section reveals a total thickness of some 155 m of sediments within the *Carbonicola lenisulcata* and *C. communis* zones of the Lower Coal Measures. However, the *G. subcrenatum* marine band, marking the base of the Coal Measures, is exposed just above a thrust in the **inlet S of Settling Nose** (SM 8600 1550), and the band is repeated by another thrust at Haroldstone Bridge about 180 m further S (SM 8592 1540). The overlying sediments comprise a major coarsening-upwards cycle some 50 m thick, which is exposed for some 650 m to the S from the marine band exposure. The basal 25 m is essentially shale and mudstone, succeeded erosively by 8 m of alternating fine sand and mud laminae ('oscillatory facies') displaying current and wave ripple marks and abundant evidence of bioturbation. The overlying thick arenite is well exposed in the two anticlines which occur in the **bays** immediately S of Black Point (SM 8595 1510). Cross bedding in the sandstone indicates transport towards the SW, but minor silt- and sand-filled channels in the uppermost few metres of the sandstone have

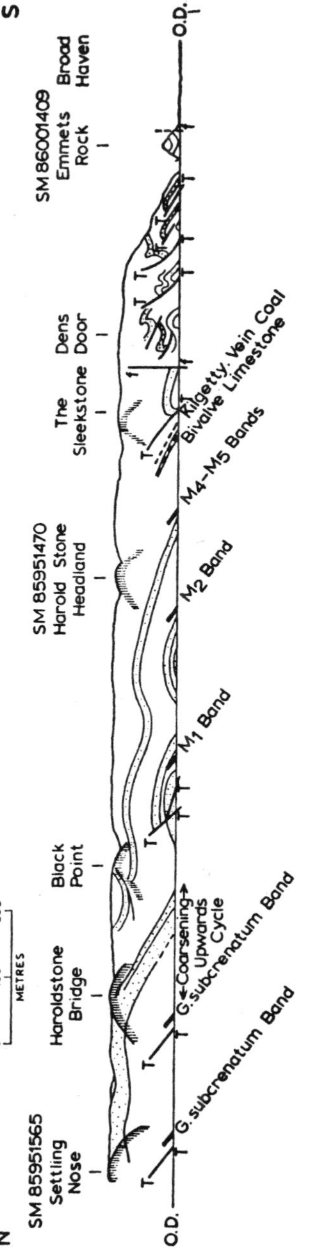

Fig. 12. Section showing the structure and sequence of Westphalian A strata between Settling Nose and Broad Haven.

an E-W orientation (Williams 1966, fig. 45) and may be tidal channels. This entire coarsening-upward cycle is interpreted as a major offlap sequence, the basal 'delta slope' muds being overlain by intertidal mudflat, sand bar, and tidal channel deposits, which migrated to the S and W with time.

Renewed marine transgression is indicated by the 4 m band of dark shales with *Lingula mytilloides* (M1 band) which overlies the thick sandstone (Jenkins 1962, p. 87). Another cross bedded sandstone, 6 m thick, erosively succeeds the marine shale and fines upwards to be capped by a mudstone and fireclay. From the **N side of the headland** at SM 860 151 to the thrust at the **Sleekstone monocline** (SM 8604 1480), the gentle southwards dip reveals a further 80 m of largely argillaceous sediments, including at least three further bands of marine shale, carrying fish fragments, *Planolites,* and foraminifera. Several thin coals and underclays also occur and some of these cap additional coarsening-upward cycles. A 2 m bed of buff limestone (ankeritic siltstone), rich in non-marine bivalves and overlain by a thick underclay and coal (?Kilgetty Vein), occurs in the **S part of the bay** just N of the Sleekstone (SM 8600 1451).

The thrust at the base of the famous Sleekstone monocline repeats the upper part of the sequence just described. Excellent ripple marks and deformation features may be observed in the sandstones forming the overfold. S of the Sleekstone, elucidation of the sequence is complicated by a normal fault running NNE-SSW and probably downthrowing to the E. This fault runs just to the E of the isolated stack of **Dens Door** (SN 8598 1435) and through the **headland immediately to the S** (Fig. 12). The cliff section E of the fault and as far S as **Emmets Rock** (SM 8600 1408) contains at least four thrust-displaced anticlinal overfolds. These repeat a 25 m sequence comprising at least five thin coarsening-upward cycles each capped by an underclay or coal. This succession has been assigned tentatively to the upper part of the *communis* Zone (Jenkins 1962, p. 87).

The sequence of Lower Coal Measures sediments exposed between Black Point and Emmets Rock indicates a series of minor marine transgressions and regressions across a coastal plain environment which was occasionally emergent, allowing peat-swamp development. The sands are mainly of coastal barrier aspect and transport directions are consequently very variable.

6. Nolton Haven. The cliffs and foreshore on the NW side of Nolton Haven (SM 858 185) yield exposures of sediments within the *Anthraconauta phillipsii* Zone of the Upper Coal Measures (Jenkins 1962, pl. 5). The gentle dip of the beds to the SW is interrupted by two normal faults which form prominent gullies ascending the cliff. The exposed sequence is some 45 m thick and is predominantly sandy. A thin coal (Black Cliff Vein) above a thick underclay is exposed about **85 m E of the headland** (SM 8571 1845).

Below this, to the NE, a floodplain sequence of alternating siltstones and fine sandstones (6 m) with minor channelling passes down into a cross- and parallel-bedded subgreywacke arenite (15 m), the whole succession representing a fining-upward, fluvial channel fill cycle, very similar to those observed in the Pennant Measures of the main coalfield of South Wales (Kelling 1968, 1974).

The sediments forming the **NW headland of Nolton Haven** occur above the Black Cliff Vein coal and underclay and include a further 25 m of beds, most of which comprise a further fluvial fining-upward sequence. In this cycle the basal part of the thick substratum arenite is conspicuously conglomeratic (mainly ironstone pebbles), with numerous, gently inclined, internal erosion surfaces. The upper few metres of the sandstone contain several contiguous minor channels, floored by lag-breccias rich in ironstone clasts. Channel truncation of the overlying topstratum siltstones by the basal arenite of the succeeding cycle may be discerned on the foreshore at the headland.

The orientation of cross bedding, ripple marks, and minor channels within the fluvial cycles of Nolton Haven all indicate sediment transport to the W or WSW (Williams 1966, fig. 55), and probably result from the westwards extension of the major W- flowing drainage system of Lower Pennant times detected in the main coalfield (Kelling 1968, fig. 11).

REFERENCES

AARIO, R. 1972. Associations of bed forms and palaeocurrent patterns in an esker delta, Haapajärvi, Finland. *Suomal. Tiedeakat. Toim.* Series 3 No. 111, 55 pp.

ARCHER, A. A. 1965. Notes on the Millstone Grit of the north crop of south Pembrokeshire. *Proc. Geol. Ass.* **76,** 137-150.

COLEMAN, J. M. & GAGLIANO, S. M. 1965. Sedimentary structures: Mississippi River deltaic plain. *In* MIDDLETON, G. V. (ed.). *Primary sedimentary structures and their hydrodynamic interpretation. Spec. Publs. Soc. econ. Paleont. Miner. Tulsa,* **12,** 133-148.

DIXON, E. E. L. 1921. The geology of the South Wales Coalfield, Part 13. The country around Pembroke and Tenby. *Mem. geol. Surv. U.K.* i-vi, 220 pp., 5 pls.

ELLIOTT, T. 1978. Deltas. pp. 97-142 *In* READING, H. G. (ed.), *Sedimentary environments and facies.* Blackwell.

GEORGE, G. T. 1970. *The sedimentology of Namurian sequences in South Pembrokeshire.* Unpublished PhD thesis, University of Wales (Swansea).

JENKINS, T. B. H. 1962. The sequence and correlation of the Coal Measures of Pembrokeshire. *Q. Jl geol. Soc. Lond.* 118, 65-101.

JOHNSON, H. D. 1978: Shallow Siliciclastic Seas. pp. 207-258 *In* READING. H. G. (ed.). *Sedimentary environments and facies.* Blackwell.

JONES, D. G. 1969. The Namurian succession between Tenby and Waterwynch. Pembrokeshire, *Geol. J.* **6,** 267-272.

JONES, D. G. 1974. The Namurian Series in South Wales. pp. 117-132 *In* OWEN, T. R. (ed.), *The Upper Palaeozoic and post-Palaeozic rocks of Wales.* viii + 426 pp. Univ. Wales Press, Cardiff.

JOPLING. A. V. & WALKER, R. G. 1968. Morphology and origin of ripple-drift cross-lamination, with examples from the Pleistocene of Massachusetts. *J. Sedim. Petrol.* **38,** 971-984.

KELLING, G. 1968. Patterns of sedimentation in Rhondda Beds of South Wales. *Bull. Am. Ass. Petrol. Geol.* **52,** 2369-2386.

KELLING, G. 1974. Upper Carboniferous sedimentation in South Wales. pp. 185-224 *In* OWEN, T. R. (ed.), *The Upper Palaeozoic and post-Palaeozoic Rocks of Wales.* viii + 426 pp. Univ. Wales Press, Cardiff.

KELLING, G. & GEORGE, G. T. 1971. Upper Carboniferous sedimentation in the Pembrokeshire Coalfield. pp. 240-259 *In* BASSETT, D. A. & BASSETT, M. G. (eds.), *Geological excursions in South Wales and the Forest of Dean.* 267 pp. Geologists' Association, South Wales Group, Cardiff.

KELLING, G. & STANLEY, D. J. 1976. Sedimentation in canyon, slope and base-of-slope environments. pp. 379-435 *In* STANLEY, D. J. & SWIFT, D. J. P. (eds.), *Marine Sediment Transport and Environmental Management,* Wiley.

KUENEN, PhH. 1948. Slumping in the Carboniferous rocks of Pembrokeshire. *Q. Jl geol. Soc. Lond.* **104,** 365-385.

LEITCH, D., OWEN , T. R. & JONES, D. G. 1958. The basal Coal Measures of the South Wales coalfield from Llandybie to Brynmawr. *Q. Jl geol. Soc. Lond.* **113,** 461-486.

OWEN, T. R. 1971. The relationship of Carboniferous sedimentation to structure in South Wales, *Compt. Rendu 6me Cong. Inter. Strat. Geol. du Carbonifere* (Sheffield, 1967) **111,** 1305-1316.

OWEN, T. R. 1974. The Variscan Orogeny in Wales. pp. 285-294 *In* OWEN, T. R. (ed.), *The Upper Palaeozoic and post-Palaeozoic Rocks of Wales.* viii + 426 pp. Univ. of Wales Press, Cardiff.

OWEN, T. R., RHODES, F. H. T., JONES, D. G. & KELLING, G. 1965. Summer (1964) field meeting in South Wales. *Proc. Geol. Ass.* **76,** 463-496.

OWEN, T. R., BLOXAM, T. W., JONES, D. G., WALMSLEY, V. G. & WILLIAMS, B. P. 1971. Summer (1968) field meeting in Pembrokeshire, South Wales. *Proc. Geol. Ass.* **82,** 2-60.

RAMSBOTTOM, W. H. C. *et al.* 1978. A correlation of Silesian rocks in the British Isles. *Spec. Rep. geol. Soc. Lond.* No. 10. 81 pp.

RUPKE, N. A. 1978. Deep clastic seas. pp. 372-415 *In* READING, H. G. (ed.), *Sedimentary Environments and Facies.* Blackwell.

SULLIVAN, R. 1964. The Lower Carboniferous rocks of Castle Hill fault block, Tenby, Pembrokeshire. *Geol. Mag.* **101,** 113-115.

WILLIAMS, P. F. 1966. *The sedimentation of the Pembrokeshire Coal Measures.* Unpublished PhD thesis, University of Wales (Swansea).

WILLIAMS, P. F. 1968. The sedimentation of Westphalian (Ammanian) measures in the Little Haven — Amroth coalfield, Pembrokeshire. *J. sedim. Petrol.* **38,** 332-362.

WILLIAMS, P. F. 1969. Notes on some deformation structures of sedimentary origin in the Little Haven — Amroth coalfield, Pembrokeshire. *Geol. Mag.* **106,** 395-411.

11

SEDIMENTOLOGY OF THE UPPER SANDSTONE GROUP (NAMURIAN G_1) IN SOUTH-WEST DYFED: A CASE STUDY

by G. T. GEORGE

Maps *Topographical:* 1 : 50 000 Sheets 157 St David's and Haverfordwest, 158 Tenby

1 : 25 000 Sheets SM81, SM91, SN00, SN01, SN10

Geological: 1 : 50 000 Sheets 226/227 Milford Haven, 228 Haverfordwest, 244/245 Pembroke and Linney Head

THROUGHOUT the Carboniferous coalfield area of SW Dyfed [Pembrokeshire Coalfield], the Upper Sandstone Group (Namurian G_1), previously known as the Farewell Rock (see discussion in excursion 10, this volume) is represented by a single fining-upward sequence. The lower part of the sequence is composed of sandstones, up to 22 m thick, that are deeply eroded into the Middle Shale Group, while the upper part of the sequence is composed of a variable succession of siltstones, mudstones and plant-bearing shales with thin coal seams. Nowhere does the erosive base of the sandstone extend below the *Gastrioceras cancellatum* marine band, and the top of the sequence is overlain abruptly everywhere by the *G. subcrenatum* marine band. Thus the Upper Sandstone Group, as defined, occurs entirely within the Yeadonian Stage (G_1) of the Namurian.

It is evident from the Geological Survey maps that the sandstone described above (named Farewell Rock on the maps) forms a continuous outcrop, with gentle dips to the S, along the entire N crop of the coalfield syncline. Along the S flank of the coalfield the sandstone outcrop is laterally discontinuous, due largely to overthrusting of pre-Namurian strata and folding.

There are excellent exposures of the Group along the coast of Carmarthen Bay at Amroth and Tenby, and N of Broad Haven in St Brides Bay (see excursion 10, fig. 1). Inland exposures are generally poor, although there are a number of interesting outcrops along the banks of the Cleddau and Cresswell estuaries.

[pp. 203-214 *In* BASSETT, M. G. (ed.). 1982. Geological excursions in Dyfed, south-west Wales.]

ITINERARY

This itinerary provides an opportunity to study in detail the Upper Sandstone Group cyclothem. It is intended to be used as a field project requiring approximately 8 — 10 hours fieldwork and some supplementary evening work, although the localities can be combined with those described in excursion 10 if a more general excursion is required. The case study illustrates how diagnostic sedimentary criteria, such as vertical sequence, sedimentary structures, palaeocurrents, and sandstone geometry, can be utilised to interpret a specific depositional environment.

1. The best exposure of the Upper Sandstone Group in SW Dyfed occurs on the **coast E of Amroth** between Telpyn Point (SN 186 072) and a small bay at SN 183 073 (Fig. 1a). Telpyn Point is only accessible between medium and low tide although the upper part of the cycle, exposed in the small bay, is normally accessible at high tide. From the bay a path leads up to the Pendine-Amroth road through a small, fault-defined valley and this path should be used when tides restrict access to the New Inn, Amroth (SN 175 073) via the shorter route along the foreshore.

At this locality the complete cycle is 19.5 m thick (Fig. 2a). The erosive base of the channel can be examined at SN 1860 0724 where it contains a mélange zone, up to 2 m thick, composed of large silty mudstone rafts with contorted lamination and irregular coal streaks and lenses. Here the base of the channel lies 0.5 m above a prominent convoluted siltstone bed, while 250 m further E in the cliffs it lies approximately 5 m above this marker bed. The overlying sandstone decreases in thickness by an almost equivalent amount (4.5 m) in this direction (Fig. 1a). Palaeocurrent data from the sandstone (Fig. 2a) indicate that the cliff section is approximately normal to the palaeoflow direction, i.e. the channel axis. Using the above information it can be calculated that the channel has a width to depth ratio of around 140. This calculation is made on the assumption that the channel is symmetrical and that it reaches its maximum observed thickness of 14 m at Telpyn Point.

The sandstones above the erosional base of the channel are trough cross-stratified and the sets are apparently isolated in massively bedded, mutably erosive sandstone (Fig. 2a, 0 - 6 m). Many of the troughs have minor lag concentrates on their bases and some are side-filled. A prominent erosional plane with a thin lag deposit occurs about 6 m above the base of the channel and displays sets of interference ripples and orientated casts of *Calamites*. The overlying strata (6 - 14 m) display an interesting series of vertical and lateral facies transitions (Fig. 3). This part of the sequence consists of a number of minor storeys, each beginning with an erosionally-based massive or cross stratified sandstone and passing up transitionally into finer micro-trough cross laminated sandstones. Large flute casts, up to 1 m in diameter, are common on these erosional surfaces. Many of the cross stratified sets have ripple marked and/or ripple laminated accretion faces, which appear to

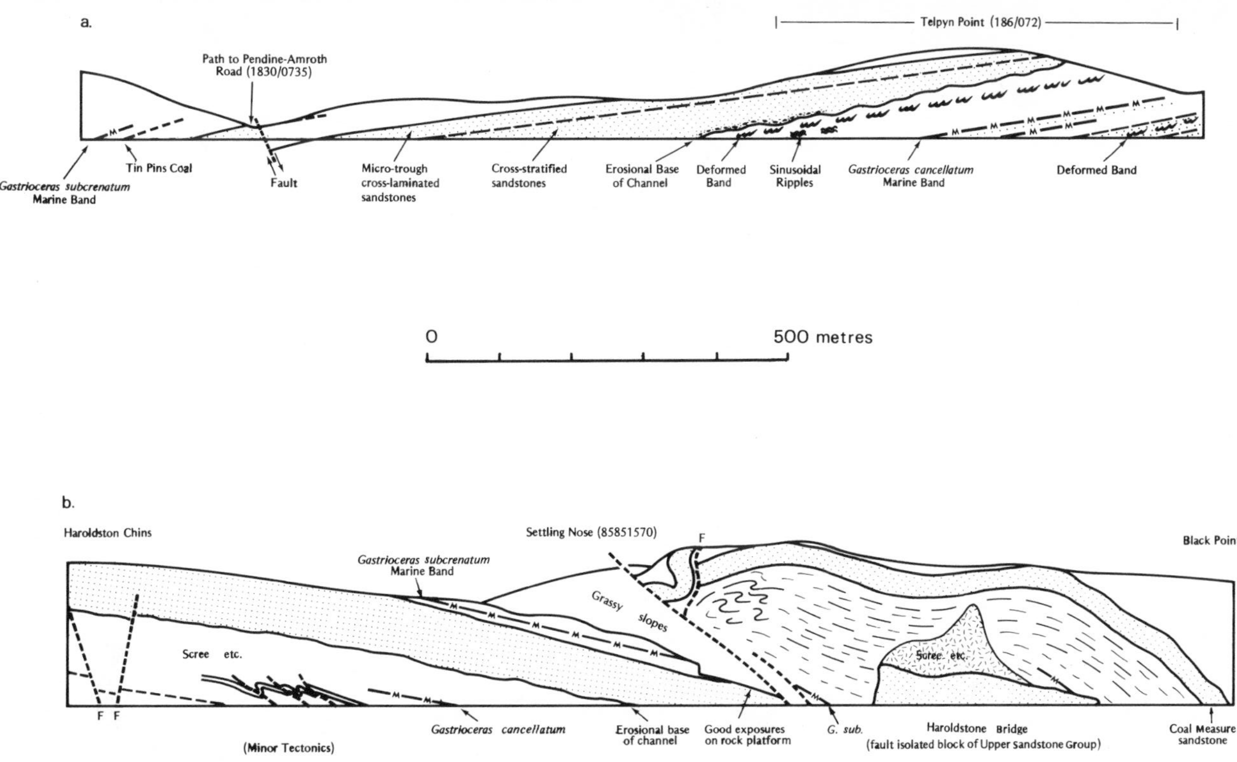

Fig. 1. Cliff profiles showing the structure and distribution of the Upper Sandstone Group and related strata at (a) Telpyn Point, Amroth, and (b) Settling Nose, Broad Haven.

merge laterally into the micro-trough cross laminated facies (Fig. 3). These compound cross stratified sets may represent Epsilon cross stratification

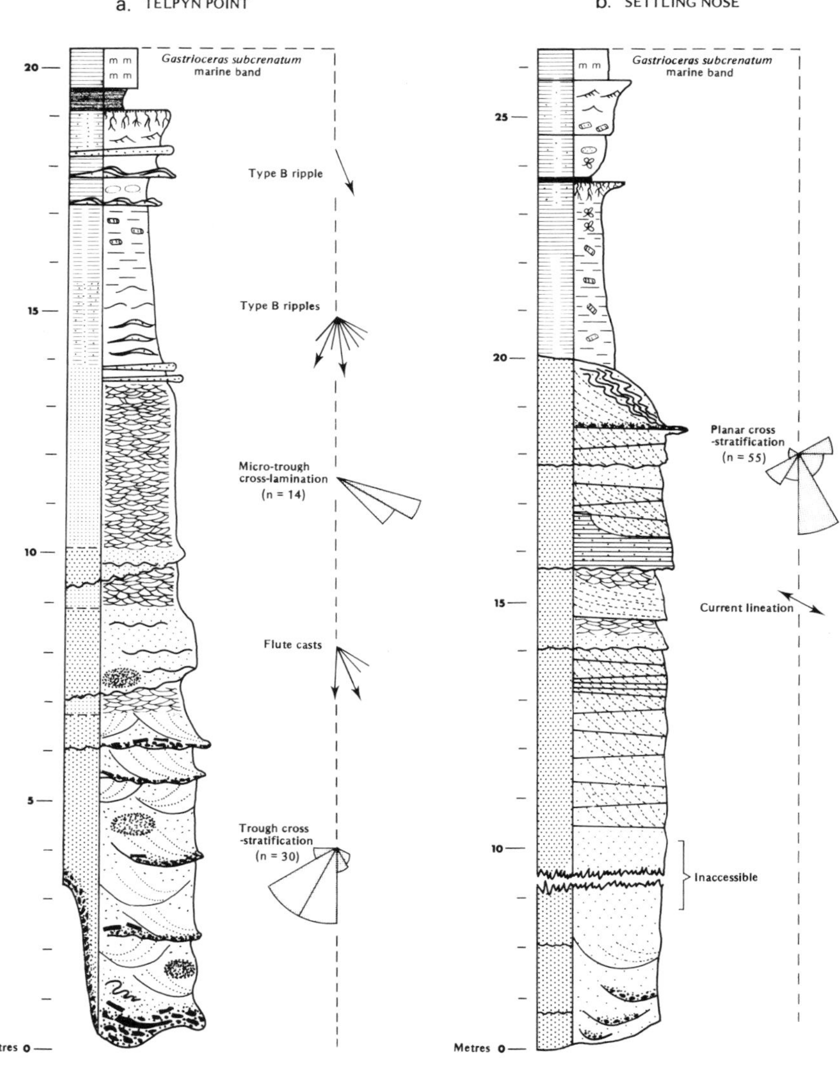

Fig. 2. Vertical sequences and palaeocurrents from Upper Sandstone Group cycles at (a) Telpyn Point, and (b) Settling Nose. (see Fig. 4 for legend).

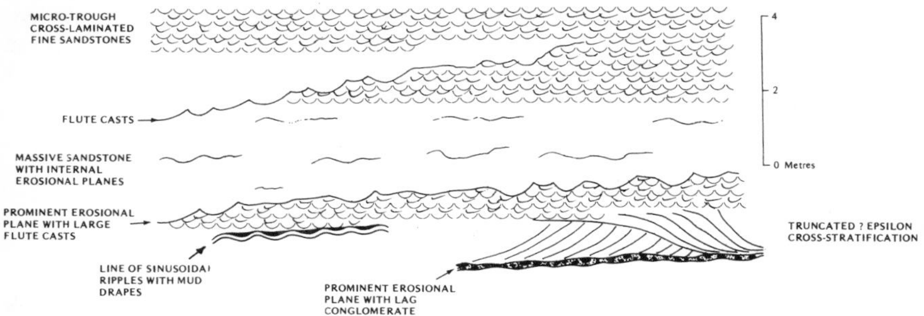

Fig. 3. Generalised vertical and lateral facies relationships at 6 — 11 m (Fig. 2a), Telpyn Point.

(Allen 1963) from which the upper argillaceous part has been removed by erosion.

There is a notable and significant variation in the palaeocurrent directions measured from the large scale cross stratified sub-facies and from the ripple cross laminated sub-facies (Fig. 2a). The vector mean directions of the grouped readings are approximately perpendicular to one another.

A number of thin, very fine grained sandstone ribs mark the contact between the micro-trough cross laminated sandstones and the overlying siltstones (Fig. 2a, 13.5 m). These siltstones display well developed type B ripple cross laminations (Jopling & Walker 1968), with heights up to 18 cm and wave lengths around 50 cm. A small coarsening-upward unit, capped with a seatearth and thin coal, marks the top of the sequence. The coal (Tin Pits Vein) can be located by digging on the **small promontory** at SN 1825 0733.

An overgrown cliff fall interrupts the section between the Tin Pits Vein and overlying dark grey shales containing *G. subcrenatum,* at SN 1815 0726. This gap probably conceals the easterly continuation of a fault that can be traced along the foreshore towards the New Inn (Jenkins 1962).

2. Settling Nose (SM 858 157) can be approached from Broad Haven either on foot, by walking 2 km N along the Pembrokeshire Coast Path, or in a small vehicle which can be parked near the sharp bend (SM 863 161) on the minor coast road to Nolton Haven. At Settling Nose the lower part of the sequence is inaccessible, although the upper part can be examined on the rock platform to the S of the point (Fig. 1b) at all states of the tide. A traverse along the foreshore from Druidston Haven to Settling Nose, to examine the Middle Shale Group, should only be attempted during a good low tide.

The sandstone in the **cliffs to the N of the point** has an erosive base, but with no prominent lag deposit, and is about 26 m thick. The uppermost 10 m of the sandstone sequence (Fig. 2b 10 - 20 m) consists predominantly of cross stratified, medium grained sandstones with thinner horizontally bedded and ripple laminated horizons. When viewed from a distance, on bedding plane exposures, the foresets of the cross stratified sets form very broad arcuate units. Primary current lineation is common on the surface of the flat beds and on the low angle foresets. The prominent erosional planes and vertical changes in the types of sedimentary structures indicate the multistorey character of the sandstone body.

Unlike the channel sequences at Telpyn Point and Tenby, the Settling Nose sandstone does not grade up into a ripple laminated, fine grained sandstone. Instead, the medium grained cross stratified sandstones are abruptly overlain by silty mudstones. The top of the sandstone is pebbly and at one locality the external form of a dune, with deformed foresets, is preserved.

The overlying silty mudstones contain plant remains and coal smuts between 22.5 - 24.5 m (Fig. 2b). A small coarsening-upward unit with symmetrical and asymmetrical ripples occurs below the *G. subcrenatum* marine band. The index goniatite at this locality was first recorded by Jenkins (1962) although the marine band was discovered by Cantrill (1910). A calcareous siltstone at the base of this horizon contains abundant brachiopods including *Orthotetes cantrilli* (Thomas 1910).

In the cliffs to the N of Settling Nose the sandstone can be seen to rise in stratigraphical level and approaches the dark shales bearing *G. subcrenatum* (Fig. 1b).

3. At **Tenby** the Upper Sandstone Group is repeated by folding at two localities along the coast, (1) **First Point** (SN 135 013), and (2) **S of Waterwynch Bay** (SN 136 018). It is thus possible to examine the effects of lateral facies change within the fining-upward sequence. Again good low tides (e.g. low tide around noon; height at low tide <1.0 m) are necessary to study the sequences in detail. Such tides give a working time of up to four hours at First Point and Waterwynch Bay. From the latter locality the Coast Path can be taken back to Tenby, noting the fine views of Carmarthen Bay.

At First Point the channel sandstone has been folded into a rather tight syncline with a slightly inverted southern limb (see excursion 10, this volume, fig. 9). The basal part of the channel is well exposed in the S limb of this syncline, where it contains a good lag deposit of well rounded ironstone pebbles and mudstone clasts. A plant bed yielding *Alethopteris* (Dixon 1921) is present in the mélange zone seen at the base of the cliff. On the N limb of the syncline the base of the channel can be proved to be 6.5 m lower in the succession by reference to a prominent loaded horizon, 53 cm thick, in the underlying strata (Kelling & George 1971).

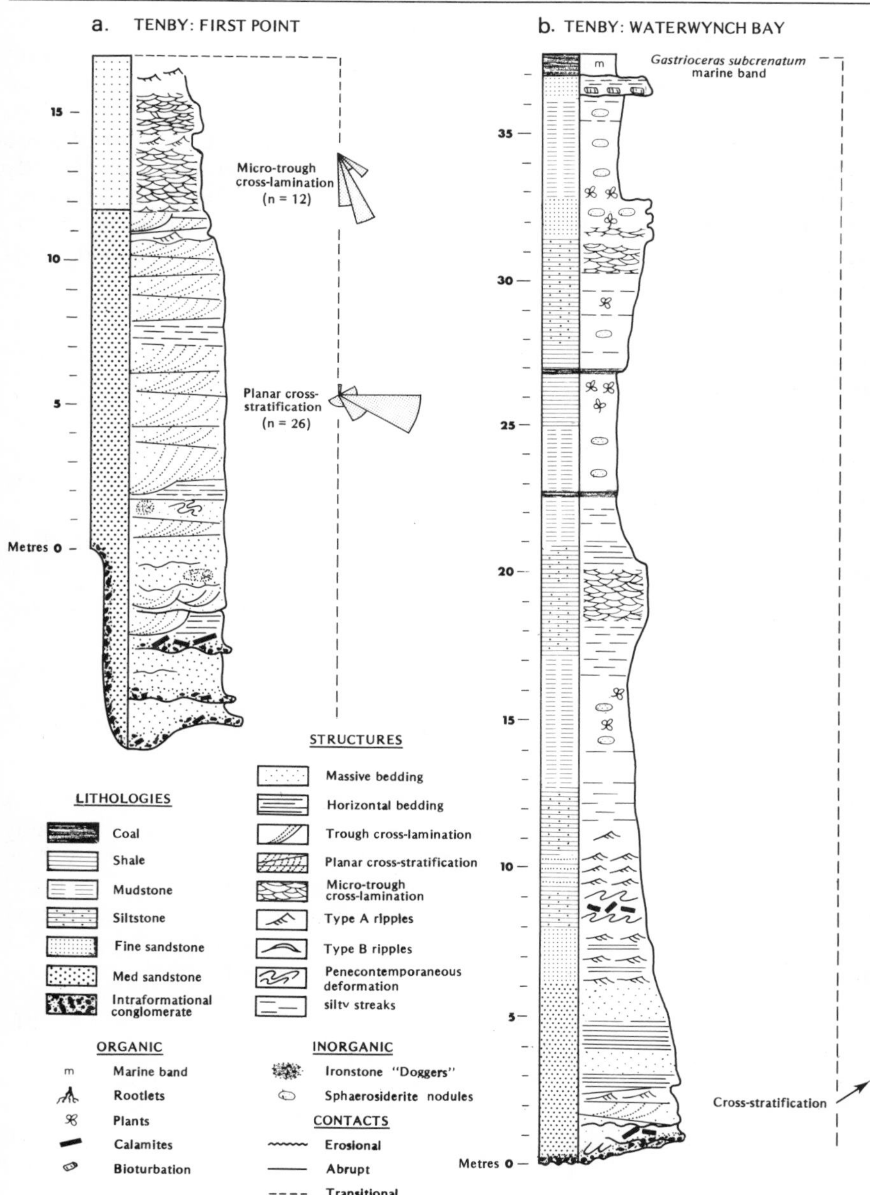

Fig. 4. Vertical sequences and palaeocurrents from Upper Sandstone Group cycles at (a) First Point, and (b) Waterwynch Bay, Tenby.

The maximum thickness of the sandstone, measured on the N side of the point, is approximately 22 m (Fig. 4a). Here the sequence commences with predominantly massive, medium grained sandstones with internal erosional planes bearing minor lag concentrates and casts of *Calamites*. Penecontemporaneous deformation structures are evident in some of these massive beds. Above, the sandstones display well developed, apparently planar, cross stratification (2.0 - 11.5 m, Fig. 4a). However, the sets have asymptotic foresets, many of their basal erosion planes are curved, and some sets are cut out laterally. These features are more typical of trough cross stratification.

Above 11.5 m (Fig. 4a) the cross stratified sandstones are replaced by finer grained, ripple laminated sandstones, displaying substantial divergence in palaeocurrent readings (Fig. 4a).

To the **S of Waterwynch Bay,** this sandstone member is exposed in the inverted northern limb of a major anticline (excursion 10, fig. 9). Here the erosional base of the channel occurs 1 m above a shale band from which Jones (1969) has recorded *Gastrioceras cumbriense,* and 37 m below the *G. subcrenatum* marine band. The channel fill consists of only 8 m of sandstones (Fig. 4b) compared with the 22 m of similar facies at First Point.

Above the channel sandstone, a deformed siltstone with disorientated plant remains occurs at 8.5 m, and two coarsening-upwards units are developed between 15 - 21 m and 27 - 33 m. These units begin with carbonaceous mudstones and shales and pass up into streaked silty mudstones, and then into medium scale trough cross laminated siltstones and fine ripple laminated sandstones.

By reference to marine marker bands in the Middle Shale Group it is possible to calculate that the channel has an erosional relief of approximately 40 m between First Point and Waterwynch Bay (see excursion 10, fig. 11). Moreover, taking account of tectonic shortening, it can be calculated that the channel has a width to depth ratio of approximately 105. This assumes that the channel is more or less symmetrical in cross section. Palaeocurrents indicate that the channel axis is perpendicular to the cliff section.

4. Inland outcrops of the Upper Sandstone Group are rather inaccessible and are not recommended for large field parties. The exposures of the sandstone facies at **Cresswell Quay** (SN 049 068), **Eastern Cleddau** (SN 024 127), **Millin Pill** (SM 994 131), and the **Western Cleddau** (SM 968 128) are sufficiently good to make general lithological observations and to measure palaeocurrents. At Millin Pill the silty mudstones below the *G. subcrenatum* marine band (SM 9939 1301) show evidence of wave reworking, viz. low angle planar cross stratification, symmetrical and asymmetrical ripples, giving a polymodal palaeocurrent distribution.

ENVIRONMENTAL INTERPRETATION

From the above descriptive itinerary it is evident that the Upper Sandstone Group displays similar facies and facies developments throughout the coalfield area of SW Dyfed. Features of interpretative value, common to the various cycles, include: (1) erosively-based fining-upward sequences; (2) sandstone bodies with channel geometry and width/depth ratios of 100 to 140; (3) multi-storey sandstone facies; (4) unimodal palaeocurrents; and (5) thin coals and rootlet beds in the argillaceous facies.

These features are characteristic of sequences deposited in modern, and ancient, alluvial channels and delta-distributary channels (e.g. see Collinson 1978; Elliott 1978). In both environments the process of channel formation, associated with lateral channel migration and/or abandonment, results in decreasing flow velocity and the deposition of erosively-based fining-upward sequences.

A number of factors suggest that the deposition of the Upper Sandstone Group sequences occurred in distributary channels, dominated by fluvial processes. Firstly, the low width/depth ratios of the channels (100-140) appear to be more typical of distributary channels, which tend to switch their courses more frequently than rivers. At Settling Nose the abandonment process appears to have been very rapid, resulting in the absence of a ripple laminated sandstone facies. Secondly, the channels are erosive on sequences that have been interpreted as shelf and delta slope deposits (see excursion 10, figs. 6, 9). Only limited rejuvenation would be required for delta distributaries to erode to this level, but a more catastrophic event would be required for alluvial channels to reach a similar base level. Lastly, there is no evidence of emergence (e.g. rootlets) in the channel sandstones or in the directly overlying argillaceous facies. Rootlet horizons, associated with thin coals, do not appear until relatively late in the deposition of the argillaceous facies. This suggests deposition in water depths greater than those normally associated with alluvial floodplains and backswamps.

The actual distributary channels appear to have been from 2.0 - 2.5 km wide and up to 25 m deep. Evidence for point bar deposition (e.g. the Epsilon cross stratification at Telpyn Point) and the prominent divergence in palaeocurrent directions measured from cross stratified and ripple laminated facies, within the same channel (Figs. 2a and 4a), suggest that the channels were moderately sinuous at low stage, although probably straight at bank-full stage. Multistorey fills suggest that the distributaries were subject to frequent, periodic fluctuations in stage. The continuous outcrop pattern of the sandstone, especially on the N crop, suggests that the distributary network consisted of a series of close spaced, multilateral, channels.

The argillaceous facies that overlies the distributary channel sandstones are interpreted as interdistributary bay deposits. Within this environment

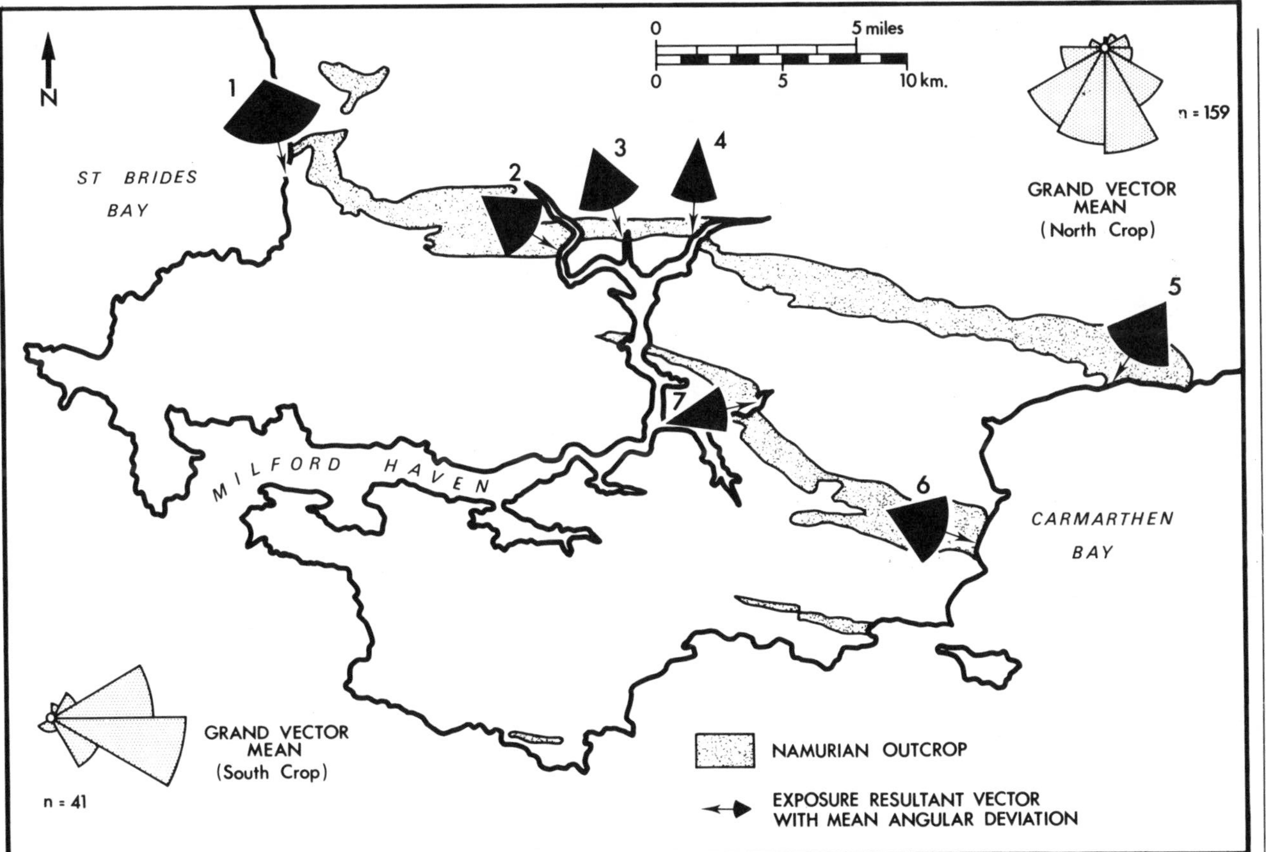

Fig. 5. Upper Sandstone Group palaeocurrents based on large scale cross stratification. Localities: 1, Settling Nose; 2, Western Cleddau; 3, Millin Pill; 4. Eastern Cleddau; 5, Telpyn Point; 6, Tenby.

suspension deposition in quiet water is recorded by the fine grained mudstones and shales, while flood generated processes appear to have been largely responsible for the deposition of the minor coarsening-upward units. The two well developed coarsening-upward units at Waterwynch Bay (Fig. 4b, 15 - 21 m and 27 - 33 m) both appear to be of levee origin. The absence of rootlets at the top of the first unit suggests that it was purely subaqueous, while their presence in the second unit indicates emergence. The deformed plant-bearing siltstones at 8.5 m in the same sequence probably represent bank collapse material.

PALAEOCURRENTS AND PALAEOGEOGRAPHY

An important aspect of the case study is the systematic collection and interpretation of palaeocurrent data. Directional structures such as large scale cross stratification and ripple cross lamination are abundant in the sequences and their measurement is straightforward (viz. maximum foreset dip or trough axis orientation). However, because of the folding at Tenby it is necessary to correct the palaeocurrent readings for tectonic dip (see Potter and Pettijohn 1963, p. 259). Grouped readings of current vectors can be summarised as rose diagrams or as arcs that represent the mean angular deviation (see Reyment 1971, p. 26).

The dispersal systems revealed in Fig. 5 are based on the measurement of palaeocurrents from large scale cross stratification. From analysis of the data, it is apparent that in the N crop dispersal was to the S, off St George's Land, while in the S crop there was a dominant easterly flow. These two major fluvio-deltaic systems may have been separated by a zone of tectonic instability located along the E-W line of the present Ritec Fault (see also Kelling 1974). As a response to early Yeadonian uplift, the deltas advanced to the S and E across the area, and their channels cut deeply into pre-existing shelf and delta slope deposits belonging to the Middle Shale Group.

Provenance studies of the Upper Sandstone Group suggest that most of the sediment was derived from fairly local source rocks similar in composition to those of the Lower Palaeozoic of north Dyfed. The proximity of this source suggests significant rejuvenation of Caledonian structures such as the Teifi and Towy anticlines and a southern extension of the Bala fault during late Namurian times. This factor also suggests that the contributive network supplying the late Namurian distributaries was a short-headed alluvial system.

Towards the end of Yeadonian times the distributary channels switched their courses and migrated out of the coalfield area. Since sandstones with similar (Upper Sandstone Group/Farewell Rock) lithology occur above *G. subcrenatum* in the main South Wales basin, it appears that the main locale of delta deposition migrated to the NE. This retreat was associated with accumulation of a variety of interdistributary bay deposits and later marine deposits formed during the *G. subcrenatum* transgression.

REFERENCES

ALLEN, J. R. L. 1963. The classification of cross-stratified units, with notes on their origin. *Sedimentology,* **2,** 93-114.

CANTRILL, T. C. 1910. *Summ. Progr. geol. Surv. Lond.* 13-22.

COLLINSON, J. D. 1978. Alluvial sediments. pp. 15-60 *In* READING H. G. (ed.), *Sedimentary environments and facies.* Blackwell.

DIXON, E. E. L. 1921. The geology of the South Wales Coalfield. Part XIII: The Country around Pembroke and Tenby. *Mem. geol. Surv. UK.* 220pp.

ELLIOTT, T. 1978. Deltas. pp. 97-142 *In* READING, H. G. (ed.), *Sedimentary environments and facies.* Blackwell.

JENKINS, T. B. H. 1962. The sequence and correlation of the Coal Measures of Pembrokeshire. *Q. Jl geol. Soc. Lond.* **118,** 65-101.

JONES, D. G. 1969. The Namurian succession between Tenby and Waterwynch, Pembrokeshire. *Geol. J.* **6,** 267-272.

JOPLING, A. V. & WALKER, R. G. 1968. Morphology and origin of ripple-drift cross-lamination, with examples from the Pleistocene of Massachusettes. J. sedim. Petrol. **38,** 971-984.

KELLING, G. 1974. Upper Carboniferous sedimentation in South Wales. pp. 185-224 *In* OWEN, T. R. (ed.), *The Upper Palaeozoic and post-Palaeozoic Rocks of Wales.* viii + 426pp. Univ. Wales Press, Cardiff.

KELLING, G. & GEORGE, G. T. 1971. Upper Carboniferous sedimentation in the Pembrokeshire Coalfield. pp. 240-259 *In* BASSETT, D. A. & BASSETT, M. G. (eds.), *Geological Excursions in South Wales and the Forest of Dean.* 267 pp. Geologists' Association, South Wales Group, Cardiff.

POTTER, P. E. & PETTIJOHN, F. J. 1963. *Palaeocurrents and basin analysis.* 330 pp. Springer Verlag, Berlin.

REYMENT, R. A. 1971. *Introduction to quantitive palaeoecology.* 226 pp. Elsevier, Amsterdam.

THOMAS, I. 1910. The British Carboniferous Orthotetinae. *Mem. geol. Surv. U.K. (Palaeontology),* **1,** 177,188.

12
VARISCAN STRUCTURES IN SOUTH-WEST DYFED

by P. L. HANCOCK, W. M. DUNNE, *and* M. E. TRINGHAM

Maps *Topographical:* 1 : 50 000 Sheets 157 St David's and Haverfordwest, 158 Tenby

1 : 25 000 Sheets SM00, SM80, SM81, SN10, SR89, SR99, SS09

Geological: 1 : 50 000 Sheets 226/227 Milford, 228 Haverfordwest, 244/245 Pembroke and Linney Head

Because most users of this guide will organise excursions principally to examine stratigraphical successions, many of which will contain the structures described here, this chapter is not in the form of an itinerary. Following a brief introduction to Variscan tectonics there are three sub-sections in which structurally interesting localities are described.

VARISCAN STRUCTURAL ELEMENTS (P. L. Hancock)

THE Precambrian and Palaeozoic rocks within the segment of the Variscan belt that extends through SW Dyfed belong to part of the outer margin of that orogen where it converges with the paratectonic Caledonides. Comprehensive reviews of Variscan tectonics in the area are given by Hancock (1973) and Hancock *et al.* (1981, in press). They divide the region into zones on the basis of structural assemblages (Fig. 1). Zone I contains evenly distributed folds and strike faults, mainly of WNW trend, whereas deformation in Zone II is largely restricted to four WSW trending disturbance belts. Large amplitude, gently plunging macrofolds relatively uncomplicated by congruent parasitic mesofolds characterise Zone Ia. In this account macrofolds are regarded as those with an axial plane separation in excess of 150 m, while mesofold axial planes are less than 150 m apart. The more general term mesostructure is used to embrace any planar or linear structure which is exposed in its entirety within a single exposure, and hence its dimensions are commonly measured in centimetres or a few metres. In the E of Zone Ia most folds face (the direction of younging along an axial plane and normal to a hinge line, Fig. 2) outwards and upwards with respect to the Orielton anticlinorium (Dixon 1921), the principal macrofold. The outwards-facing folds are accompanied by thrusts whose senses of translation

[pp. 215-248 *In* BASSETT, M. G. (ed.). 1982. Geological excursions in Dyfed, south-west Wales.]

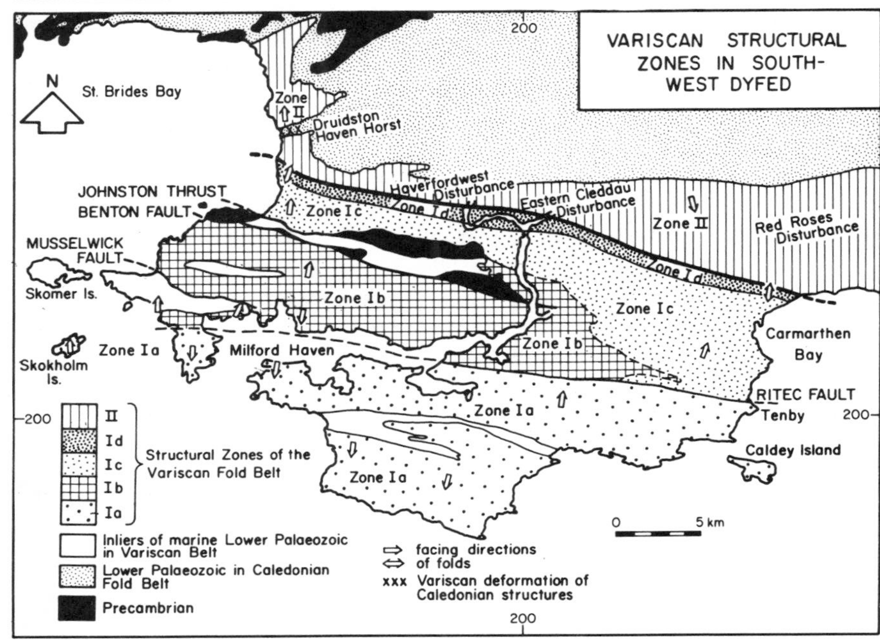

Fig. 1. Map of structural zones in SW Dyfed (from Hancock *et al.* 1981, fig. 2.)

are in accord with the fold facing directions. Although mesofolds are uncommon, the direction of vergence (see Fig. 2) of asymmetrical anticlinal-synclinal couplets is towards adjacent macroanticlinal hinge lines. The majority of folds are upright or steeply inclined, *i.e.* their axial planes dip between 60° and 90°. Throughout Zone Ia there is a conjugate system of wrench faults symmetrically orientated about fold axial traces, the NNW trending set being dextral, the NE set sinistral. Some of the wrench faults developed during the later stages of folding, and thus they are tear faults. Minor wrench faults in Zone Ia are also symmetrically orientated about folds in three dimensions; the obtuse bisector between them being parallel to the hinge line of the displaced fold and the acute bisector perpendicular to its axial plane (Fig. 3). Flattening of strain markers and the relative development of cleavage in all lithologies are more noticeable in the W of the zone. The Ritec Fault is a high-angle reverse fault.

Although the average amplitude of macrofolds is lower in Zone Ib than Zone Ia, they are complicated by numerous mesofolds which are outwards facing with respect to the principal anticlinorial system. Most folds plunge E between 20° and 40° and are accompanied by a cleavage in most lithologies. A well developed system of conjugate wrench faults symmetrically orientated about folds is not present; but cross-faults displaying either dextral strike-slip or normal dip-slip displacements are abundant.

Many N-facing and verging mesofolds complicate the limbs of relatively low amplitude macrofolds, Zone Ic, which corresponds with the S part of the Coalfield. Folds are generally tighter, more asymmetrical and more overturned as the Johnston Thrust or Ritec Fault are approached; and compared with other zones, non-cylindrical folds and minor décollement surfaces are more abundant. The Johnston Thrust (Fig. 1) juxtaposes Precambrian igneous rocks and the Westphalian Coal Measures as a consequence of transport to the N. There was later and subordinate dextral strike-slip on the fault, which resulted in the local refolding of some of the earlier N-facing folds (Tringham 1979). Cleavage in mudstones is generally restricted to fold hinge zones, except at Tenby where it is more widespread. Cleaved sandstones are common throughout Zone Ia. Strike faults include normal faults and thrusts, some of the latter being folded, while cross-faults show either normal or dextral strike-slip displacements.

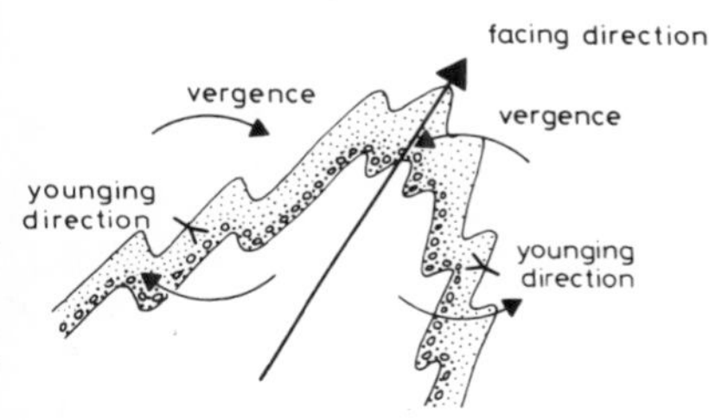

Fig. 2. Schematic profile to explain the meanings of the terms vergence, younging direction, and facing direction. The usage of vergence adopted here follows that proposed by Roberts (1976) for the horizontal direction in the plane of the fold-profile, towards which the upper component of rotational asymmetry shown by inequant folds is directed.

Zone Id, also within the Coalfield, comprises a 1 km wide belt of conjugate folds and associated reverse faults, and according to Hancock *et al.* (1981, in press) it may be used to define the location of the Variscan front in SW Dyfed.

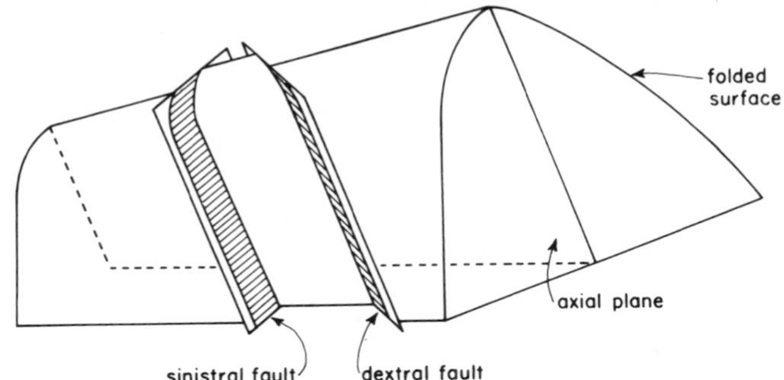

Fig. 3. Block diagram showing the geometrical relationship between conjugate small wrench faults and folds in Zone Ia.

Of the four disturbances in Zone II only the westernmost, the Druidston Haven Horst, a structure bounded by major normal faults, is exposed on the coast. A S-facing Caledonian fold within the horst is coaxially refolded by Variscan structures.

At many localities the best exposed structures are planar mesostructures, especially cleavages, shear zones, kink bands, veins, small faults, and joints. Variscan deformation resulted in a single cleavage generally arranged in convergent fans about axial planes, but less commonly in divergent fans or perfectly axial plane. Except within a few folds the bedding-cleavage lineation (defining the *b* direction) is parallel to hinge lines. Relative cleavage development is generally better in the W, persisting N of Zone Ic in sandstones but not in mudstones. Using Powell's (1979) morphological classification of cleavage styles the following types of cleavage occur in the three common sedimentary rocks. Cleaved mudstones are cut by smooth to rough disjunctive, spaced cleavage domains in which opaque minerals and phyllosilicates are concentrated. The cleavage domains separate microlithons up to 0.1 mm wide, some of which contain flattened quartz grains and phyllosilicates. Where mudstones are weathered and the cleavage fabric is weak the field expression of the structure is commonly an anastomosing array of superficial extension fissures subparallel to the fabric. Cleavage in sandstones is also spaced, ranging from smooth, disjunctive surfaces less than 5 cm apart, to rough disjunctive surfaces up to 30 cm apart. Some cleavage domains in sandstones display a grain fabric oblique to the domain, which offsets bedding planes in a series of small normal steps up to about 2 cm in height. Cleaved limestones, which are largely restricted to the W of Zone Ia, are also cut by a spaced cleavage which is disjunctive and commonly anastomosing. The principal process involved in cleavage development was pressure solution (for details of cleavage genesis see Hobbs *et al.* 1976).

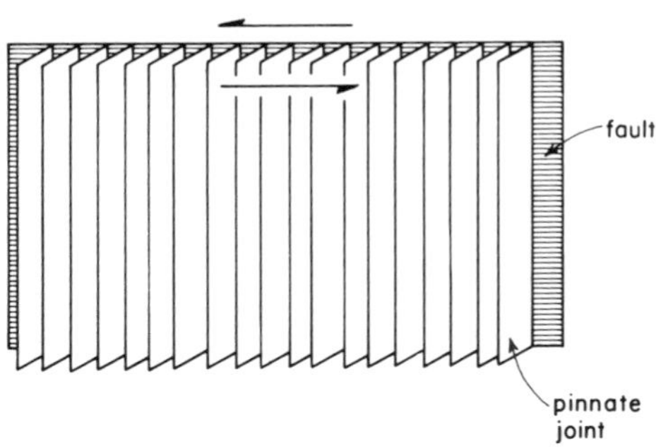

Fig. 4. Pinnate joints related to a fault.

Most mesofractures are symmetrical with respect to fold geometry. A few, such as small scale wrench faults and accompanying arrays of pinnate joints (Fig. 4), are symmetrical with respect to the axial plane and hinge line of the fold which they cut (Fig. 3), but many, especially within Zone Ia, are symmetrical with reference to the dip of beds and the plunge of the nearest fold hinge line. A concise way of describing the geometry of these fractures is to relate them to an orthogonal fabric axial cross in which bedding defines the *ab* plane, the fold hinge line the *b* direction, and the normal to

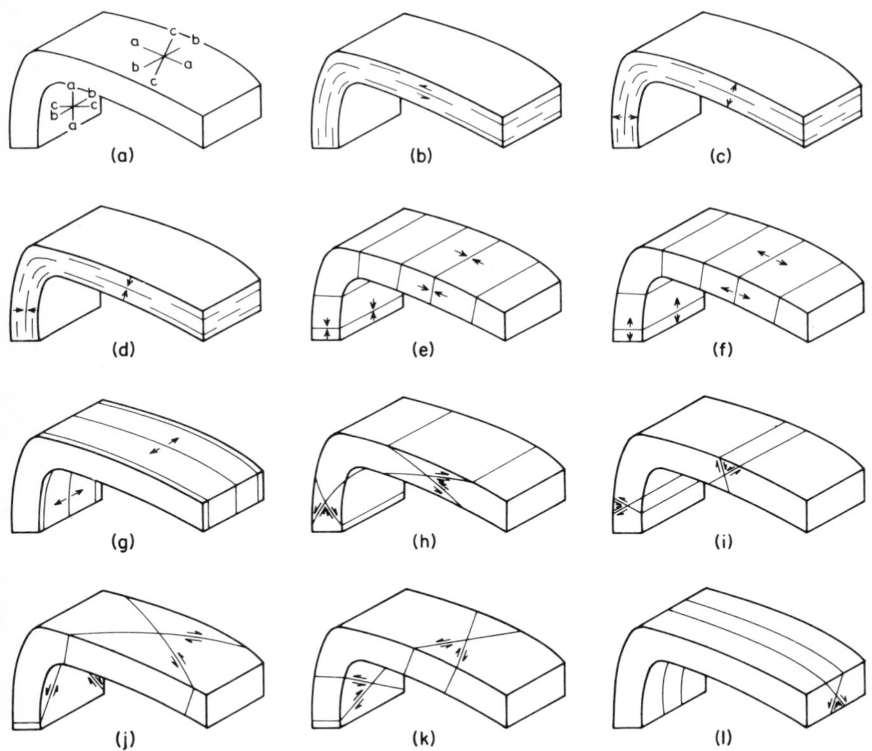

Fig. 5. Block diagrams showing geometrical relationships between planar mesoscopic structures and folds in Zone Ia. a, definition of the fabric axial cross; b, shear surfaces in *ab;* c, extension fractures in *ab;* d, stylolitic and other pressure solution surfaces in *ab;* e, pressure solution surfaces in *bc;* f, extension fractures in *bc;* g, extension fractures in *ac;* h, conjugate *h*0*l* shear fractures enclosing an acute angle about *a; i, conjugate h*0*l* shear fractures enclosing an acute angle about c; j, conjugate *hk*0 shear fractures enclosing an acute angle about *a;* k, conjugate *hk*0 shear fractures enclosing an acute angle about *b;* l, conjugate 0*kl* shear fractures enclosing an acute angle about *c.*

bedding is the *c* direction (Fig. 5). Surfaces containing two axes are said to be in *ab, ac* or *bc,* while those oblique to two axes but containing one are in *hk*0, *h*0*l* or 0*kl.* Conjugate *hk*0, and *h*0*l* sets are each divided into two systems according to whether they enclose acute angles about *a, b* or *c.*

Mesofaults are either minor representatives of wrench faults, normal faults, or thrusts, or they are extension or contraction faults in *h*0*l,* the former elongating layers, the latter shortening them (Fig. 6). According to whether the sense of shear on a fault supports or opposes that presumed to act along bedding during folding they are called synthetic or antithetic. Many mesofaults are accompanied by arrays of *pinnate joints* intersecting them along lines normal to the slip vector, and facing against the sense of shear (Fig. 4). Denudation of a fault surface intersected by an array of pinnate joints and cut by a set of cleavage surfaces leads to the development of microrelief resembling a staircase (Fig. 7).

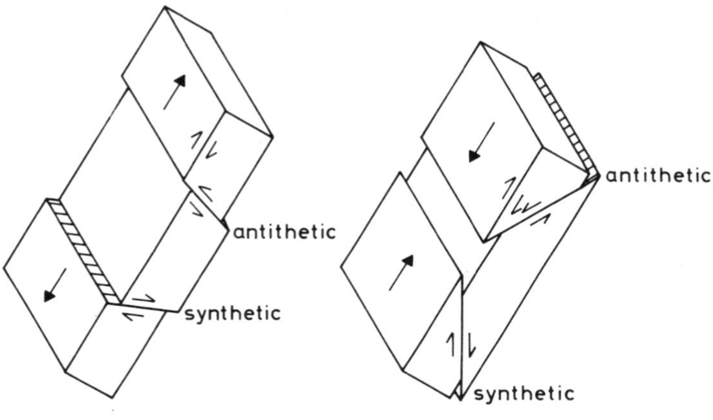

Fig. 6. Block diagrams showing the geometry of extension and contraction faults.

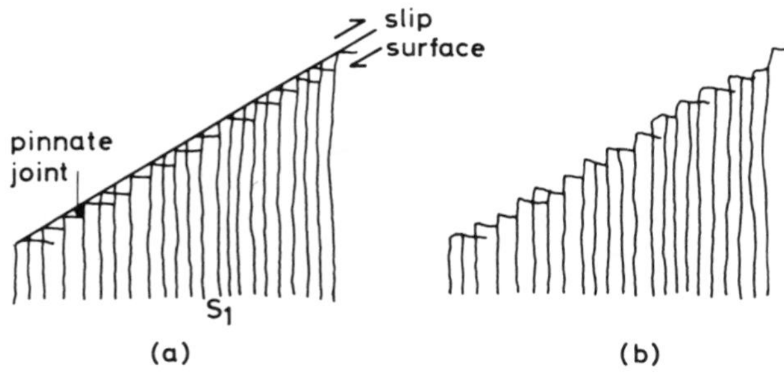

Fig. 7. Evolution of a microstaircase relief as a result of the denudation of pinnate joints and cleavage surfaces (S_1) intersecting a fault surface; a, before denudation of the structures in the footwall; b, after denudation.

Shear zones, that is semi-brittle to ductile fault zones of finite width (Ramsay 1980), are defined by either an array of second-order en échelon veins facing against the sense of shear, or a secondary foliation also oblique to the zone but facing with the sense of shear, or by a combination of both

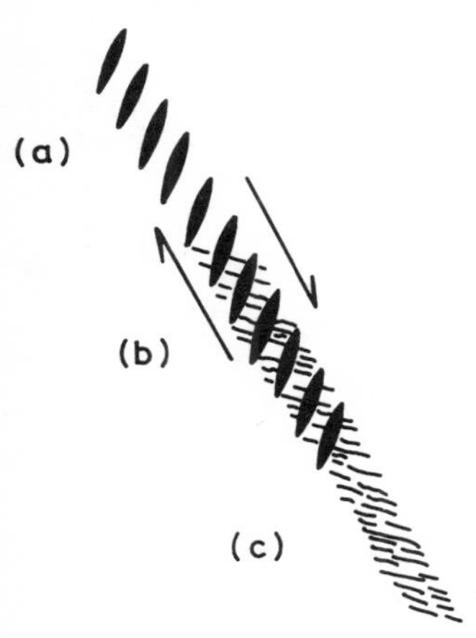

Fig. 8. Categories of shear zones; a, containing an array of en échelon veins; b, containing veins and a foliation oblique to the zone; c, containing a foliation restricted to the zone.

(Fig. 8). Such shear zones are largely restricted to sandstones and limestones, especially those in the *hk*0 system enclosing an acute angle about *a*, or the *h*0*l* system at an acute angle about *c*. *Kink bands* in which cleavage or sedimentary lamination is rotated in a tabular fold zone generally belong to one of the *h*0*l* systems.

Stylolitic pressure solution surfaces are largely restricted to limestones and are generally layer-parallel *(ab)* although some are in *ac*. Quartz or carbonate *veins,* some containing *growth fibres,* (Durney & Ramsay 1973) are common in many sets, especially those in *ac, bc* or *hk*0. Some *h*0*l* extension faults and some bedding planes display a *crystal fibre slickenside lineation* within *accretion steps;* the lineation and steps can be employed to determine slip directions along fractures. *Joints* are the most abundant mesofractures; those in *ac* or *bc* are extension joints, those in *hk*0, *h*0*l* or 0*kl* belong to conjugate sets of shear joints.

STRUCTURES SOUTH OF THE COALFIELD (W. M. Dunne & P. L. Hancock)

1. Freshwater East (car park at SS 015 978). Stratigraphical details at this locality are given in excursions 7 and 9, this volume, The nearly vertical beds on the N limb of the W-plunging Freshwater East anticline are cut by numerous conjugate wrench faults (Fig.9), which in three dimensions are symmetrical about the attitude of the axial plane and hinge line of the anticline (Fig. 3). An 800 m traverse along the **foreshore from the W end of the section** reveals many examples of the wrench faults, some showing displacements of less than 5 m and hence not shown in Fig. 9.

Arrays of nearly vertical pinnate fractures related to faults are common; those visible at locality **A** (inset **A,** Fig. 9) are unusual because one of the fractures in a set pinnate to a small dextral fault is itself accompanied by pinnate joints. At locality **B** the geometrical relationships between *bc* extension joints and conjugate *hk*0 shear joints enclosing an acute angle about *a* are clearly exposed in a nearly vertical bed of green sandstone (inset **B,** Fig. 9). The orientation of the *b* fabric axis is known from the geometry of the fold, but because cleavage is only weakly developed the direction is not immediately obvious as a bedding-cleavage lineation. Conjugate *hk*0 joints and *bc* joints are also well exposed in another green sandstone at locality **C.**

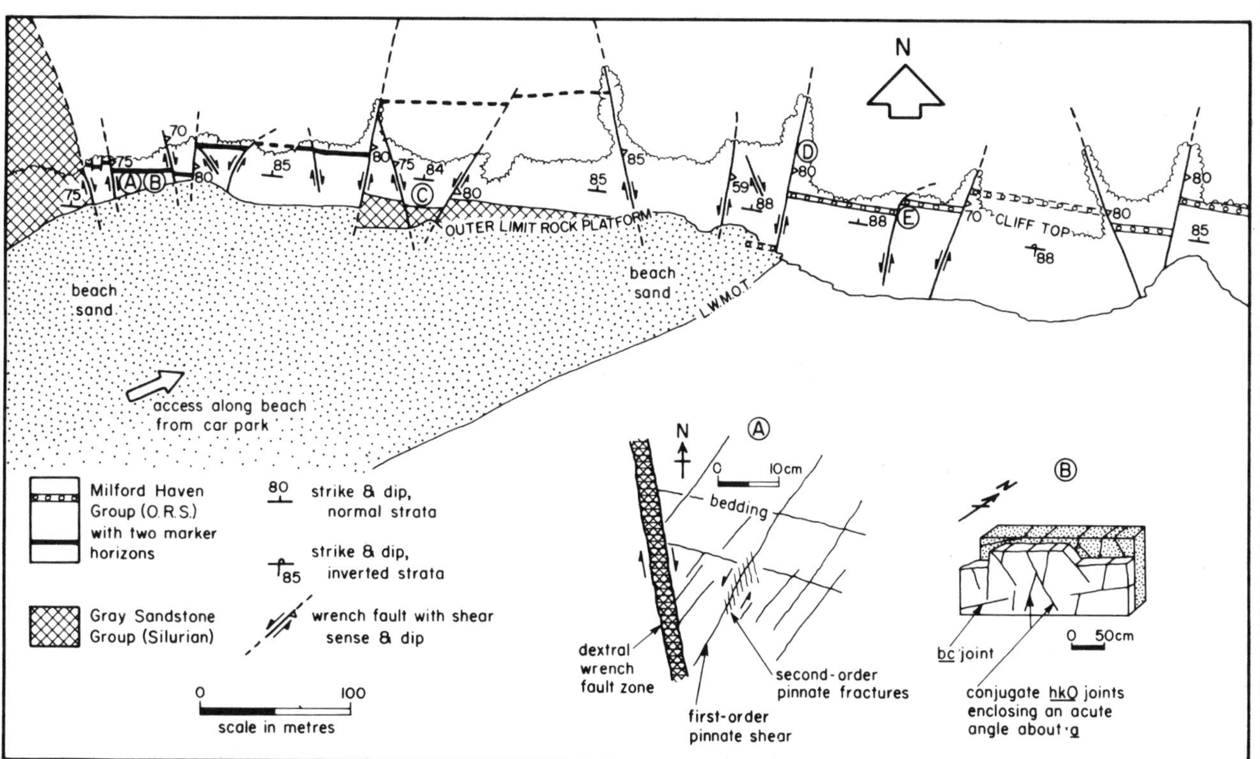

Fig. 9. Structural map of part of the N side of Freshwater East; insets show examples of mesofractures referred to in the text.

Antithetic *h*0*l* extension faults (Fig. 6) displace beds a few centimetres at locality **D,** where it is also possible to inspect lineated gilgai (pseudoanticlinal) surfaces cutting the feeble cleavage. Chains of cylindrical pedogenic (calcrete) concretions which were statistically normal to bedding at the time of formation now subtend angles of about 70° with bedding as a consequence of there having been shear strain during folding. At locality **E** a sinistral wrench fault, which is steeply inclined where it crosses the wave-cut platform, curves as it ascends the cliff until it becomes intermediate in attitude between a wrench fault and a N-dipping overthrust.

2. Stackpole Quay (car park SR 991 958) The Old Red Sandstone and Carboniferous Limestone Series are deformed by S-facing, E-plunging folds. which are displaced by two dextral wrench faults active during the late stages of folding (Fig. 10). To visit localities **A, B** and **C** a rope is needed to aid descent of the steep path into North Cove.

Mudstones at the top of the Milford Haven Group dip and young to the S and are cut by a cleavage dipping steeply N (locality **A,** Fig. 10). Formerly spherical reduction spots have been deformed to triaxial ellipsoids, with their long and intermediate axes *(X & Y)* subparallel to cleavage. Arrays of pinnate joints (Fig. 4) accompany oblique-slip faults which displace some mudstones.

First Point headland is dissected by several gaps eroded along sinistral wrench faults (locality **B**) which displace beds of conglomerate within the Skrinkle Sandstones Group. The tops of these beds expose the traces of conjugate *hk*0 shear zones containing en échelon veins. Several synthetic *h*0*l* extension faults (Fig. 6) cut the beds. The Lower Limestone Shales at locality **C** are overturned and dip steeply N. Mudstones are cut by a cleavage which also dips N but less steeply than the beds. In upwards-facing folds this bedding/cleavage relationship indicates that the rocks are on the inverted limb of a fold.

On the **N side of Middle Cove** (locality **D**) a high-angle reverse fault displaces a marker bed of calcareous mudstone within a sequence of overturned limestones, which S of the fault are cut by conjugate *hk*0 shear zones containing arrays of en échelon veins.

The hinge zone of an overturned, S-facing, E-plunging syncline is preserved in the **large stack in the centre of Middle Cove** (locality **E**). Micrite filled burrows on the steep or overturned N limb are orientated with their long axes parallel to cleavage. A spaced pressure solution cleavage intersects the bedding to give a well defined lineation subparallel to the hinge line of the fold. A few *h*0*l* contraction faults (Fig. 6) cut the limestones in the fold core.

A metric-scale, S-verging fold couplet deforms limestones in **Third Point** (locality **F**); up-plunge these folds amplify and are exposed again in **Stackpole Quay quarry (G),** where they are laterally offset about 100 m to the N across

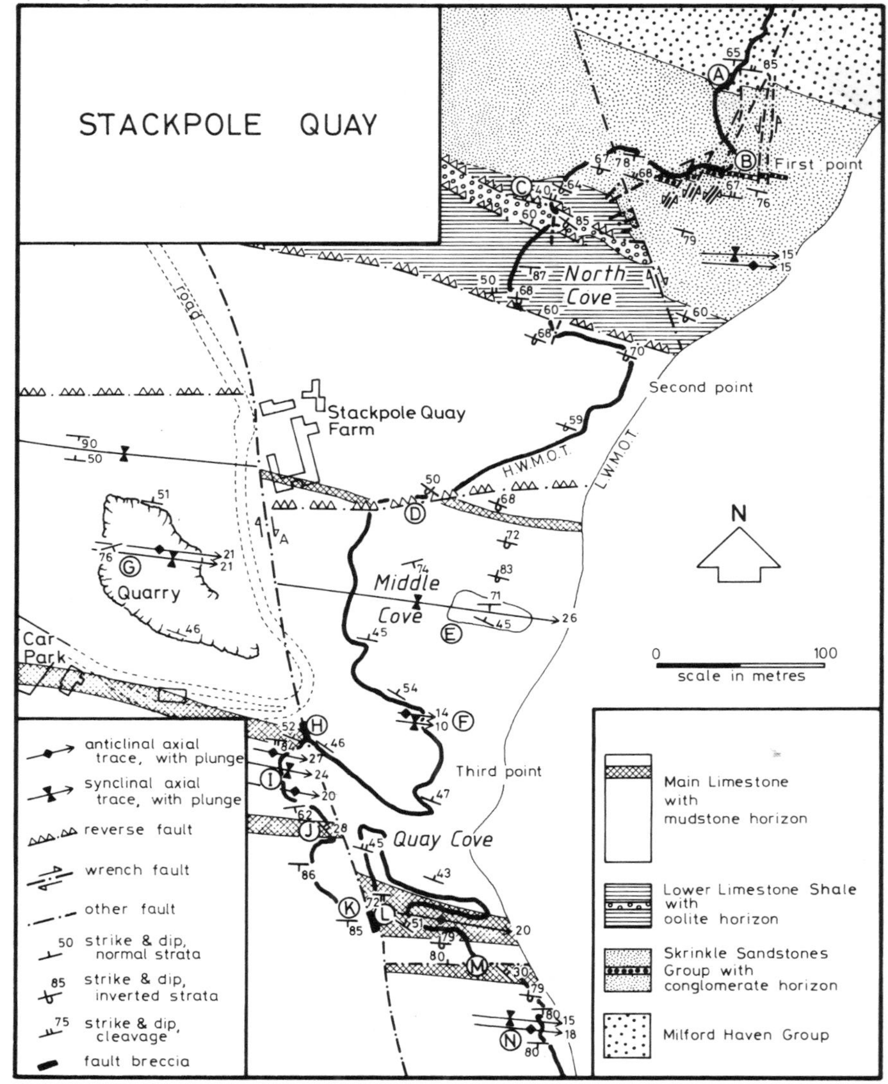

Fig. 10. Structural map of the Stackpole Quay region; some faults in North Cove are after Marshall (1977, fig. 13).

the Stackpole Quay Fault. The fault, which dips steeply E, is exposed at locality **H** (Fig. 10). It is accompanied by a 1 m wide zone of fine grained breccia and gouge, and on the E by a wider zone of shattered limestones. The

N-dipping calcareous mudstones to the W of the fault are cut by a set of anastomosing, disjunctive, pressure solution cleavage surfaces dipping S. They are also cut by nearly vertical pinnate fractures related to the fault. The symmetrically buckled core of the Stackpole Quay anticline emerges on the coast at locality **I.** Limestones deformed by the buckles are cut by a well developed, spaced pressure solution cleavage and by arrays of en échelon veins. Locality **J** exposes the marker mudstone on the steep S limb of the anticline. The cleavage cutting it dips gently N, whereas, as will have been noted, it dips steeply S at locality **H** on the N limb, thus defining a strongly convergent fan about the axial plane of the Stackpole Quay anticline.

Locality **K** is the underside of a steeply S-dipping bed of limestone. It exposes an inaccessible pair of conjugate vein arrays and a pair of conspicuously fissured conjugate *hk*0 joints (Fig. 5). At locality **L** the axial trace of the Stackpole Quay anticline plunges E, and by looking NW the approximately 100 m dextral offset of the trace across the Stackpole Quay Fault can be seen. The mudstones and limestones on the N limb of the fold dip moderately to the N and are cut by a S-dipping cleavage which is especially well developed in the marker mudstone horizon. Coincident with the bedding in the mudstone are arrays of en échelon calcite veins which indicate that the upper beds were displaced towards the crest of the anticline. Conjugate *h*0*l* extension faults cut the cleavage and shear zones. The S limb of the anticline at locality **L** is slightly overturned and the mudstones are cut by a cleavage dipping moderately NE.

Locality **M** (accessible only at low tide) exposes a steeply dipping normal lag-fault separating the marker mudstone horizon from overlying limestones. A final stop should be made at locality **N** which is reached from the cliff top. The limestones are deformed by a spectacular N-verging, but S-facing, anticlinal-synclinal couplet. In the hinge zone of the anticline there are several slightly folded *h*0*l* contraction faults which developed during the later stages of folding. Some of these faults are shear zones comprising arrays of en échelon veins.

3. Freshwater West (park at SR 886 994). On the S side of Freshwater West an Ordovician to Carboniferous succession crops out on the S limb of the S-facing, E-plunging Castlemartin Corse anticline (Fig. 11), a fold with an amplitude of at least 3 km. Stratigraphical details are described in excursions 7 and 9, this volume. Cutting the **headlands of Great and Little Furzenip and the intervening wave cut platform** is the trace of the Flimston Bay Fault, which achieves a dextral displacement of about 50 m in the N near Little Furzenip, but one of 200 m in the S near Great Furzenip. The foreshore S of Little Furzenip exposes many splay faults (Fig. 11), structures which commonly develop where a major strike-slip fault is dying out.

Whether the folded and cleaved *Didymograptus bifidus* Shales (locality **A**) are exposed depends not only upon the state of the tide, but also whether the low reef is covered by sand, a common situation. The numerous folds in the shales are probably accommodation structures close to the core of Castlemartin Corse anticline, whose axial trace lies not far to the N.

Little Furzenip stack (locality **B**) is separated from the mainland by a gully following the trace of the Flimston Bay Fault. Nearly vertical mudstones and fine grained sandstones near the N end of the gap show examples of cleavage refraction. Two-thirds of the way S through the gap there are two small, nearly vertical sinistral wrench faults exposed on the side of the stack. The faults, which are pinnate to the Flimston Bay Fault, are themselves

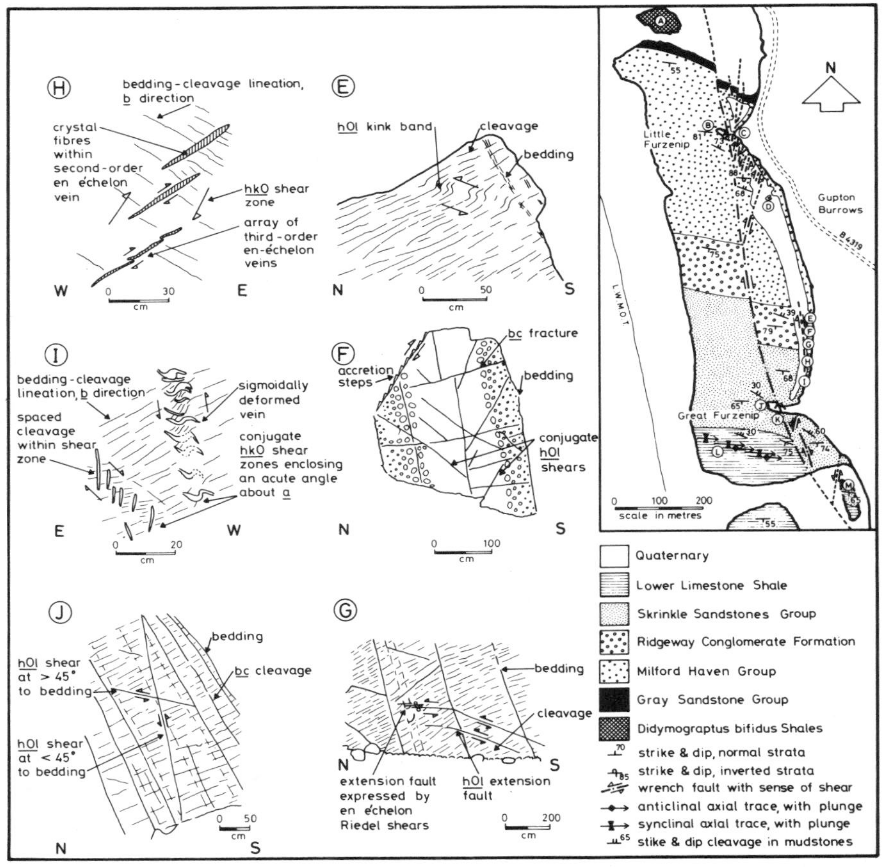

Fig. 11. Structural map of the S part of Freshwater West; insets show examples of mesostructures referred to in the text.

accompanied by nearly vertical pinnate joints restricted to their NW sides. The **SE face of the stack** is cut by conjugate *hk*0 fractures enclosing an acute angle about *a,* and an obtuse angle about the moderately plunging *b* lineation formed by the bedding-cleavage intersects. The more gently inclined set comprises quartz veins and joints, while the steeply inclined set mainly consists of joints.

At **C, opposite the stack,** there are excellent examples of: (1) cleavage refraction; (2) cylindrical pedogenic (calcrete) concretions aligned with their long axes parallel to cleavage; (3) synthetic *h*0*l* extension faults; (4) arrays of pinnate joints related to the extension faults; and (5) dextral splay faults branching from the Flimston Bay Fault.

A **small stack** (locality **D**) exposes a nearly vertical bed of cleaved mudstone cut by an array of pinnate joints in the footwall of a synthetic *h*0*l* extension fault. The upper surface of the stack displays a particularly good example of the microstaircase relief, which arises from the denudation of pinnate joints and cleavage surfaces intersecting a fault (Fig. 7). S of locality **D** the section is within the Castlemartin Range; **permission to enter** must be obtained from the Commandant.

Locality **E** is a bed of calcretised mudstone in which the N-dipping cleavage is deformed in a negative (reverse) kink band parallel to nearby synthetic *h*0*l* extension faults (inset **E,** Fig. 11). Another **low stack** within the Ridgeway Conglomerate (**F**) is formed by a bed of steeply dipping conglomerate (inset **F,** Fig. 11) cut by a set of *bc* joints and conjugate sets of *h*0*l* fractures enclosing an acute angle about *c*. Some fractures in the N-dipping *h*0*l* set bear a crystal fibre slickenside lineation normal to the fracture-bedding intersect *(b)*. The risers of the asymmetrical accretionary steps face up the footwalls of the fractures and demonstrate that the sense of shear was that of an antithetic extension fault.

Steeply S-dipping mudstones are cut by refracted cleavage planes and synthetic *h*0*l* extension faults at locality **G** (inset **G,** Fig. 11). The long axes of pedogenic (calcrete) concretions are orientated within cleavage planes and perpendicular to the bedding-cleavage *(b)* lineation. One of the synthetic extension faults terminates to the N in an array of Riedel shears, each of which is a negative kink band deflecting cleavage, and one of which displaces a large calcrete concretion.

S of the disconformity between the Ridgeway Conglomerate and the Skrinkle Sandstones Group the upper surface of a sandstone at locality **H** exposes conjugate shear zones. The widest zone (inset **H,** Fig. 11) comprises en échelon second-order fractures, most of which are single veins with growth fibres oblique to their margins. One second-order direction is composite, consisting of an array of third-order veins. Locality **I** exposes further examples of conjugate shear zones enclosing an obtuse angle about the bedding-cleavage lineation (the *b* direction) and containing sigmoidally deformed veins associated with a spaced cleavage (inset **I,** Fig. 11). At the **W end of Great Furzenip** it is possible to inspect spaced *bc* cleavage surfaces cut by *h0l* extension and contraction faults (inset **J,** Fig. 11). The **S face of the headland** and a **stack immediately to the S** of it (locality **K**) are good sites to appreciate the high degree of symmetry between conjugate *hk0* shear zones and the bedding-cleavage lineation *(b)*.

At locality **L,** N-verging buckle folds deform the Lower Limestone Shales, which immediately to the E of the folds is dragged against the trace of the Flimston Bay Fault. A final stop at locality **M** allows a well developed disjunctive spaced cleavage in pebbly sandstones to be examined.

4. West Angle Bay (car park at SM 854 032). The most readily appreciated structures lie **immediately N of the centre of the bay,** beneath which lies the axial trace of the Angle syncline. The limestones at locality **A** are deformed by a meso-anticline cut by spaced pressure solution cleavage surfaces giving rise to a bedding-cleavage *(b)* lineation parallel to the hinge line of the fold (Fig. 12). A S-dipping thrust separates the Lower Limestone Shales in the hanging wall from the Main Limestone in the footwall at **B.** An array of en échelon calcite veins in a shear zone is visible at **C.** Excellent examples of layer-parallel *(ab)* and through-rock *(ac)* styolites cut limestones at **D.**

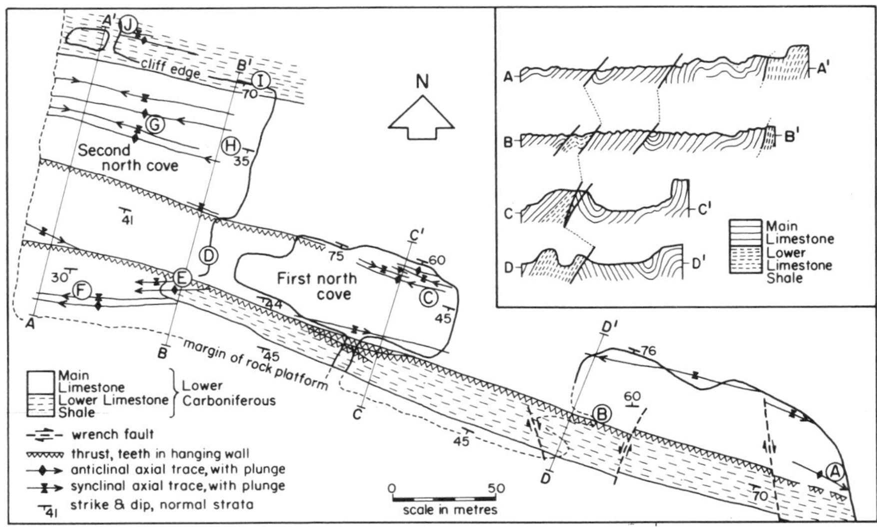

Fig. 12. Structural map and cross sections of folds and faults exposed on the N side of West Angle Bay.

At **E** the same thrust as at **B** again juxtaposes the Lower Limestone Shales and the Main Limestone. The thrust plane, polished and lineated by groove slickensides, is accompanied by a narrow zone of mylonitised limestone in the hanging wall. Also within the hanging wall, a N-verging and facing fold-couplet, which plunges moderately W, is responsible for the sinuous outcrop of the contact between the shales and limestones. Crinoid ossicles and stems which have been flattened in the core of the syncline give rise to an approximately axial plane foliation. Locality **F** exposes another anticlinal-synclinal couplet. Nearly upright elongate periclines cut by *ac* calcite veins occur in the region of **G** (Fig. 12). An array of en échelon calcite veins in a shear zone of *h*0*l* extension fault geometry can be seen at **H.** Many of the veins are truncated at bedding stylolites.

The calcareous mudstones at **I** are cut by a steep, N-dipping cleavage, which is deformed by numerous negative (reverse) kink bands. Conjugate *hk*0 joints enclosing a small angle about *a* also cut the slates. At **J** the cleavage can be seen to be axial plane with respect to a small anticlinal-synclinal couplet.

N of the area depicted in Fig. 12 there are further examples of planar mesostructures; perhaps the most instructive assemblage occurs at SM 8495 0377 in a bed of pebbly sandstone within the Skrinkle Sandstones Group. The bed is cut by five sets of joints; a single extension set in *bc,* and two systems of conjugate shears in *hk*0 (Fig. 5).

5. St. Anne's, Milford Haven. Exposed on the **foreshore** at SM 0888 0537 is the core of an anticline accessible from St. Anne's beach to the W. Within the fold is a channel-fill sequence with an unconformable base (Fig. 13a), across which the hinge line shifts from **X** to **Y** and the attitudes of the fold axis and axial plane change. Thus, it is possible to infer that the occurrence of a pre-existing sedimentary feature has influenced the style and the location of a subsequent tectonic structure. A sandstone at the channel base displays a bedding-cleavage lineation which is curvilinear and nearly normal to a set of veins which are cut by the cleavage, suggesting that axial extension occurred during folding when the cleavage was developing.

In the hinge zone at SM 0888 0538, quartzitic sandstones less than 10 cm thick display a disjunctive spaced cleavage with a separation of less than 4 cm. Some of the cleavage surfaces are continuous, without refraction into the more frequently developed cleavage zones in the interbedded mudstones. This latter cleavage is deflected by up to 30° near bedding surfaces, on which there is a crystal fibre slickenside lineation. In the **cliff immediately to the N** is a sub vertical cross-fault accompanied by several splays. Between the main surface and the splays are a set of surfaces (Fig. 13b) with a spacing of less than 10 cm, some of which show offset indicating that they are splays to the splays.

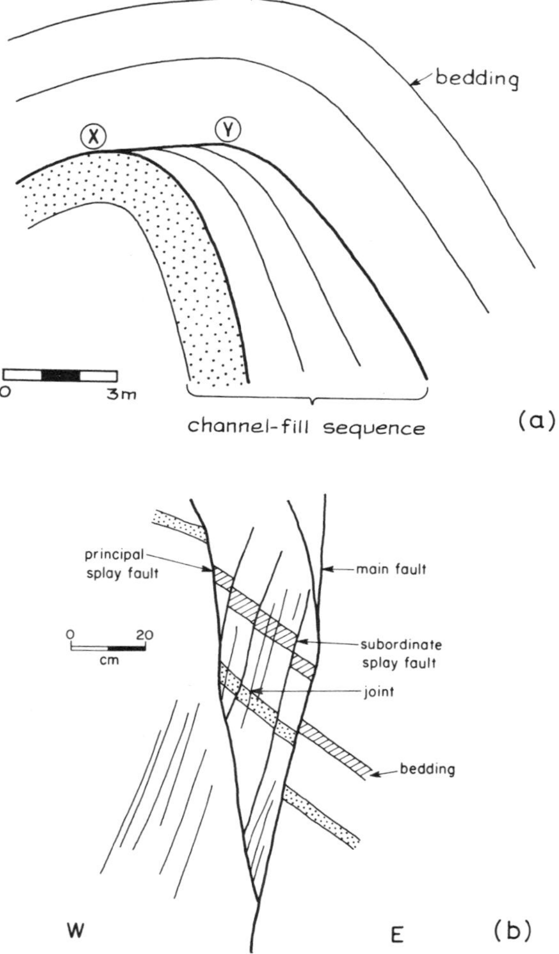

Fig. 13. a, variations in the location of the hinge line of an anticline at St. Anne's, Milford Haven; b, cross section of faults exposed at St. Anne's, Milford Haven.

6. Little Wick to Kilroom Bay. This section, which extends around South Hook Point (SM 8677 0553), may be reached by a coastal path and road from Gelliswick Bay (SM 886 057, Fig. 14). Localities **D** to **L** are accessible via **A,** an overgrown stairway, **B,** South Hook Point, and **C,** a gully in the cliff.

On the N limb of the Kilroom Bay syncline at **D** are *h0l* kink bands which elongate the beds parallel to their dip. The gently N-dipping bands deflect the cleavage and contain arrays of Riedel shears offsetting the cleavage (inset

D, Fig. 14). At **E,** the core of the Kilroom Bay syncline, an upright, parallel fold with a broad subrounded hinge zone, is exposed. The frequency of cleavage surfaces increases from the limbs to the core.

N of the South Hook Point syncline, at **F,** is a fault typical of the minor, dextral strike-slip cross-faults in this section. The fault zone is about 1 m wide with 2 m dextral offset, and has an orientation of 160/82E. On the W side of the fault is a set of splay faults which are generally planar and discontinuous, with a spacing of 5-15 cm. Between the faults bounding the zone is an array of minor dextral Riedel faults. At **G**, in the core of the South Hook syncline, is an excellently developed disjunctive spaced cleavage cutting sandstones, and there is also a good example of a contraction fault in the fold hinge zone (inset **G,** Fig. 14). The cleavage zones, in which bedding is deflected or discontinuous, are less than 1 cm wide and are separated by microlithons 1-3 cm in width. Although the convergent cleavage zones are closely spaced they are not periodic. On the N limb of the syncline a 1.5 m wide contraction fault zone contains three main surfaces and several minor surfaces. The rock between the faults is unfractured sandstone rather than fault breccia or gouge. Many of the fault surfaces are calcite veins displaying a crystal fibre slickenside lineation. The veins are less than 2 cm thick and multi-layered, indicating that there were several episodes of slip.

In the anticline at **H** there are interlaminated sandstones and mudstones disturbed and dissected by sedimentary water-escape structures which superficially resemble tectonic crenulations. The overall fold style is similar as a consequence of flow of the mudstones into the hinge zone of the fold; the majority of folds in the Variscan area of SW Dyfed are parallel or nearly parallel in style. Also, the fold is unusually tight with an interlimb angle of less than 60° in an 8 m wide hinge zone.

On the S limb of the anticline at **I** an unusually well developed crystal fibre slickenside lineation is exposed on a bedding plane. There are more than five layers of fibres, which truncate older veins within the beds.

7. Little Castle Head. This section exposes an anticlinal-synclinal couplet deforming the Milford Haven Group and repeating the outcrop of the Townsend Tuff Bed (for stratigraphical details see excursion 8, locality 5, this volume). Access is from **A, B** or C (Fig. 15). The **S slope of the headland at C** is an eroded contraction fault surface forming a staircase, in which the risers are nearly vertical cleavage planes and the treads are nearly horizontal pinnate joints. If the thicknesses of the sedimentary units involved in the fold-couplet are measured it is clear that within the shared middle limb they are nearly half as thin as in the external limbs to the N and S. Because the thickness variations are accompanied by changes in rock type, it is more likely that they are related to original sedimentary differences than to subsequent tectonic deformation. Indeed, the sedimentary variations may

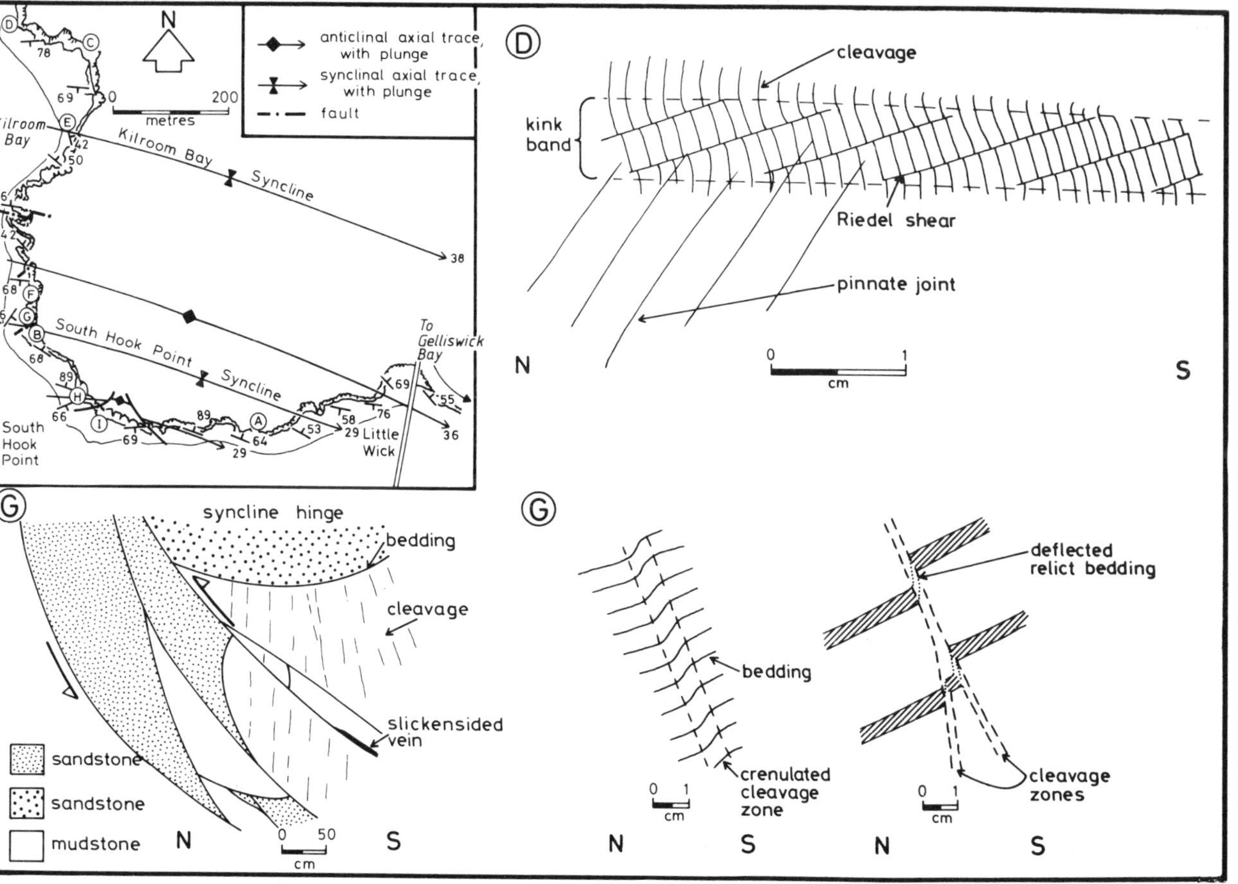

Fig. 14. Structural map of the area between Little Wick and Kilroom Bay; insets show examples of structures referred to in the text.

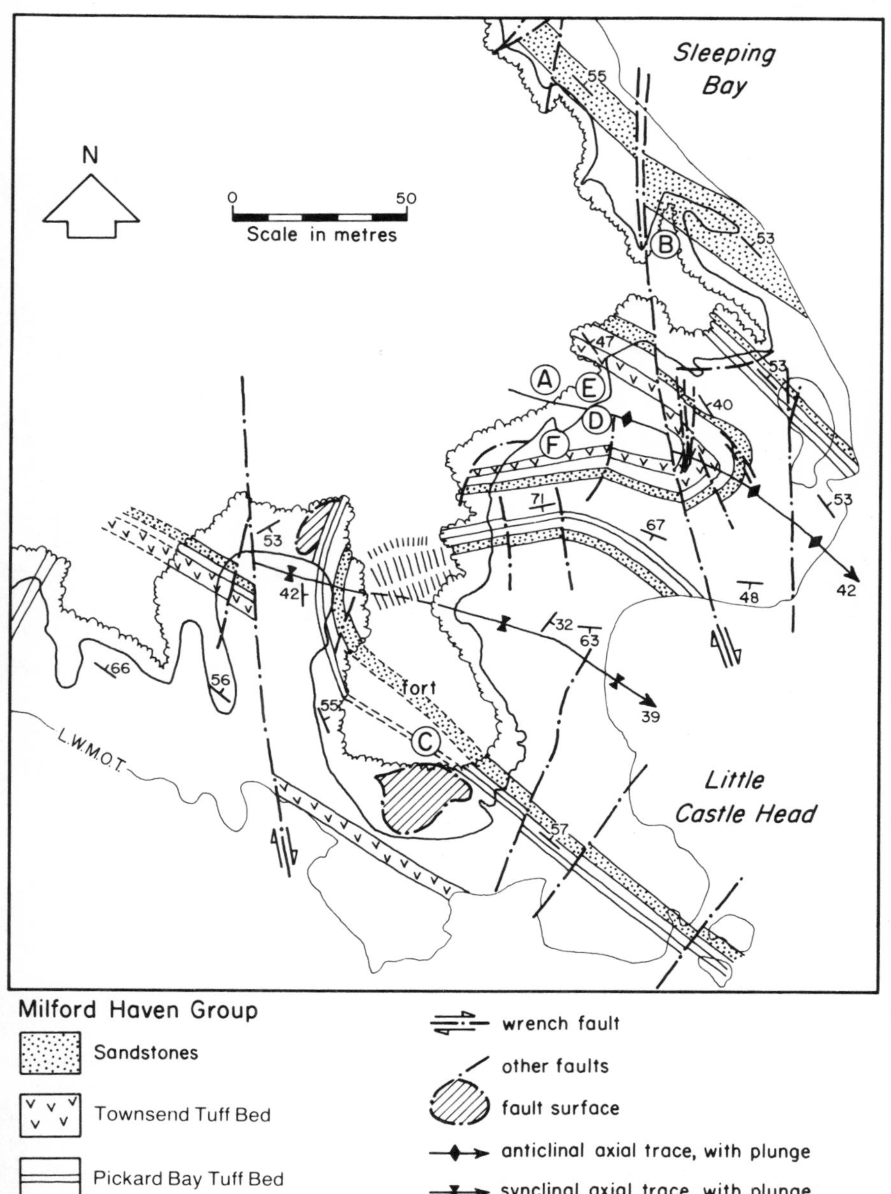

Fig. 15. Structural map of Little Castle Head.

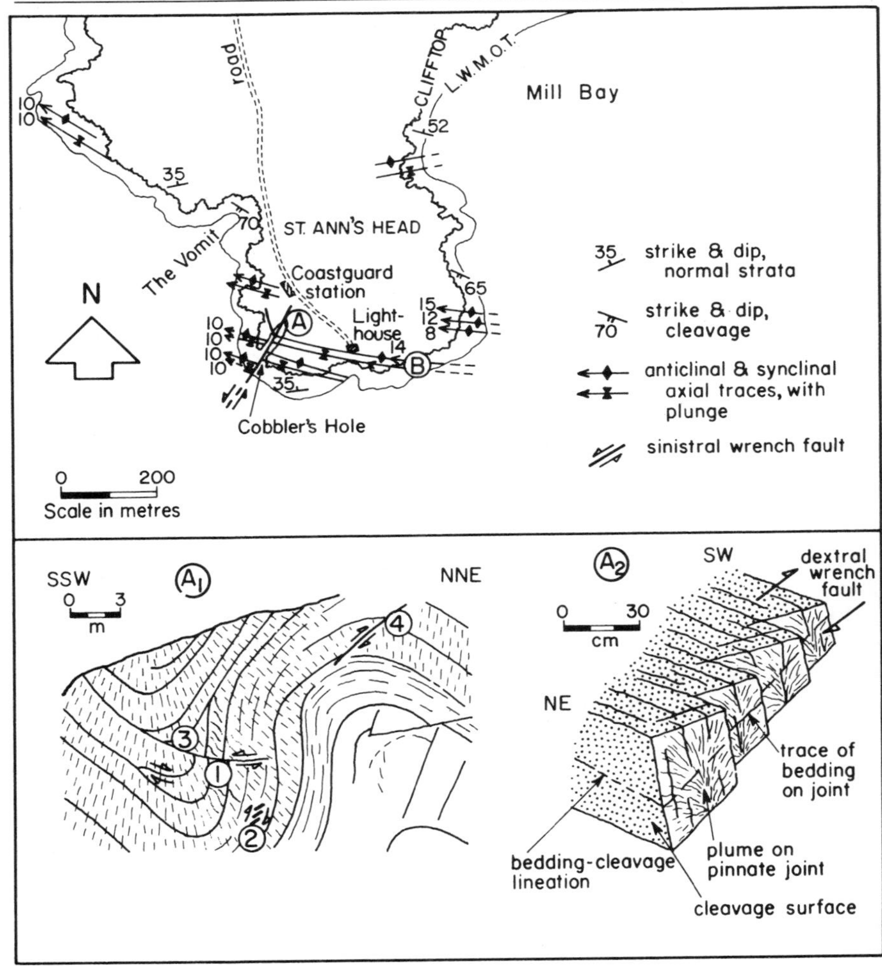

Fig. 16. Structural map of St. Ann's Head, Dale; insets show examples of structures referred to in the text.

have caused the folds to initiate here. One consequence of folding this sequence of uneven thickness has been to produce an anticline in which the hinge line makes an angle of about 20° with the bedding-cleavage lineation (locality **D**). Within most folds in SW Dyfed these two directions are parallel or subparallel. At **E** there is a multi-layered quartz vein parallel to bedding. The pitches of crystal fibre slickenside lineations within the layers vary by up to 38°, suggesting that interlayer slip directions changed during folding, perhaps in response to the sedimentary thickness variations.

The most abundant joints are orientated 030/80W and belong to one set in the conjugate *hk*0 system, which encloses an obtuse angle about the fold axial direction. The spatial distribution of the joints is not uniform. As can be seen at **F** they are mainly restricted to zones up to 5 m wide and 20 m long, within which joint separation is generally in the range 2 to 7 cm.

8. St Ann's Head, Dale (car park at SM 803 042). The Milford Haven Group on the S limb of the Angle syncline is deformed by several S-verging fold-couplets. From the **SE side of Cobbler's Hole** (locality **A**) a magnificent example of one couplet may be viewed (inset **A1**, Fig. 16.). Cleavage is moderately convergent about axial planes and at position **1** (inset **A1**) is refracted. An array of en échelon veins (position **2, A1**) indicates that there was interstratal shear during folding, a process which also gave rise to the accommodation structures visible at positions **3** and **4.**

From the **top of the inlet** at SM 8054 0283 follow a grassy track to about one-third of the way down the slope. From here it is possible to inspect refracted cleavage domains from which quartz was selectively removed during pressure solution, and in which there is now an oblique grain-shape fabric. An array of pinnate joints related to a small dextral wrench fault intersects the cleavage surfaces, and as a consequence of denudation a microstaircase relief has developed (inset **A2**, Fig. 16 and Fig. 7). Many of the pinnate joints bear plumose marks with nearly vertical axes aligned parallel to the direction of joint propagation.

Locality **B** (Fig. 16), reached via a cliff path starting at SM 8086 0285, exposes another asymmetrical fold-couplet which is of special interest because on a gently dipping bedding plane there are several cross sections through deformed *Beaconites antarcticus* burrows. Before deformation the sections would have been approximately circular, but they are now elliptical with a short to long axis ratio (Y/X) of about 0.5. The longer axes (X) of the ellipses are parallel to the bedding-cleavage lineation.

9. Marloes Sands. Details of the stratigraphical succession at this locality are described in excursions 7 and 8, this volume. The full sequence from the Skomer Volcanic Group to the Milford Haven Group is cut by several varieties of planar mesostructure. Perhaps the most spectacular are the conjugate shear zones containing en échelon quartz veins such as at localities **A1** to **A3**. Vein arrays (inset **A1**, Fig. 17) are approximately normal to bedding, the mean orientation of the dextral and sinistral sets being 088/42N and 024/54W respectively. Conjugate arrays enclose an acute angle which is approximately symmetrical about bedding strike. In addition to en échelon veins many shear zones also contain a quartz grain-shape fabric and a set of disjunctive pressure solution cleavage surfaces (Knipe & White 1979). A common arrangement of these structures within a shear zone is that the end

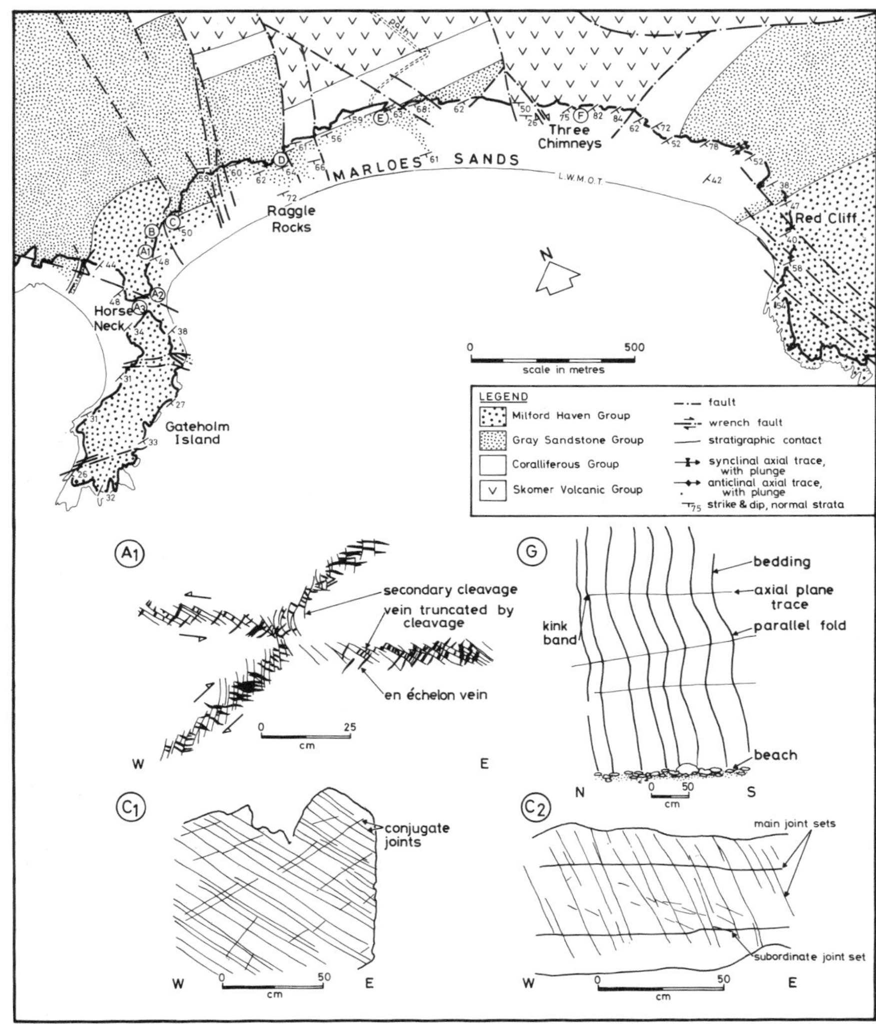

Fig. 17. Structural map of Marloes Sands; insets show examples of structures referred to in the text.

of a zone contains only the shape fabric, whereas towards the middle of a zone veins and cleavage are developed in addition to the shape fabric. Sigmoidally deformed veins and second generation veins are present within some zones.

At **B** it is possible to examine the relationship between deformed reduction spots and cleavage planes. While some small, green spots are triaxial ellipsoids, others are irregular in shape, suggesting that not all of them were spherical before deformation. The ellipsoids have their long (*X*) and intermediate (*Y*) axes lying within cleavage planes, and *Y* is subparallel to the bedding-cleavage lineation.

At **C** a well developed set of joints orientated 132/62N cuts brown, medium grained sandstones in the Milford Haven Group. The joints, 1 to 10 cm apart, are almost precisely planar (inset **C**1, Fig. 17). Although representatives of the same joint set cut green sandstones in the Gray Sandstone Group a few metres to the N they are shorter, less frequent, and subordinate to surfaces belonging to two older joint sets (inset **C**2, Fig. 17).

In the **small embayment at D** there is a 15-20 cm wide fault zone containing poorly sorted, angular breccia clasts cemented by granular calcite. Inner and outer zones of calcite veining indicate that there were at least two phases of displacement on the fault. About 15 m to the S, very thin lenses of sandstone interbedded with mudstone contain small, lenticular quartz veins sub-perpendicular to bedding and totally absent in the mudstones.

Near Sandy Lane at **E** is a sequence of rocks in which the mudstone content decreases to the S, with the cleavage becoming correspondingly less well developed. Where the cleavage is well developed, indications of inter-layer slip in the form of crystal fibre slickenside lineations are abundant. They are orientated 228/58, and if they developed normal to the hinge line of the Marloes anticline it is possible to infer that its plunge is moderate and to the SE.

Within the Skomer Volcanic Group **near Three Chimneys (F)** there is an anomalous bedding/cleavage relationship. The cleavage dips moderately S and cuts nearly vertical beds. In an upwards-facing fold this relationship would normally indicate that the direction of younging was to the N. However, sedimentary structures such as erosion surfaces and graded bedding show that these beds young to the S. This anomalous relationship has been explained as a consequence of tilting the Skomer Volcanic Group before deposition of the Coralliferous Group and subsequent development of the Variscan cleavage (Graham *et al.* 1977).

Though they occur elsewhere at Marloes Sands, minor asymmetrical folds and kink bands which deform the cleavage are best seen at **G** within the Skomer Volcanic Group. Here, the gentle, nearly recumbent folds change in style from parallel to kink-like with decreasing amplitude (inset **G**, Fig. 17). The kink bands only occur where there are thin, infrequent, sandstones interbedded with mudstone, and they are incongruent parasites to the recumbent folds.

10. St. Bride's Haven. The mudstones and sandstones of the Milford Haven Group at St Bride's Haven are displaced a total of about 50 m by numerous dextral cross-faults concentrated in a 100 m wide fault zone (Fig. 18). The

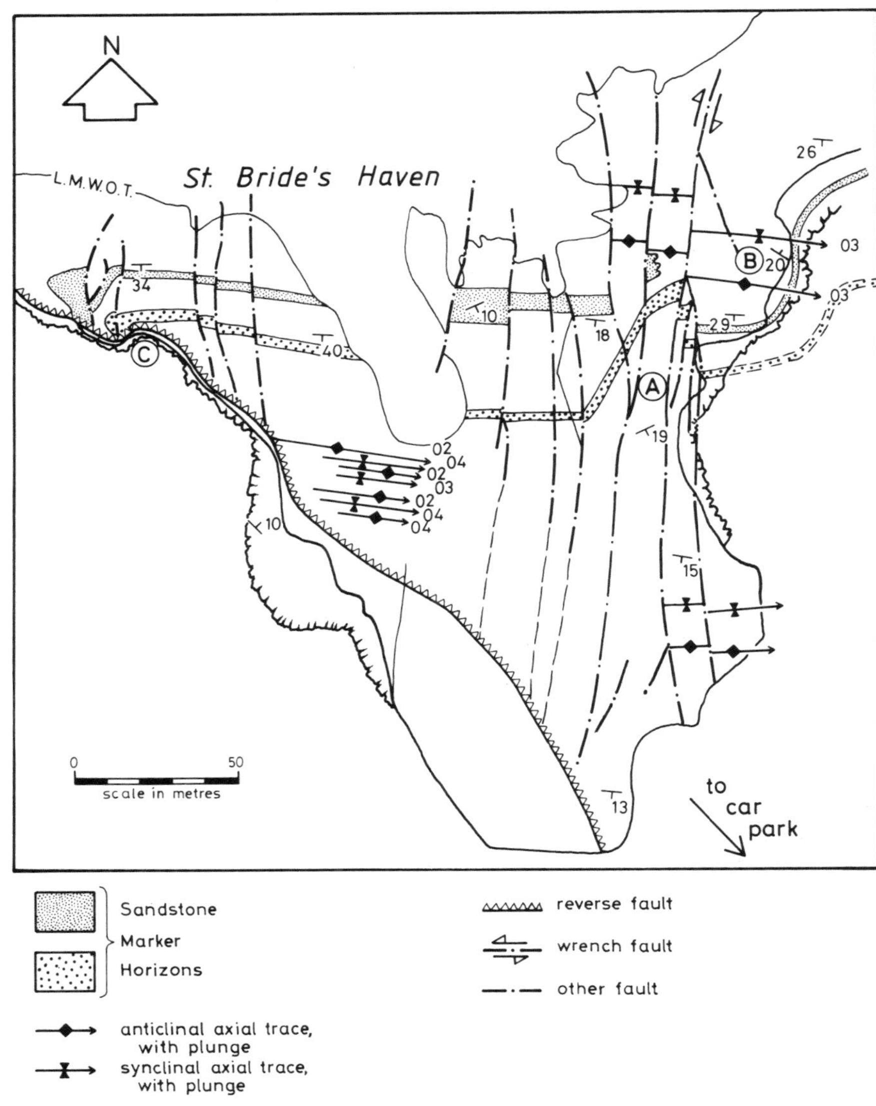

Fig. 18. Structural map of St. Bride's Haven.

nearly vertical faults which strike N-S have been eroded into narrow gullies. At locality **A** the principal fault within the zone displays a dextral offset of about 20 m, and is accompanied by N-S trending splay faults which branch from the point where the main fault curves out of its general N-S alignment. Pinnate joints related to the fault are also present.

At locality **B** an open anticline and syncline are exposed. Their style is typical of many of the folds which deform the Old Red Sandstone on the W coast. Axial planes are nearly vertical, hinge lines nearly horizontal, and limbs are generally straight and separated by rounded hinge zones. A bed of sandstone involved in the fold couplet is cut by conjugate *h0l* contraction faults, one set of which follows the foresets of cross bedding surfaces within the layer. The mudstones enclosing the sandstone have shortened by the development of an axial plane cleavage which is absent in the sandstone cut by the contraction faults.

On the W side of the haven at **C** there is a reverse fault orientated 116/20S. It bears a slickenside lineation which plunges on a bearing of 204°, indicating that shear was dominantly dip-slip. The beds in the hanging wall dip N, while those in the footwall dip S, and thus the fault emplaces the S limb of a syncline on its N limb. An unusual feature of this reverse fault is that it cuts some of the N-S cross-faults which elsewhere in SW Dyfed are generally younger than reverse strike faults.

STRUCTURES WITHIN THE COALFIELD AREA (M. E. Tringham)

11. Amroth. Near Amroth, deformed Coal Measures are exposed in the cliffs (Fig. 19). Stratigraphical and sedimentological details in this area are described in excursions 10 and 11, this volume. Structures include folds and

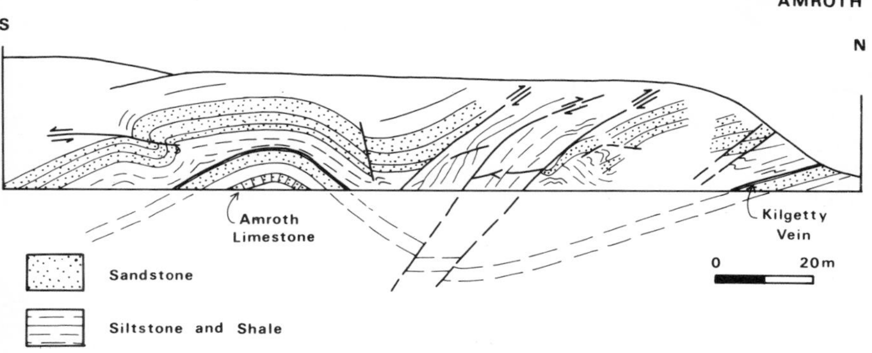

Fig. 19. Cross section showing structures visible in the cliffs SW of Amroth; the structures are projected onto a N-S section, perpendicular to fold axes and strike faults.

strike faults which trend E-W oblique to the coast. SW from Amroth (SN 1618 0694), the faulted N limb of a syncline is visible, the prominent seat earth of the Kilgetty Vein dipping moderately to the S. Within the complex faulted section steeply dipping reverse faults occur with associated minor folds.

Further SW, the Kilgetty Vein and its seat earth again crop out in the core of the Amroth anticline (SN 1576 0677). This anticline is of particular interest, because it contains a parasitic anticline-syncline fold pair which face S, the majority of folds in the coalfield facing N. The parasitic folds are visible in the cliff approximately 5 m above beach level, accompanied by a small overthrust to the S. The deformed sandstone is folded concentrically, with radial quartz veins developed on the outer arc of the parasitic syncline. At beach level, close examination of bedding surfaces on the seat earth, and the Amroth freshwater limestone, reveals traces of a spaced pressure solution cleavage trending parallel to fold axes. The cleavage forms narrow anastomosing seams perpendicular to bedding, across which there was pressure solution. Close to the axial trace of the Amroth anticline (SN 1591 0684), normal cross-faults intersect the cliff, with displacements of a few metres. One pair of N-S trending cross-faults forms a small graben recessed into the cliff.

12. Saundersfoot. At Saundersfoot, **between the harbour** (SN 1381 0458) **and the Ladies Cave anticline** (SN 1388 0433), a mainly argillaceous coal-bearing sequence is complexly deformed. Where coals have been thrust over sandstones, there are a series of steps, formed as a result of the thrust having been refracted either parallel or oblique to layering. In addition, small scale folds, normal strike faults and cross-faults, all add to the complexity of the section. Some normal strike faults are slightly curved, convex upwards, with sandstones thickened across them, indicating that they may have been sedimentary growth faults.

S of the complex section, the Ladies Cave anticline forms a small headland. This well known anticline is an example of a chevron fold, the fold possessing long straight limbs, and a narrow hinge zone. In common with other folds in this structutral zone, the anticline is inclined, the axial surface dipping steeply S. Minor accommodation features include limb thrusts, and small saddle reefs, where thin shale beds have flowed into the hinge zone. In the fold core, shales are cut by a convergent cleavage fan, and ironstone beds are shortened by minor contraction faults and small scale buckles.

13. Monkstone Point. At Monkstone Point (SN 1484 0326), an anticline presents some unusual features. The fold has a sub horizontal E-W trending axis, and an axial surface inclined steeply to the S. There are three natural cross sections through the fold, and these reveal complications thought by Tringham (1979) to be partly sedimentary and partly tectonic in origin. Features include bedding discontinuities, disharmonic minor folds, deformed mudstones with slumped balls, coal 'rafts', and lens shaped bodies of conglomerate (Fig. 20). The sedimentary and tectonic assemblage is interpreted as having formed by folding of a large channel sandstone, tectonic folds and reverse faults being superimposed on a wide variety of earlier sedimentary structures.

14. Waterwynch. In the coastal section near Waterwynch, folds and thrust faults affect the uppermost Namurian and basal Westphalian rocks (Fig. 21). Details of the succession in this area are described in excursion 10, this volume. In the **first bay N of Waterwynch (SN 1391 0226)**, a gently dipping thrust fault intersects the section. Above the thrust, Namurian rocks lie parallel to the thrust surface. Quartz fibre slickenside lineations are visible on bedding surfaces in the reefs, their orientations indicating that some bedding plane slip was oblique to the dip of the thrust surface. In the cliff, the thrust surface forms a 20 cm thick carbonaceous fault gouge, below an overhanging sandstone. Below the thrust, sandstones, shales and coals form a complex mélange. On **the headland** (SN 1397 0225), moderately plunging mesofolds occur on the inverted limb of an overturned syncline, the overturned nature of the rocks being determined from ripple marks and load structures in the sandstones. In the **bay to the N,** folds are visible in the cliff section; they are intersected by strike faults, which displace their hinges (SN 1406 0237).

In the **Bay S of Waterwynch** (SN 1362 0190), the faulted core of an overturned syncline forms an inlier of Westphalian rocks (Fig. 21).

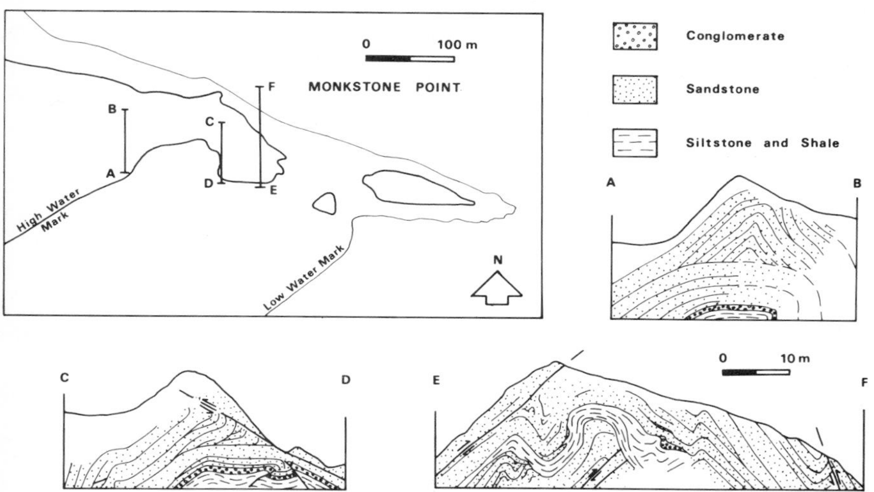

Fig. 20. Map and cross sections of Monkstone Point; the approximate locations of the three natural sections are shown on the map; see text for details.

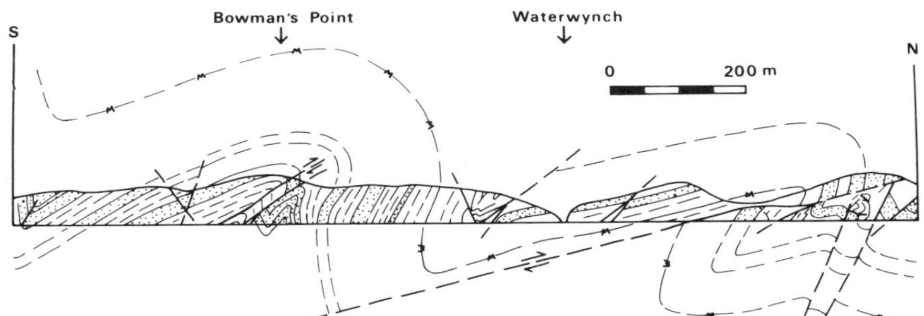

Fig. 21. Cross section of structures exposed near Waterwynch; 'M' marks the horizon of the *Gastrioceras subcrenatum* marine band, the base of which is the boundary between the Namurian and Westphalian; legend as for Fig. 20.

In the core, minor symmetrical folds of 'W' sense are visible, together with a number of strike faults. To the S as far as **Bowman's Point** (SN 1368 0161) the Namurian sequence is entirely inverted, bedding surfaces dipping S between 40° and 60°. At Bowman's Point an anticline-syncline fold pair are present. The folds are of chevron geometry, sandstones displaying accommodation effects such as limb thrusts and bulbous hinge zones. In the **bay to the S** (SN 1356 0157), the core of a large scale anticline is visible, the fold hinge plunging gently E. Shales within the fold core display a slaty cleavage, and thrust faults which displace the overturned N limb of the fold pass into bedding-parallel shears on the normal limb.

15. Tenby North Sands. Details of the stratigraphy and sedimentology of this locality are described in excursions 10 and 11, this volume. In the **cliff section** at North Beach, asymmetrical and inclined chevron folds are present (Fig. 22). In the siltstone-shale sequence, the competent silty beds are of

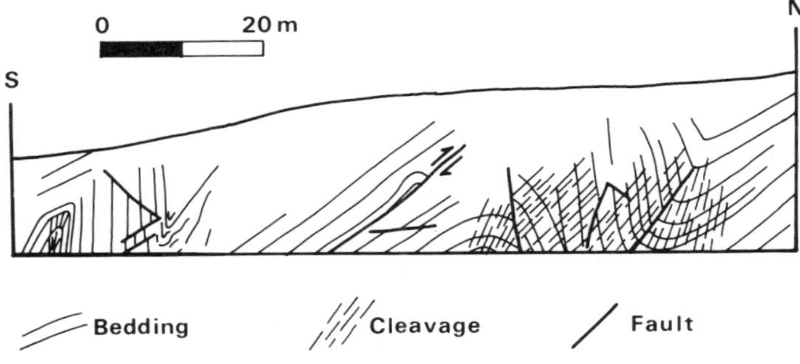

Fig. 22. Cross section showing structures present in Namurian rocks at North Beach, Tenby.

particularly constant thickness, thus facilitating chevron fold formation. One chevron fold possesses a slightly box-like shape (SN 1333 0106), perhaps attributable either to some minor refolding, or to accommodation effects in the hinge zone. Here, slaty cleavage is strongly developed, and forms convergent fans around the folds (Fig. 22). In some thick shale units it is difficult to recognise bedding because cleavage predominates.

16. Musselwick Bay near Little Haven. At Musselwick Bay (SM 8505 1237), 1 km SW of Little Haven, a wide variety of structures have developed. Here, the Johnston Thrust superimposes Precambrian diorites of the Johnston 'Series' on Upper Carboniferous rocks (Fig. 23). From the cliff top, some structural features are visible. To the W, the Johnston Thrust crops out **half way up the cliff, in a cove close to a small promontory** (SM 8467 1238). The trace of the thrust then passes westwards beneath the mooring in Goultrop Roads, to reappear at the **foot of the cliff at Borough Head** (SM 8400 1274). Below, in **Musselwick Bay,** the axial trace of the overturned Musselwick syncline is visible in the reefs at low tide (SM 8504 1239), outcrops forming 'V' shapes, the syncline plunging moderately W.

After descent into the bay, tight folds, strike faults, and cross-faults are

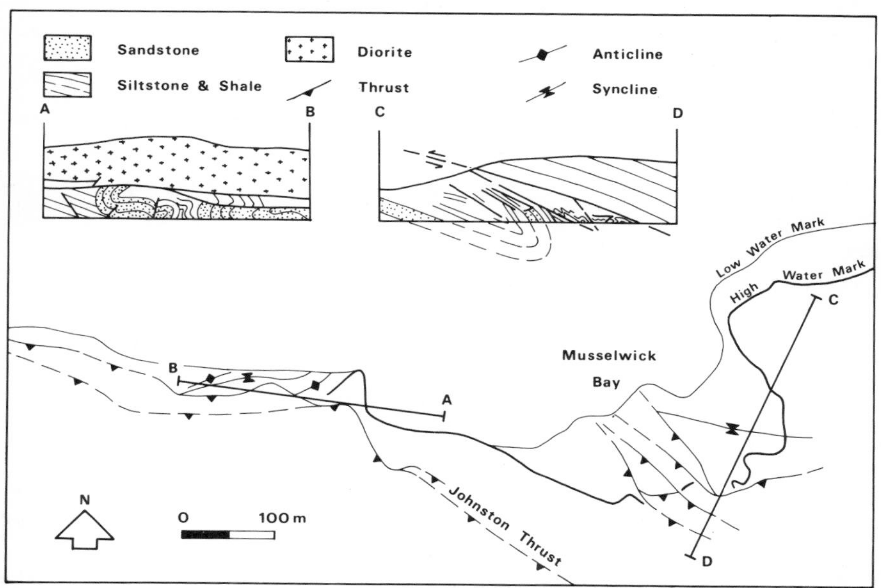

Fig. 23. Map and cross sections of Musselwick Bay, showing folds and faults close to the Johnston Thrust; section A-B illustrates reclined, W-facing, S-plunging folds; section C-D shows the overturned W-plunging Musselwick syncline, together with a complex of thrusted units, which also contain S-plunging folds.

visible both in the **cliff and foreshore.** The folds occur in three thrust-bounded units, each of which contains folds of different axial trend. The SW unit forms a complex fault-mélange, in which brecciated sandstone layers are enclosed in crenulated shales (SM 8496 1232). Minor folds in this unit trend N-S, an anomalous orientation for the Variscan fold belt. The assemblage of structures at Musselwick is interpreted by Tringham (1979) to have formed during complex polyphase deformation, which included late dextral strike-slip and E-W compression in the Johnston Thrust zone.

17. Little Haven. N of Little Haven, many folds and strike faults are visible in the **cliff section** (Fig. 24). Here, the effects of lithology on deformation styles are well displayed. At the mouth of the haven (SM 8568 1310), a thick sandstone unit forms a large concentric anticline, the core of the fold comprising the partially mined **Fox Hole.** In the **cave roof,** minor faults displace sandstone beds by a few tens of centimetres, the faults having presumably formed as compressional accommodation features in the inner arc of the fold.

In contrast, coal-bearing cyclothems exposed in the **Settlands** contain numerous mesofolds intersected by strike faults. The folds are overturned and asymmetrical, and contain thickened shale beds in hinge zones. The hinge zone of one nearly recumbent fold is particularly interesting (SM 8585 1332). It comprises a strongly cleaved sideritic seat earth separated from the remainder of the fold by faults. The spaced cleavage traces are sub-horizontal and gently refracted through the bed.

Between the Settlands and Broad Haven, the rocks are inverted, the section forming the overturned N limb of a large composite anticline (Fig. 24). In a **small inlet immediately N of the Rain** (SM 8584 1343), an unusual fault-

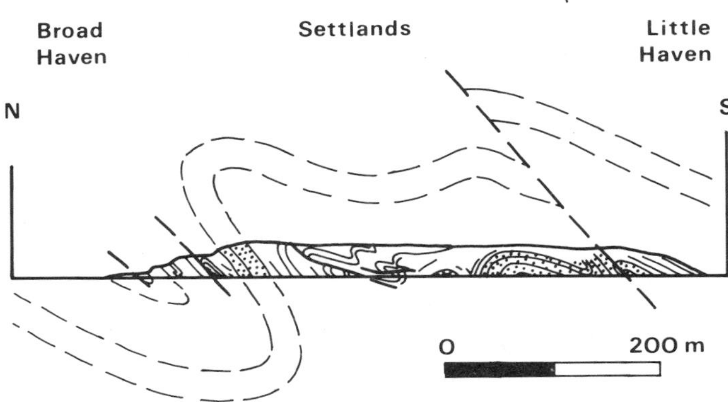

Fig. 24. Cross section of the cliffs between Little Haven and Broad Haven; legend as for Fig. 23.

bounded zone contains tight, downwards-facing mesofolds. The folds have developed within a coal-bearing siltstone and shale unit, and are accompanied by numerous thrust faults. One possible explanation for these anomalous downwards-facing folds is that they were developed during localised compression, before the larger scale folds had formed.

18. Broad Haven. Stratigraphical and sedimentological details in this area are described in excursions 10 and 11, this volume. In the cliff and foreshore on the N side of Broad Haven, numerous mesofolds and strike faults are exposed (Fig. 25). These complex structures deform shaly, coal-bearing cyclothems. The lateral impersistence of the structures is well displayed on the foreshore, where a seemingly chaotic array of en échelon folds and strike faults occurs. **In the cliff,** an asymmetrical N-facing anticline possesses some noteworthy features (SM 8603 1417). The overturned N limb of the fold is intersected by a subhorizontal thrust, which when traced to the normal limb comprises a bedding-parallel shear. The thrust surface is curved, some folding presumably having taken place after fault initiation. Within the fold, sandstone units are deformed in a disharmonic manner, irregular spaces between the units being infilled by thickened shaly beds. In the fold core, a seat earth contains a spaced pressure solution cleavage, the bedding-cleavage lineation being slightly oblique to the fold hinge line.

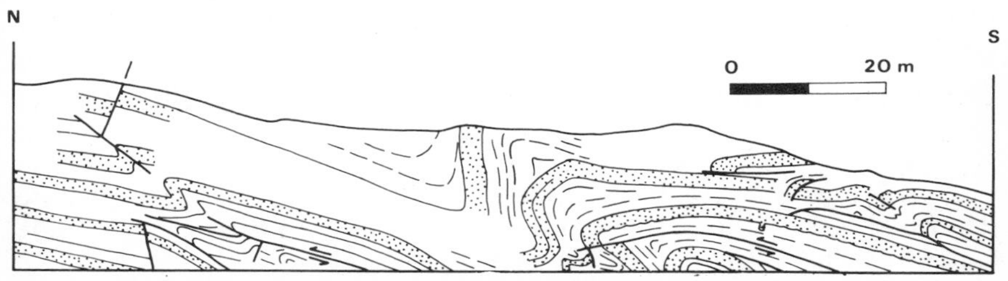

Fig. 25. Cross section of structures visible in the cliffs N of Broad Haven; legend as for Fig. 23.

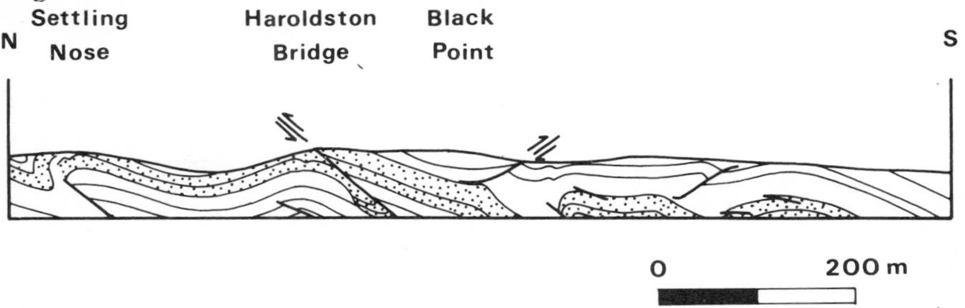

Fig. 26. Cross section of the cliffs near Black Point; for clarity, units of 'Farewell Rock' which are displaced by faults at Settling Nose and Haroldston Bridge have been omitted; legend as for Fig. 23.

To the N, at **Lion Rock** (SM 8599 1430) the cliff is intersected by a NE-SW trending zone of normal cross-faults, with a predominant downthrow to the SE. Nearby, **in the cliffs and stacks,** sandstones contain en échelon quartz veins in arrays parallel to the faults. At the **Sleek Stone** (SM 8595 1446), the well known anticline forms a promontory, the overturned fold plunging seawards at about 10°.

N from the Sleek Stone to **Black Point** (SM 8589 1531), folds of box-like geometry are visible **in the cliff** (Fig. 26). The folds and accompanying faults make up Zone Id in the structural scheme of Hancock *et al.* (1981). Features of interest include thrust faults, some overthrusting to the N, and some to the S. Some fault surfaces are curved, and pass laterally into bedding-parallel shears. The box-like geometry of folds, is well displayed at SM 8594 1505, where the flat crest of an anticline forms a small promontory. The headlands of **Haroldstone Bridge** (SM 8590 1541) and **Settling Nose** (SM 8572 1571) form fault-displaced units of Farewell Rock sandstone. Where the normal faults intersect the sandstone, there are fault breccias, with deep slickenside grooves and quartz fibres. At Settling Nose, on the top bedding surface of the Farewell Rock, narrow ductile shear zones are visible (SM 8591 1565). The shear zones show up as approximately 2 cm wide bleached lines on the surface. Close examination of the zones and surrounding rock, reveals that quartz grains are progressively stretched and rotated where they enter the zones.

19. Druidston Haven to Madoc's Haven. The Druidston Haven Disturbance is the only Zone II disturbance that intersects a coastal section. It comprises the Druidston Haven Horst together with folds which deform Carboniferous rocks to the N of the horst. Structures within the horst are described below, and the description here is confined to structures in the Carboniferous rocks.

S of the horst (Fig. 27), the Namurian mudstones dip gently S, the only folds being a few open minor anticlines and synclines close to the S boundary fault of the horst. The throw on the N boundary fault of the horst is at least

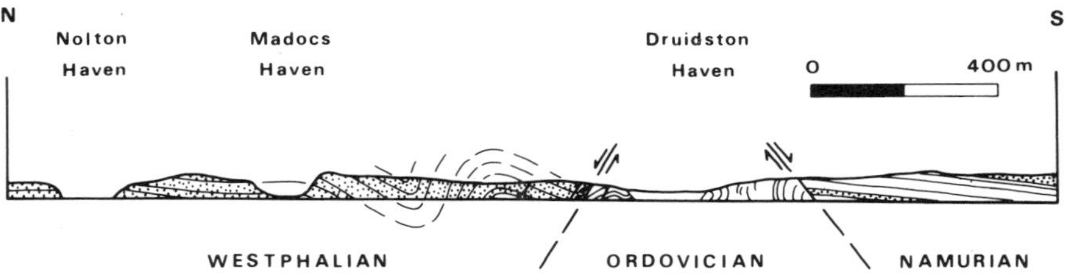

Fig. 27. Cross section showing structures present in the Druidston Disturbance; legend as for Fig. 23.

2000 m, the brecciated fault zone containing slate and sandstone fragments. N of the fault zone the Westphalian sandstones are deformed by a pair of concentric, N-facing macrofolds trending E-W, approximately parallel to other Variscan structures in the coalfield. Some sandstones are cut by a spaced pressure solution cleavage.

CALEDONIAN STRUCTURES WITHIN THE VARISCAN FOLD BELT (P. L. Hancock)

20. The Druidston Haven Horst (park at SM 863 170). Structures in Ordovician rocks within the Druidston Haven Horst are of special interest because they are the only well exposed Caledonian structures visible within the Variscan fold belt. The section through the horst, which is bounded by major normal faults, allows the influence of Variscan deformation on a S-facing Caledonian anticline to be examined. The steep S limb of the anticline in *Dicranograptus* shales (Caradoc) has been refolded, approximately coaxially, and the Caledonian slaty cleavage has been deformed into open antiforms and synforms (Fig. 28).

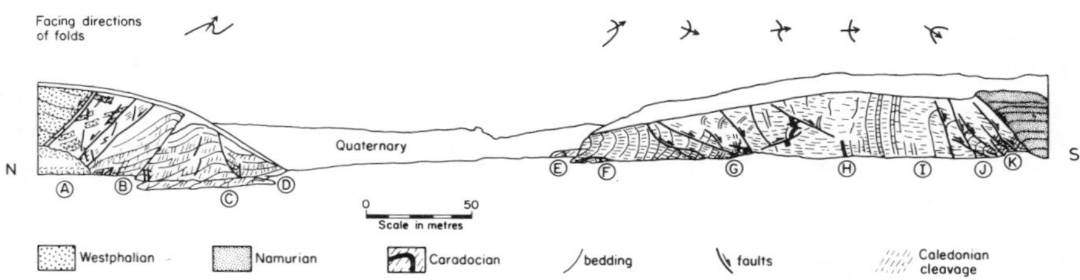

Fig. 28. Cross section of structures in Ordovician rocks within the Druidston Haven Horst.

At locality **A** (Fig. 28) the N boundary fault of the horst separates Ordovician slates from Westphalian sandstones. At **B** unmodified Caledonian slaty cleavage dips steeply N within the gentle N limb of the Caledonian anticline. A small anticlinal-synclinal couplet deforming the N limb is exposed at **C.** The special feature of locality **D** is a set of thin, planar dip veins which have not been deformed by the later Variscan movements.

S of the Quaternary sediments exposed in the centre of the Haven the effects of Variscan deformation on the older Caledonian structures are clearly displayed in the steep S limb of the Caledonian anticline. Deformed graptolites can be collected at locality **E.** A nearly recumbent, S-facing anticline has resulted from the refolding of the nearly vertical limb at **F.** Bedding is marked by thin pyrite bands which are buckled and slightly boudinaged. The Caledonian cleavage, which formerly dipped steeply N, has been folded into an open antiform. At **G** that cleavage now dips S in the core of a downwards-facing anticline cut by low angle normal faults downthrowing to the S.

Thin beds of siltstone and fine grained sandstone containing truncated ripple cross lamination and slump balls indicate that at locality **H** the beds young to the S. Here, and further S there are numerous examples of formerly planar Caledonian dip veins, which are now folded as a consequence of the superimposition of Variscan strain. Locality **I** is situated at the crest of a cleavage antiform. The clearest example of a downwards-facing fold occurs at **J** where there is an antiformal syncline whose axial plane dips moderately S. Parallel to the bedding there are quartz/pyrite veins deformed by centimetric-scale folds with hinge lines oblique to the fibre lineation within the veins. At this locality the formerly N-dipping Caledonian cleavage now dips S on the S limb of a cleavage antiform, and the whole assemblage of structures is displaced by a normal fault dipping S. At **K** the slates are brecciated in the southern boundary fault zone separating the Ordovician rocks from the Namurian shales.

REFERENCES

DIXON, E. E. L. 1921. The geology of the South Wales Coalfield. Part 13. The country around Pembroke and Tenby. *Mem. geol. Surv. U.K.* 220 pp.

DURNEY, D. W. & RAMSAY, J. G. 1973. Incremental strains measured by syntectonic crystal growths. pp. 67-96 *In* DE JONG, K. A. & SCHOLTEN, R. (eds.), *Gravity and Tectonics*. Wiley, New York.

GRAHAM, J. R., HANCOCK, P. L. & HOBSON, D. M. 1977. Anomalous bedding-cleavage relationships in Silurian rocks at Marloes Sands, S. W. Dyfed (Pembrokeshire), Wales. *Proc. Geol. Ass.* **88,** 179-181.

HANCOCK, P. L. 1973. Stuctural zones in Variscan Pembrokeshire. *Proc. Ussher. Soc.* **2,** 509-520.

HANCOCK, P. L., DUNNE, W. M. & TRINGHAM, M. E. 1981. Variscan structures in southwest Wales. *Geologie Mijnb.* **60,** 81-88.

HANCOCK, P. L., DUNNE, W. M. & TRINGHAM, M. E. (in press). Variscan deformation in southwest Wales. *In* HANCOCK, P. L. (ed.), *The Variscan fold belt in the British Isles.* Hilger, Bristol.

HOBBS, B. E., MEANS, W. D. & WILLIAMS, P. F. 1976. *An outline of structural geology.* 571 pp. Wiley, New York.

KNIPE, R. J. & WHITE, S. H. 1979. Deformation in low grade shear zones in the Old Red Sandstone, S. W. Wales. *J. struct. Geol.* **1,** 53-66.

MARSHALL, J. D. 1977. *Sedimentology of the Skrinkle Sandstones Group (Devonian-Carboniferous) South West Dyfed.* Unpublished Ph.D. thesis, University of Bristol.

POWELL, C.McA. 1979. A morphological classification of rock cleavage. *Tectonophysics,* **58,** 21-34.

RAMSAY, J. G. 1980. Shear zone geometry : a review. *J. struct. Geol.* **2,** 83-99.

ROBERTS, J. L. 1976. The structure of the Dalradian rocks in the North Ballachulish district of Scotland. *J. geol. Soc. Lond.* **132,** 139-154.

TRINGHAM, M. E. 1979. *Structures in Upper Carboniferous rocks in the Pembrokeshire Coalfield, Dyfed, Wales.* Unpublished Ph.D. thesis, University of Bristol.

13
ARENIG ROCKS OF THE CARMARTHEN-LLANARTHNEY DISTRICT

by R. M. OWENS *and* R. A. FORTEY

Maps *Topographical:* 1 : 50 000 Sheet 159 Swansea and the Gower
1 : 25 000 Sheets SN41, SN42, SN51, SN52
Geological: 1 : 50 000 Sheets 229 Carmarthen, 230 Ammanford

In Dyfed, rocks of the lower Ordovician Arenig Series extend in an almost unbroken outcrop from Whitesand Bay in the west to Llanarthney in the east. The study of these rocks and their contained fossils is not easy, since in the western coastal sections, where they are well exposed, they are strongly cleaved, whilst inland exposure is poor. The latter factor, however, is partially compensated for by the fact that towards the eastern end of the outcrop, especially around Whitland and Carmarthen, they are little affected by cleavage, and fossils are well preserved and quite easy to obtain.

In the district between Carmarthen and Llanarthney a large part of the Arenig sequence can be studied within a fairly small area (Fig. 1). This part of the outcrop is described in detail in the Carmarthen and Ammanford memoirs (Strahan *et al.* 1907, 1909), and a modern interpretation, with descriptions of the more important fossils in the lower part of the sequence is given by Fortey & Owens (1978). These latter authors suggest that the sequence represents a progressive deepening of the sea during the Arenig, with the coastline somewhere in the region of the present Bristol Channel, and open ocean towards the north. Thus the earliest strata are coarse conglomerates and sandstones (Allt Cystanog Member) which give way in turn to fine sandstones and siltstones (Bolahaul Member), mudstones (Pibwr Member), and finally to a series of mudstones and turbidites (Cwmffrŵd, Cym yr Abbey members and Tetragraptus Shales) Fig. 2). These lithological changes are accompanied by faunal changes, so that the earlier faunas are of shallow water origin, and these progressively give way to deeper water ones higher in the succession.

In Arenig times, southern Britain, together with western and central Europe are believed to have been situated in the southern hemisphere at high

[pp. 249-258 *In* BASSETT, M. G. (ed.). 1982. Geological excursions in Dyfed, south-west Wales.]

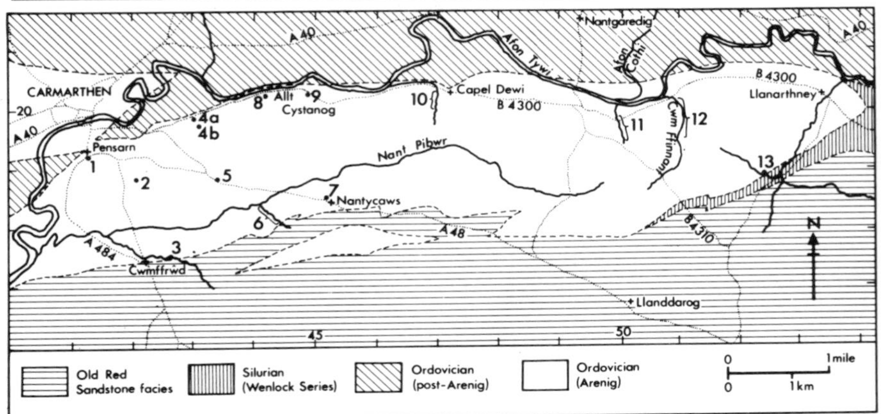

Fig. 1. Simplified geological map of the Carmarthen-Llanarthney district, showing positions of localities.

latitudes, on the continental margins of the southern part of the proto-Atlantic or Iapetus Ocean. Shallow water faunas from this region are quite different from contemporaneous equatorial faunas, found today in such areas as Spitsbergen and North America, which were on the opposite (northern) side of Iapetus. Deeper water faunas, however, are much more similar in all regions, since such barriers as temperature and depth which prevented migration between widely separated shallow water regions did not affect the more uniform, deeper water environments to such a great extent.

ITINERARY

Arenig rocks in the area are much affected by folding and faulting, and large parts of the outcrop are covered by a thick blanket of drift. Exposures are limited and scattered, and the best are in stream sections. It is difficult to set out a simple itinerary through the succession, and instead a series of localities is described, from west to east, with several alternatives offered for each part of the sequence. Visitors can select from these a set which is best suited to their purpose and interests.

None of these localities is suitable for large parties, and access by large vehicles or by large numbers of vehicles is not possible. Therefore we recommend that this itinerary is not attempted by groups of more than six or seven people; it is most suitable for individuals or pairs. Wellington boots are the most suitable footwear for the stream sections, and a small trenching tool or mattock is an invaluable addition to one's field equipment.

1. Roman Road, Pensarn (SN 4133 1918). In Pensarn village, take the

STRATIGRAPHY		LITHOLOGY	IMPORTANT FOSSILS	INFERRED ENVIRONMENT	LOCALITIES
TETRAGRAPTUS SHALES		mudstones	*Pricyclopyge* extensiform *Didymograptus*	quiet, deep water	10
		mudstones and thin turbidites	*Ogyginus* cf. *hybridus*	deep water with regular turbidite influxes	13
		mudstones and thick turbidites	*Ogyginus* cf. *hybridus*		12
CARMARTHEN FORMATION	Cwm yr Abbey Member	mudstones	*Porterfieldia punctata* *Merlinia rhyakos*	quiet, deep water	3 11
	Cwmffrŵd Member	mudstones and thick turbidites	*Bienvillia praecalva* *Merlinia rhyakos*	deep water with regular turbidite influxes	7
	Pibwr Member	mudstones	*Merlinia selwynii* infaunal bivalves	relatively deep, quiet water	6
OGOF HÊN FORMATION	Bolahaul Member	silty mudstones sandstones	*Merlinia murchisoniae* *Ampyx cetsarum* *Orthambonites alata*	shallow water	1 9
	Allt Cystanog Member	siltstones thin mudstone seams sandstones conglomerates		very shallow subtidal	4 2 8 5?

Fig. 2. Summary of Arenig succession, lithologies, faunas and environments in the Carmarthen-Llanarthney district, with stratigraphical ranges exposed at each locality.

minor road which runs uphill and eastwards from the A484. In about 40 m pass a chapel on the right, and almost immediately afterwards turn right into the old Roman road. About 30 m from the junction, past a house on the left, is an exposure of silty mudstone belonging to the upper part of the Bolahaul Member. Although badly weathered these rocks yield a fairly abundant fauna of benthonic brachiopods *(Orthambonites alata)* and trilobites *(Merlinia murchisoniae)*. Further exposures of a similar horizon occur on either side of the road, extending for about 200 metres up the road. In addition to the forms named above, these exposures have yielded the trilobite *Ampyx cetsarum* and orthoconic nautiloids. The Roman Road section is the type locality for *0. alata* and *M. murchisoniae,* which were first described from here by Murchison (1839) in his *Silurian System*.

2. **Quarry beside lane leading to Cilwaunydd** (SN 4207 1881). Take the lane leading E from the Cwmffrŵd-Pensarn road 1.4 km N of Cwmffrŵd (SN 4190 1878) and follow it for 140 m to the point where it makes a sharp right bend. Here a long abandoned quarry exposes typical Allt Cystanog Member rocks — a series of fine sandstones and conglomeratic grits of shallow water origin. No fossils have so far been found at this locality.

3. **Nant y Glasdwr, Cwmffrŵd** (SN 4255 1748 — SN 4266 1747). Take the minor road which runs E from the village, and park on the verge near Gwynion Dale, having first obtained **permission** at Bryn-cyrnau-ganol Farm (SN 4300 1750). The best point to enter the stream is opposite Gwynion Dale. From here downstream as far as the road bridge there is a strike section in which mudstones of the Cwm yr Abbey Member of the Carmarthen Formation are exposed. These mudstones were formerly described as the 'Peltura punctata Beds', and were once thought to be of Tremadoc age (Crosfield & Skeat 1896). They are richly fossiliferous, and this is one of the best localities for obtaining the olenid trilobite *Porterfieldia punctata,* complete specimens of which are not infrequent. The large asaphid trilobite *Merlinia rhyakos* occurs less commonly. One specimen of the pelagic, large-eyed cyclopygid trilobite *Microparia grandis* has been found here, and it would be appreciated if further finds were reported to the Department of Geology, National Museum of Wales. The exposures along the stream banks here should **not** be hammered indiscriminately, since they support road and field boundaries, and plenty of fossils can be found in the loose scree.

The exposure continues on the other (north) side of the road bridge around SN 4255 1748, where the mudstones have yielded common *P. punctata* and *M. rhyakos*, the rare olenid trilobite *Hypermeraspis venerabilis* and uncommon dendroid graptolites *Callograptus (Pseudocallograptus) salteri* and *Palaeodictyota* sp.

4. **Star Cottage.** The top of the Allt Cystanog Member and the base of the Bolahaul Member are exposed here.

4a. (SN 4293 1982 — SN 4294 1981). Proceed along the B4300 for 600 m from its junction with the A48 at the edge of Carmarthen and turn right (south) onto the **narrow road beside Star Cottage.** Exposures of micaceous siltstones belonging to the lower part of the Bolahaul Member crop out at and just above road level behind Star Cottage and up to 20 m to the south. Fossils are difficult to obtain, although *O. alata, M. murchisoniae* and *Neseuretus* sp. have been collected. This locality is best used to see the relationship of the Bolahaul Member with the underlying Allt Cystanog Member.

4b. (SN 4306 1973). Walk about 200 m up the track from Star Cottage to a **disused quarry** on the W side of the track, which exposes the top of the Allt Cystanog Member. The typical sequence of fine sandstones, siltstones and mudstone seams is well developed, with characteristic horizons with ripple-drift lamination. No fossils have been recorded, but should be sought. This quarry lies on a prominent escarpment formed by the top of the resistant Allt Cystanog Member where it passes up into the more easily weathered Bolahaul Member.

5. Cutting on N side of A48 east of Login (SN 4345 1875 — SN 4360 1870). A good exposure showing a sequence of siltstones, sandstones, conglomerates and thin mudstone seams. This section was previously described as being of Tremadoc age (Cope *et al.* 1978, p. 196), but the subsequent discovery of dichograptid stipes not unlike those of known Arenig forms casts doubt on this interpretation. Fossils are not abundant, the commonest being *Lingulella* sp., some specimens of which are found in growth position. Rare graptolite fragments (see above), trilobites *(Asaphellus* sp.) orthid brachiopods, and trace fossils *(Cruziana*-type tracks) have also been recorded. Further finds of trilobites, graptolites and articulate brachiopods could be extremely helpful in elucidating the stratigraphical position of this section, and we would be grateful if these were to be reported to the Department of Geology, National Museum of Wales.

6. Allt Pen-y-Coed (SN 4426 1823 — SN 4444 1805). **Permission** must be obtained from Pen-y-Coed Farm (SN 4480 1808). Take the minor road leading S from the A48, 500 m W of Nantycaws, and enter the stream at SN 4422 1825, near the point where four minor roads meet. This dingle provides a splendid section through the upper part of the Pibwr Member and the Cwmffrŵd Member. The regional dip is to the south (upstream), although the strata are affected by a large number of minor faults and folds. Fossils occur throughout, and reflect deepening conditions upwards through the succession.

The Pibwr Member is exposed over the first 170 m upstream from the bridge, and its typical blocky mudstones form a more or less continuous exposure. The lowest part of the Pibwr Member exposed in this section is most easily studied at about 25 m from the bridge, where the asaphid trilobite *Merlinia selwynii* and bivalves are particularly common, accompanied by rare examples of the olenid trilobite *Bienvillia praecalva*. The higher parts of the Pibwr Member are well exposed between 120 and 170 m from the bridge. *M. selwynii* is still common, but bivalves become rare whilst *B. praecalva* becomes more abundant; the trinucleid trilobite *Myttonia* cf. *fearnsidesi* occurs infrequently.

The base of the Cwmffrŵd Member is marked by the beginning of a steep-sided gorge, and the prominent turbidite bands give rise to a series of small cataracts. The mudstone bands between the turbidites yield *B. praecalva* and *M. rhyakos*, typical deeper water forms. Rare *H. venerabilis* have been found in this section. Exposure continues upstream for about 150 m from the beginning of the gorge, and after about 300 m of non exposure rocks belonging to the Old Red Sandstone are reached, close to the point where the stream bifurcates. The junction with the Arenig is obscured, so that its exact nature is uncertain.

7. Nantycaws dingle (SN 4508 1843). Vehicles can be parked along the minor road leading N from the A48 in Nantycaws village. Climb down the steep bank into the dingle. There are good exposures of the Cwmffrŵd Member, extending as far as the A48 road bridge, and these continue in the dingle on the S side of the road. The exposure shows the characteristic thick turbidites with thin intervening mudstones, which yield the typical deep water trilobites *B. praecalva* and *M. rhyakos*.

8. North side of Allt Cystanog (SN 4410 2023). Adjacent to the B4300, 2 km E of its junction with the A48 on the edge of Carmarthen are exposures of the Allt Cystanog Member, showing typical massive shallow water sandstones. Here there is an old level running into the hillside, which was excavated in a mineralised fault zone, and which runs southwards across Allt Cystanog. It is one of three such fault zones on Allt Cystanog which were worked primarily for lead (galena) in the second half of the nineteenth century, although the galena was also extracted for its small silver content (average 2.1 oz silver per ton of lead). Climbing up through the wooded hillside, and proceeding about 250 m to the SE one encounters an old level and large spoil tips from the next fault zone to the E, which in addition to the country rock yield abundant vein quartz, baryte, and a little galena and blende. There are also pieces of silty shale belonging to the Bolahaul Member, showing that the level followed the fault from the Allt Cystanog Member southwards across the boundary. These shales yield occasional examples of the brachiopod *Orthambonites*. There are numerous exposures hereabouts of the Allt Cystanog Member.

9. East end of Allt Cystanog (SN 4483 2030). Adjacent to the B4300, 750 m E of locality **8.** Roadside exposure of silty shales at an horizon low in the Bolahaul Member, yielding occasional *Orthambonites* and hyolithids.

10. Capel Dewi stream section (SN 4706 2032 — SN 4702 2015). Situated S of the B4300 at the W end of the hamlet of Capel Dewi, 2.2 km W of its junction with the B4310. **Permission** should be sought at Capel-Dewi-isaf Farm (SN 4717 2045). Enter the field just E of the B4300 road bridge, and walk back to the stream, entering it immediately S of the bridge. From here, for some 200 m upstream there is an excellent section through grey Tetragraptus Shales. The fauna suggests that the section is near the top of the Tetragraptus Shales, high in the Arenig Series and within the *Didymograptus hirundo* Zone. These higher Tetragraptus Shales lack the dominant turbidite units so typical of the earlier Tetragraptus Shales as seen, for example, at Cwm yr Abbey (locality **11**) and Cwm Ffinnant (locality **12**). Immediately S of the bridge the shales yield the trilobites *Pricyclopyge binodosa, Ectillaenus* cf. *bergaminus* and *Ormathops* sp. In the outcrops between 135 and 200 m S of the bridge, trilobites *(P. binodosa, Bergamia* sp. nov., *Placoparia* sp., and a large asaphid), long stipes of an extensiform *Didymograptus*, and inarticulate brachiopods occur.

These faunas are a typical Arenig deep water association: pelagic graptolites and large-eyed trilobites *(P. binodosa)* together with small-eyed or blind benthonic trilobites *(Ectillaenus, Ormathops, Bergamia,* and *Placoparia)*.

11. Cwm yr Abbey (SN 5002 1988 — SN 5013 1943). The B4300 crosses this stream 670 m E of the B4310 turning to Nantgaredig. The section extends N and S of the road, and exposes the Cwmffrŵd and Cwm yr Abbey members of the Carmarthen Formation and the lower part of the Tetragraptus Shales. The strata generally young northwards, although the succession is complicated by numerous small faults and folds. The section is described from the top (stratigraphically lowest) end.

Enter the dingle at the B4300 road bridge and follow it upstream for a distance of some 350 m as far as the point where the stream leaves the wood. For 100 m downstream from this point the Cwmffrŵd Member is well exposed, showing its distinctive alternating thick turbidites and mudstone bands. Fossils are confined to the latter, with the richest horizons at points approximately 50, 70 and 90 m below the top of the section. At all these points the trilobites *B. praecalva* and *M. rhyakos* are common. The type locality for the latter is in this section.

The remainder of the stream section, as far as the bridge, is occupied by the Cwm yr Abbey Member, distinguished principally by its lack of thick turbidites. Fossils occur throughout, typified by the trilobites *P. punctata* and *M. rhyakos* and by orthoconic nautiloids.

Immediately N of the B4300 road bridge the top of the Cwm yr Abbey Member is exposed, here particularly rich in *P. punctata.* In a very short distance turbidite units once again become a dominant feature — marking

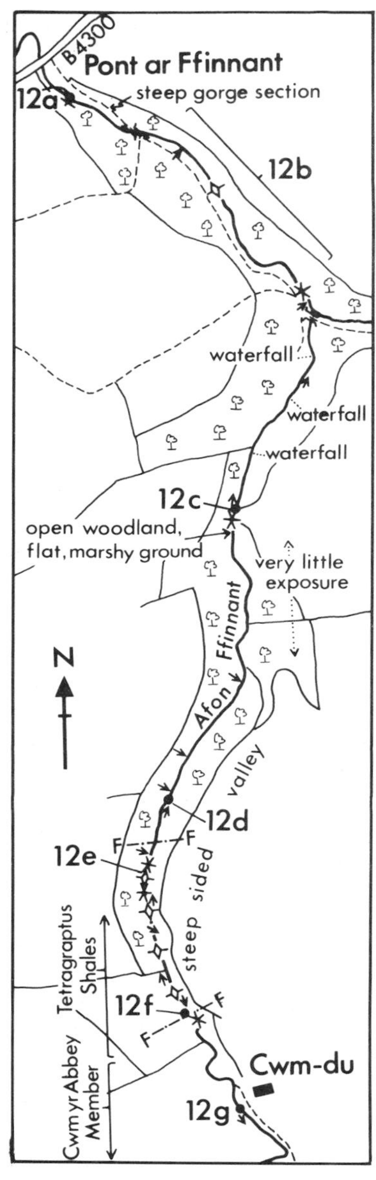

Fig. 3. Cwm Ffinnant (locality 12), showing positions of outcrops.

the base of the Tetragraptus Shales, and the remainder of the exposure, continuing for about 100 m downstream, is in this unit. Lithologically the lower part of the Tetragraptus Shales is almost indistinguishable from the Cwmffrŵd Member, but the two can be readily identified by their faunas. *P. punctata* occurs in the earliest Tetragraptus Shales, but the dominant trilobite is the asaphid *Ogyginus* cf. *hybridus.* A trinucleid trilobite *(Bergamia* sp.*)* and graptolites *(Azygograptus* spp.*)* occur in small numbers. It should be noted that great care should be exercised in moving along this part of the section, since there are many deep pools and slippery rock surfaces, and it tends to be much overgrown during the summer months.

12. Cwm Ffinnant (SN 5091 2010 — SN 5107 1924). (Fig. 3.) Park at the scenic picnic area on the N side of the B4300, 1.4 km E of the B4310 turning to Nantgaredig. Walk eastwards for 250 m to Pont ar Ffinnant, and then take the footpath on the right, which runs beside the stream. The section runs from here with some short breaks, for about 1 km upstream, nearly all in the lower part of the Tetragraptus Shales, but with a small outcrop of the Cwm yr Abbey Member near the top of the section.

In the stream **near the bridge** there is an outcrop **(12a)** of rusty weathering shales which yield *0.* cf. *hybridus.* In a short distance the stream crosses over a sequence of turbidites, which give rise to a series of steep cataracts. At this point, a return should be made to the footpath, which can be followed for some 30 m to a footbridge near the beginning of the wooded area. The section **(12b) between here and the next footbridge,** a further 250 m upstream, shows well a sequence of folded turbidites and mudstones of the Tetragraptus Shales. Fossils can be found with diligence in the mudstone bands, and include occasional graptolites (*Azygograptus* sp.) and trilobites *(O.* cf. *hybridus).* On reaching the second footbridge, leave the track, which turns off to the left up a tributary valley, and follow the main valley upstream. A similar sequence of shales and turbidites crops out in the stream for the next 170 m, until the steep sided valley gives way to a flat marshy tract in open woodland. Here **(12c)** black mudstones are exposed **in the stream bed,** and have yielded abundant trinucleid (*Bergamia* cf. *gibbsii*) and asaphid (*Ogyginus* cf. *hybridus*) trilobites and orthoconic nautiloids.

There is little exposure for the next 100 m or so, after which the stream passes through a steep sided valley; for about 150 m the strike is more or less parallel to the stream, and again the sequence is of alternating thin mudstone bands with thick turbidite units. This sequence continues upstream as far as the end of the wooded section, where it is terminated by a fault **(12f).** *O.* cf. *hybridus* has been found at localities **12d** and **12e.** South of the fault, near Cwm-du, black mudstones are seen at intervals in the stream bed, and opposite the cottage **(12g)** they have yielded *P. punctata,* indicating that they belong to the Cwm yr Abbey Member. From here return downstream to Pont ar Ffinnant.

13. Cwm Arbont (SN 5237 1891 — SN 5252 1882). Enter the stream near Arbont Cottage, about 1.75 km SSW of Llanarthney. This is one of the most easterly exposures of Arenig rocks in South Wales, and shows a sequence probably lying towards the middle of the Tetragraptus Shales. Turbidite bands crop out in the stream adjacent to Arbont Cottage, but there are few in the section downstream (E of the road). Here there is a nearly continuous exposure extending for about 180 m, consisting of dark grey silty mudstones with occasional turbidites. They have irregular dips, and have yielded *O.* cf. *hybridus* at a point 25 m downstream from the bridge, and *O.* cf. *hybridus,* a trinucleid, and *Ptilograptus* sp. 145 m further on. After the latter point, there is lack of exposure but after about a further 10 m, vertically dipping, greenish grey flaggy mudstones of the Wenlock Series are exposed. The junction itself is obscured, so its exact nature is unknown. From here return to the road.

REFERENCES

COPE, J. C. W., FORTEY, R. A. & OWENS, R. M. 1978. Newly discovered Tremadoc rocks in the Carmarthen district, South Wales. *Geol. Mag.* **115,** 195-198, pl. 1.

CROSFIELD, M. C. & SKEAT, E. G. 1896. On the geology of the neighbourhood of Carmarthen. *Q. Jl geol. soc. Lond.* **52,** 523-541, pls. 25, 26

FORTEY, R. A. & OWENS, R. M. 1978. Early Ordovician (Arenig) stratigraphy and faunas of the Carmarthen district, south-west Wales. *Bull. Br. Mus. nat. Hist.* (Geol.), **30,** 225-294, pls. 1-11.

MURCHISON, R. I. 1839. *The Silurian System, founded on geological researches in the counties of Salop, Hereford, Radnor, Montgomery, Caermarthen Brecon, Pembroke, Monmouth, Worcester, Gloucester and Stafford; with descriptions of the coalfields and overlying formations.* xxxii + 768 pp., 37pls. John Murray London.

STRAHAN, A., CANTRILL, T. C., DIXON, E. E. L. & THOMAS, H. H. 1907. The geology of the South Wales coalfield. Part VII. The country around Ammanford (Sheet 230). *Mem. Geol. Surv. U.K.* viii + 246 pp.

STRAHAN, A., CANTRILL, T. C., DIXON, E. E. L. & THOMAS, H. H. 1909. The geology of the South Wales coalfield. Part X. The country around Carmarthen (Sheet 229). *Mem. Geol. Surv. U.K.* viii + 177 pp.

14
THE GEOLOGY OF THE LLANSTEPHAN PENINSULA

by JOHN C. W. COPE

Maps	*Topographical:*	1 : 50 000 Sheet 159 Swansea and The Gower
		1 : 25 000 Sheets SN30, SN31
	Geological:	1 : 50 000 Sheet 229 Carmarthen

THE Llanstephan peninsula is situated to the SW of Carmarthen, bounded to the E and S by the river Tywi, to the W by the Tâf and its tributary the Cywyn, and to the N by a drift-covered marshy area, along the N margin of which runs the A40 road, and which must surely have been the former course of the Tywi before it breached the Old Red Sandstone ridge S of Carmarthen. Although exposure is generally poor, and the structure complex, the area is of great interest geologically, in that within it are older rocks than others known in SE Dyfed, including Tremadoc strata which are not known otherwise in South Wales. Geologically the area falls conveniently into three areas.

(i) *The Old Red Sandstone* forms the S part of the peninsula; structures in the N part of its outcrop are complex, but to the south they are much more simple. The succession becomes younger to the S (though complicated in the N part by thrusting and folding) as far as the Llandyfaelog Fault, which brings older parts of the Old Red Sandstone up again on the S edge of the area (Locality 14).

(ii) *The Llanvirn rocks* form the N limit of the area; their junction with older rocks appears on the N and NW sides of the area to be a thrust over the older rocks. Because of interbedded thick units of resistant sandstone within the Llanvirn graptolitic shales, the latter form a ridge of high ground running W for some 6 km from the Tywi valley, immediately S of Carmarthen, which then swings SW for another 3-4 km (see Fig. 3).

(iii) *The Llangynog inlier.* Between areas (i) and (ii) is a structurally complex area in which Precambrian, Cambrian, Tremadoc, and Arenig rocks are exposed, to which the name Llangynog inlier can be given, and which forms the focus of the majority of the localities described here.

[pp. 259-269 *In* BASSETT, M. G. (ed.). 1982. Geological excursions in Dyfed, south-west Wales.]

ITINERARY

The itinerary is arranged to cover the ground most economically. Inevitably, given the nature of the structures this means that the localities are not in stratigraphical order, and some familiarity with the succession is therefore necessary (Fig. 2). For details of the stratigraphy of the Arenig rocks see Fortey & Owens (1978). Because of narrow roads and shortage of places for parking, the area is unsuitable for visits by large parties or with large vehicles; at many localities parking for more than two cars is likely to prove a problem.

1. Stream section W of Pwntan. (SN 3925 1761; **permission** must be obtained from **Pwntan farm** and is likely to be granted only to small groups). This locality was first described by Crosfield & Skeat (1896). The stream exposes a good section in the Pibwr Member of the Carmarthen Formation (Fortey & Owens 1978, p. 234), and the blue-black mudstones yield abundant trilobites *(Merlinia selwynii)*. The mudstones dip N at about 20° and lie to the S of an area of Llanvirn rocks, from which they are presumably separated by a fault. Southwards too there must lie a fault as the succeeding Cwmffrŵd and Cwm yr Abbey Members dip to the S and are interpreted as lying on the S limb of a faulted anticline which plunges E (see Fig. 3).

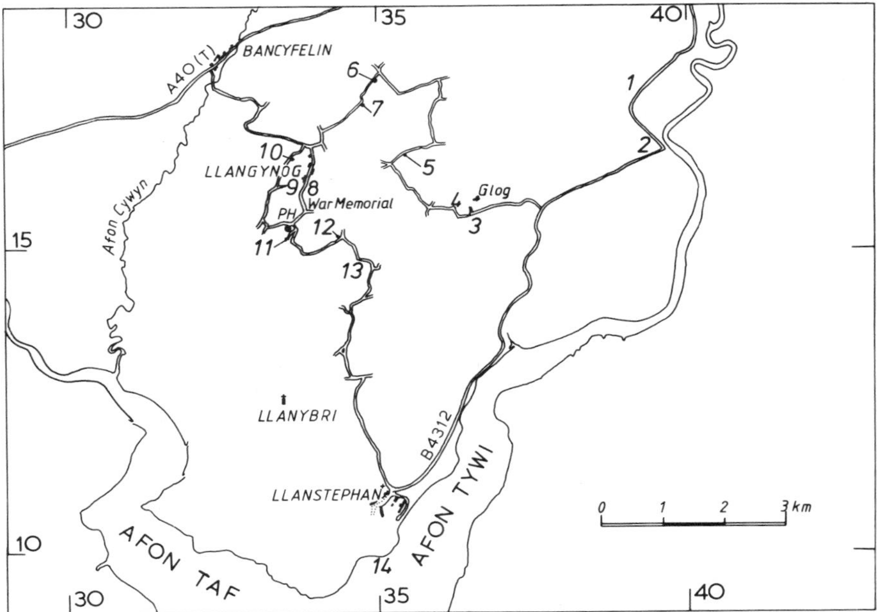

Fig. 1. Itinerary through the Llanstephan area; large numbers refer to localities described in the text; Johnstown lies just off the N margin of the map on the B4312.

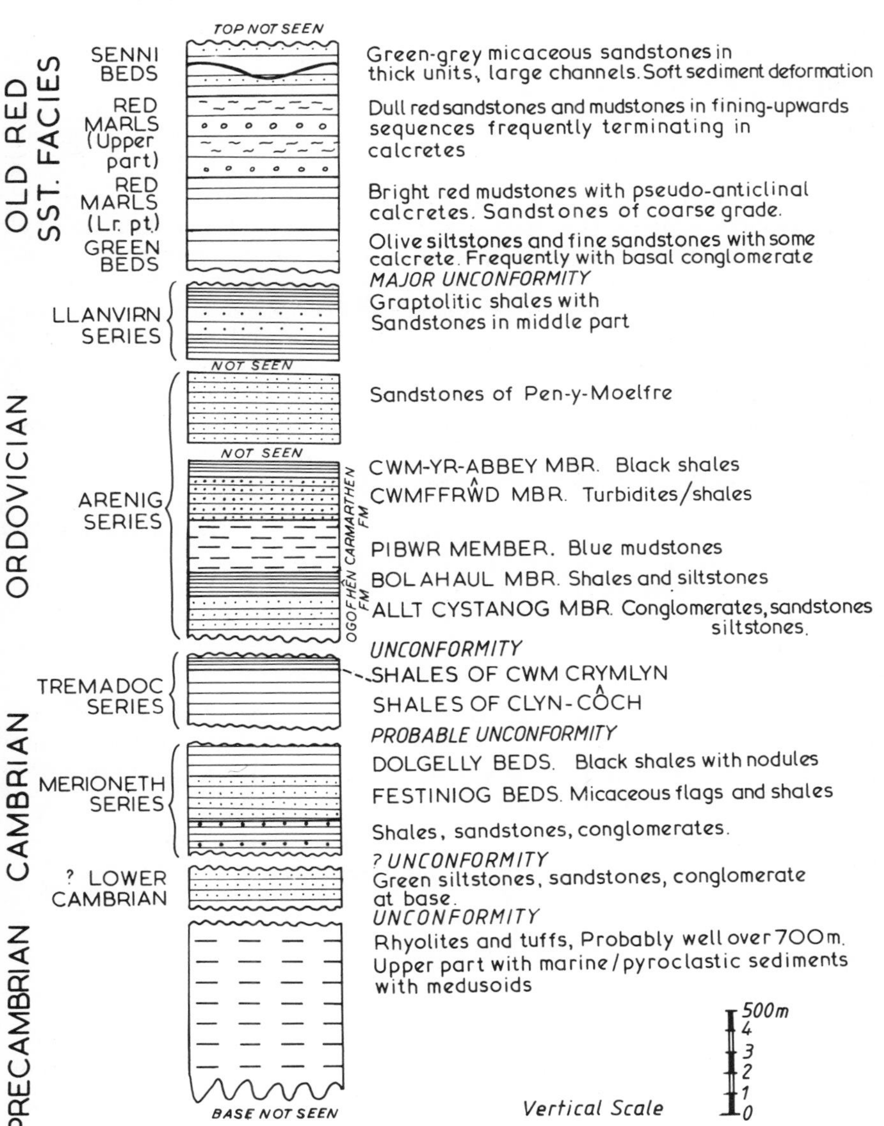

Fig. 2. Geological succession on the Llanstephan peninsula.

2. Exposures around Green Castle (SN 3960 1658). Vehicles can be parked on the W side of the road at SN 3945 1680 or alternatively on the N side of the road on the verge outside Green Castle Farm (SN 3958 1654). A **large disused quarry** (SN 3955 1672) exposes the basal Green Beds of the Old Red Sandstone, which are probably of Downton age. Much of the exposure is in olive-green siltstones and fine sandstones. There are occasional thin interbeds of more argillaceous rocks, particularly in the lower part of the succession, and calcrete nodules (or more often solution holes left by their weathering) are common. The rocks dip S at about 50° and there is a variably developed cleavage which dips N at a similar angle. To the **N of the quarry,** crags of the basal conglomeratic beds are exposed intermittently in the wood. The conglomerate consists predominantly of vein quartz pebbles together with some rhyolite, set in a greenish argillaceous matrix. Beneath the conglomerate badgers have excavated extensively into shales of the Cwm yr Abbey member. Material from these excavations has yielded the trilobites *Porterfieldia punctata* and *Merlinia rhyakos,* both species characteristic of the Cwm yr Abbey Member of the Carmarthen Formation (Fortey & Owens 1978, p. 236). The same species have been obtained by excavation into deeply weathered shale at SN 3943 1680.

From this latter point it is possible to appreciate the steep sided gorge cut by the Tywi through the Old Red Sandstone. This may have been breached initially by river capture by a headward erosion of a stream rising on the Old Red Sandstone flowing to the S. It seems likely that the earlier course of the Tywi was to the N, flowing W from Carmarthen via Bancyfelin to the Tâf river system.

Walking to the S of the quarry there is a further exposure of the Green Beds on the **bend in the road** at SN 3975 1657. The beds here are more fine grained than in the quarry and cleavage (dipping N) is stronger than the bedding (dipping S). (N.B. beware of traffic at this point.)

With **permission from Green Castle Farm** it is possible to examine another **large quarry** in the Green Beds **on the river-side** at SN 3985 1645. The succeeding Red Marl Group is well exposed in a **stream** running into the Tywi immediately S of this quarry. Typical red sandstone and mudstone units crop out here. Further to the S again lies an important thrust fault responsible for an inlier of Ordovician rocks within the main Old Red Sandstone outcrop. Exposure is very poor, but turbidite units similar to those of the Cwmffrŵd Member of the Carmarthen Formation (Fortey & Owens 1978, p. 234) around SN 394 163 are succeeded by very deeply weathered shales, probably of the Cwm yr Abbey Member, which have yielded *Merlinia* sp. at SN 3966 1623. Immediately to the S of this latter point a small pit shows basal Green Beds dipping N at about 80°. They are here inverted and young to the S.

3. Follow the B4312 road SW to SN 3765 1557 and then turn right, passing

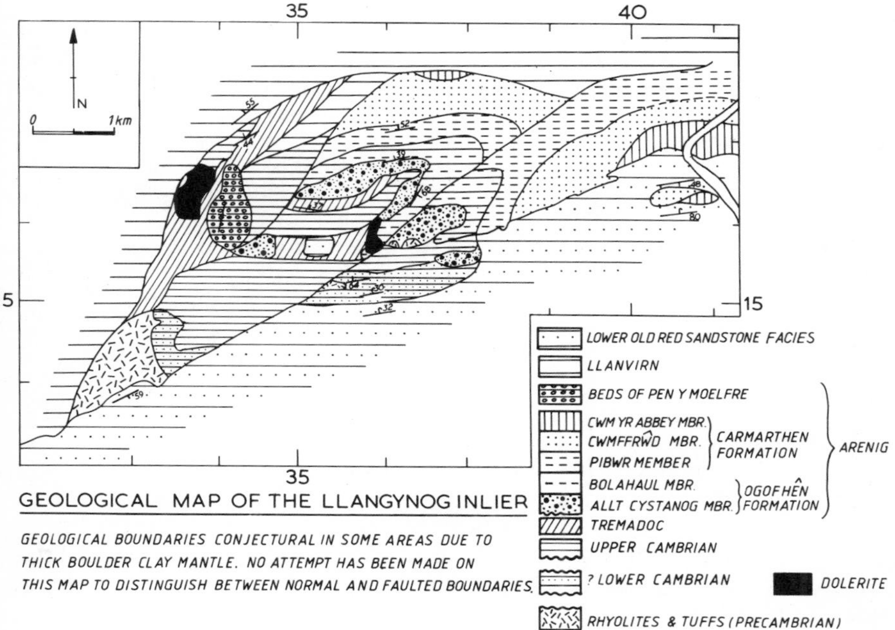

Fig. 3. Geological map of the Llangynog inlier.

Fernhill and park at the road junction to Glog at SN 3655 1551 (avoiding the gateway). This parking spot is a useful centre for several neighbouring exposures. Small groups wishing to examine the Bolahaul Member of the Ogof Hên Formation (Fortey & Owens 1978, p. 233) should **seek permission at Glog Farm** (signposted from parking place). Pass through the farmyard down the track to SN 3673 1583, where shales interbedded with conglomeratic units are sparingly fossiliferous. Some 120 m further down the track, beyond the gate and beneath a holly tree (at SN 3683 1586) another exposure of shales with thin conglomeratic units is more fossiliferous and has yielded species of the brachiopods *Orthambonites* and *Hesperonomiella*. Return may be via Glog or along the track to the E of the last exposure.

4. Walk now along the road to **Allt-y-Crug** (SN 3626 1565) where seek permission to see the following exposures:

a). Rhyolites of Precambrian age exposed **beyond the farm outbuildings** at SN 3630 1566. The rhyolites are relatively fresh here, bluish in colour and with an abundance of small pyrite cubes. The rhyolites of this region, and the more extensive though now largely afforested outcrop around Castell Cogan, (SN 327 140) were described by Cantrill & Thomas (1906), who ascribed to them a likely Arenig age. The discovery of a medusoid fauna of Ediacaran type in sediments interbedded in the upper part of this succession (Cope 1977) has led to a re-assessment of their age. Composition of these lavas and ashes appears similar to the Precambrian rhyolites of SW Dyfed (see excursion 1, this volume) and a similar age appears likely.

b). The unconformable contact of the rhyolite and an overlying conglomerate is exposed at SN 3620 1563. This exposure can be approached by leaving the N side of the road at a point 100 m to the W of the farm entrance. A few paces over the bank turn right through the gorse and the exposure lies on the left. Large subangular boulders of rhyolite together with smaller clasts rest on rhyolite which is exposed at the N corner of the exposure. The age of these conglomerates is not known. The Geological Survey after some deliberation finally ascribed them to the Old Red Sandstone (Strahan *et al.* 1909, p. 74). However, the matrix of the conglomerates tends to be dark and argillaceous and is unlike the greenish colour which seems to characterise the base of the Old Red Sandstone in the vicinity. My view (Cope 1980) that this conglomerate is of basal Arenig age, belonging to the Allt Cystanog Member of the Ogof Hên Formation (Fortey & Owens 1978, p. 233), cannot be substantiated either, but seems more probable on lithological grounds. Nearby exposures are very poor, and the outcrop is probably fault-bounded. The conglomerate is apparently uniquely coarse-grade here.

5. Return to the vehicle and continue W across the crossroads at SN 3588 1562 (the **old quarry** on the N side of the road here exposes a badly weathered dolerite) on to SN 3525 1636, and there turn right. Park in **the old quarry** at SN 3547 1654. Although partially obscured by vegetation and other debris, the typical lithology of the Allt Cystanog Member of the Ogof Hên Formation can be examined here. The conglomerates are well jointed and it is difficult to determine the bedding. Here the dip is to the N, though precise measurement does not appear possible. Clasts of rhyolite and vein quartz predominate, though there are also fragments of keratophyres and quartzose and mica-schists, the latter suggesting strongly that a Precambrian metamorphic area was undergoing erosion at no great distance (Cope 1980).

6. Continue E to SN 3594 1668 and turn left. After 1 km turn sharp left at the junction, then after another 300 m turn left again at the T junction. After a further 1 km turn sharp right. After 250 m pass through the farmyard (may be closed off by gates at milking times) and turn sharp left at the junction after a further 200 m. Shales exposed in a very small exposure on the **left hand side of the road** here (SN 3503 1784) have yielded *Didymograptus* cf. *bifidus*, showing them to be of Llanvirn age.

7. Continue along the road to SN 3480 1738, where one small vehicle may be parked; any other vehicle must be parked on the verge on the S side of the road around SN 3455 1755. Walk to examine exposures of steeply dipping Tremadoc shales at SN 3477 1735. This is locality 1 of Cope *et al.* (1978). The exposure yields a common fauna of inarticulate brachiopods and sponge spicules and anchorage spines, together with less common trilobites. Certain bedding planes are crowded with rhabdosomes of the graptolite *Clonograptus;* the full fauna includes *Clonograptus sarmentosus, C. tenellus, C. hians, Adelograptus hunnebergensis,* the inarticulate brachiopods *Palaeobolus quadratus, Eurytreta sabrinae, Broeggeria salteri* and *'Lingula'* cf. *linguae,* and the trilobites *Platypeltoides croftii, Macropyge chermi, Dichelepyge phylax, Niobella homfrayi, Parabolinella argentinensis* and *Leiagnostus* aff. *turgidulus.*

Continue along the road to the junction at SN 3413 1691, and turn left. Turn right after 200 m, then left after a further 200 m. Continue S through Llangynog vilage and park on the E side of the road N of the War Memorial (3387 1555). This is a convenient centre for several localities.

8. Walk N to SN 3386 1604, where the driveway to Pant-yr-rhedyn leads S up the hill. **Before** examining **old quarries at the N end of the drive, permission** should be sought at the farm. The quarries expose vertical beds of ill sorted conglomerates which show graded units, younging to the E, each resting on an erosive base. There is some evidence of cross bedding in the feldspathic sandstone units, and this high energy environment seems to be of shallow marine origin. No fossils have yet been found in the quarries on the farm driveway, but **another quarry** some 50 m lower in the succession around SN 3385 1595 exposes feldspathic sandstones with small specimens of *Orthambonites proava* and occasional bivalves. The same brachiopod species occurs in an **old quarry** at SN 3405 1560, where the beds, still vertical, must be some 350 m stratigraphically above the last exposure.

The strike of the rocks on this hill (Pen y Moelfre) is NNE-SSW, which is quite unlike the strike of the country around. On the E side of the hill a sandstone ridge, now thought to lie within the Upper Cambrian, runs ENE-WNW apparently straight into Pen y Moelfre. The evidence all suggests that Pen y Moelfre is a klippe and that the sandstones and conglomerates rest on a thrust. This thrust plane probably dips to the W or NW and a line of springs marks the outcrop of the thrust on the W side of the hill. A particularly prominent spring emerges around SN 3405 1557 near the entrance to the former Llangynog Vicarage. Disturbed shales below the thrust here yielded a fauna to Strahan *et al.* (1909, p. 17), which has been reinterpreted by Dr. A. W. A. Rushton as Tremadoc in age.

The age of the sandstones and conglomerates of Pen y Moelfre is not known with certainty as no diagnostic fossils have yet been found. My earlier view that the conglomerates were correlatives of the Allt Cystanog Member (Cope 1980) can no longer be substantiated, since beds below the main conglomeratic units have yielded orthids (see above). The best correlation is with beds in the Whitland area described by Strahan *et al.* (1914, pp. 14, 17) and now being re-examined by Drs. R. A. Fortey and R. M. Owens. This means that these beds appear to be the youngest Arenig rocks of the Llangynog inlier.

9. Return to the road, crossing the stile on the left at SN 3387 1605 and follow the path down to a footbridge leading to **Cerrig-yr-Wyn Quarry.** This is a large working quarry and **permission to visit** should be obtained in advance from Messrs. F. H. Gilman Ltd., Cerrig-yr-Wyn Quarry, Llangynog, Carmarthen (Tel. Bancyfelin 236).

The quarry exposes a greenish quartz dolerite intruded into Tremadoc shales. The thermally altered shales are well exposed (if the stocks of aggregate are low) at the E (footpath) approach to the quarry. There is a more permanent exposure on the W side of the intrusion at SN 3347 1597. Although no fossils have yet been found here, the greenish colour of the shales and their general lithology are typical of the lower part of the Tremadoc rocks of the region. These were described around Clyn-côch (the farm clearly visible some 700 m to the S of Cerrig-yr-Wyn Quarry) by Cope *et al.* (1978, locality 2). The shales in the **stream at the footbridge at the E entrance to the quarry** have yielded indeterminate inarticulate brachiopods, and a microflora indicative of a Tremadoc age.

10. Should a visit to the quarry not be possible, the same intrusion may be examined in a **disused quarry** around SN 336 165. The rock is here apparently faulted against dark Llanvirn shales which have yielded *Didymograptus* of the *bifidus* type.

11. 100 m to the SE of the Wern Inn (SN 337 154) take the right hand road fork, and 100 m SW of the fork it is possible to descend a steep bank down to the river. Here resistant, highly micaceous flagstones are exposed, dipping NE at about 55°. Occasional bedding planes are covered with largely broken specimens of *Lingulella davisii.* These beds lie within the Upper Cambrian Merioneth Series and correlate with the Ffestiniog Beds of North Wales. The marshy, drift-covered ground between these exposures and the Tremadoc shales of Clyn-côch some 300 m to the NW is presumably occupied by the soft black shales of the Dolgelly Beds, but there are no exposures. Dolgelly Beds do occur in other parts of the area, however, but exposure is always poor although diagnostic trilobite faunas of several zones have been found.

12. Return to the vehicles and at the road fork at SN 3372 1532 take the easterly (left hand) road over the hill; past St. Cynog's Church to a **road junction** at SN 3447 1514. Exposures on the W and S sides of this junction show small exposures of highly disturbed shales interbedded with micaceous flags which have yielded *Lingulella davisii,* and again belong to the Ffestiniog Beds.

13. Take the SE fork and after some 700 m park at the bottom of the hill near the bridge at SN 3493 1465. Walk back up the hill for 100 m to see the Lower Old Red Sandstone apparently dipping N at 55° - 60°. This quartz arenite with fine conglomeratic courses lies within the lower part of the Red Marl Group, and its inversion here can be proved by both cross bedded and graded units. The inversion means that the basal Green Beds, which are poorly exposed, lie to the N; they may be seen in the winter months in the **roadside ditches** around SN 3473 1477; they rest unconformably on Upper Cambrian (Merioneth Series) to the N, although the contact is not exposed. The Old Red Sandstone exposures here lie on the inverted S limb of a strongly asymmetrical anticline, in the core of which lie Upper Cambrian rocks. This folding in the area appears to be of Caledonian age; it involves rocks up to and including the Red Marl Group of the Old Red Sandstone; folds in the area are strongly asymmetrical and face to the S. Cleavage is axial planar dipping N, and cleavage directions within the ORS are entirely consistent with those in the Lower Palaeozoic rocks both in this area and to the N.

To the S of this last locality the Old Red Sandstone is not so highly deformed; the cleavage front of the last phase of the Caledonian movements lies just to the N of Llanybri (see Figs. 1 & 3).

14. From the last locality follow the road S to the junction at SN 3459 1393 and bear left. Take the left fork at the junction 500 m to the S. After a further 500 m turn sharp left, and then sharp right after another 200 m. 2km brings you to the apex of a bend on the B4312 road in **Llanstephan.** Cross directly over this road down Water Lane to the car park near The Green.

Between localities 13 and 14 the route crosses a generally poorly exposed area of Old Red Sandstone, consisting predominantly of the upper part of the Red Marl Group, in this region containing some thick sandstone units and dull red mudstones with calcrete horizons. In most areas the dip is gentle and southerly, and the ground appears largely unaffected by either Caledonian or Variscan movements. Certainly deformation has not been sufficiently intense to produce cleavage.

Walk SE to the beach on the E side of the castle and follow the **coast beneath the castle.** If the tide is high, the cliff path may be followed. The first rocks exposed are fine green sandstones dipping NW at angles up to 55° and with a well developed S-dipping cleavage. This S-dipping cleavage occurs only at the S end of the Llanstephan peninsula and shows that the effects of the Variscan deformation die out rapidly to the N. The Variscan cleavage front runs E-W through Llanstephan village.

On the **cliffs** beyond this point is a thick succession of calcretes, the Psammosteus Limestone of mid-Gedinnian age (Allen 1974, 1978; Strahan *et al.* 1909). These calcretes are believed to have formed at a more or less isochronous horizon over much of South Wales and the Welsh Borderland; they represent a series of pedogenic limestones, and Allen (1978, p. 79) recognised here at least six separate profiles indicating a 'long but broken period of relative geomorphic stability'.

The calcretes are the lowest rocks exposed and crop out on the N limb of an anticline with a slight plunge to the W. The axis of the fold crosses the coast further to the SW at SN 3453 0957. The anticline is asymmetrical; the S limb dips SE at angles varying from 16° to 42° (the cleavage on this limb dips S at about 40°). The dips on the N limb are close to 60° NW in the core of the fold but are generally less than this; cleavage on this limb is steeply to the SE and varies from 42° to 58°.

A major fault, the Llandyfaelog Disturbance, cuts through the Llanstephan area. Because this fault has Carboniferous Limestone outliers along its length at Llandyfaelog, at Carreg Cennen, and various other places it has usually been described as a Variscan structure. However, its Caledonian trend and geophysical evidence of subsurface geology suggest that it may have had an important pre-Variscan history (see Cope 1980).

Llanstephan Castle is built on a ridge of N-dipping fine sandstone units. The track up to the castle runs on the N side of this ridge, and around SN 1024 3512-3516 are exposures of red and green mudstones, badly fractured and disturbed; these exposures lie very close to the Llandyfaelog Fault. On the N side of the fault are higher horizons in the Red Marl Group, still dipping N at 35°-50°. These are succeeded by green micaceous sandstones belonging to the Senni Beds, which are poorly exposed on the N side of Llanstephan village.

REFERENCES

ALLEN, J. R. L. 1974. Studies in fluviatile sedimentation: implications of pedogenic carbonate units, Lower Old Red Sandstone, Anglo-Welsh outcrop. *Geol. J.* **9,** 181-208.

ALLEN, J. R. L. 1978. Llanstephan, Dyfed. pp. 79-82 *In* FRIEND, P. F. & WILLIAMS, B. P. J. (eds.), *A field guide to the Devonian of Scotland, the Welsh Borderland and South Wales*. Excursion B2. ii + 106 pp. Palaeontological Association, London.

CANTRILL, T. C. & THOMAS, H. H. 1906. On the igneous and associated sedimentary rocks of Llangynog, Caermarthenshire. *Q. Jl geol. Soc. Lond.* **62,** 223-252, pls. 23-26.

COPE, J. C. W. 1977. An Ediacara type fauna from South Wales. *Nature, Lond.* **268,** 624.

COPE, J. C. W. 1980. The early history of the southern margin of the Twyi anticline, in the Carmarthen area, South Wales. *In* HARRIS, A. L., HOLLAND, C. H. & LEAKE, B. E. (eds.). The Caledonides of the British Isles — reviewed. *Spec. Publ. geol. Soc. Lond.* **8,** 527-532.

COPE, J. C. W., FORTEY, R. A. & OWENS, R. M. 1978. Newly discovered Tremadoc rocks in the Carmarthen area, South Wales. *Geol. Mag.* **115,** 195-198, pl. 1.

CROSFIELD, M. C. & SKEAT, E. G. 1896. On the geology of the neighbourhood of Carmarthen. *Q. Jl geol. Soc. Lond.* **52,** 523-541, pls. 25-26.

FORTEY, R. A. & OWENS, R. M. 1978. Early Ordovician (Arenig) stratigraphy and faunas of the Carmarthen district, south-west Wales. *Bull. Br. Mus. nat. Hist.* (Geol.), **30,** 225-294, pls. 1-11.

STRAHAN, A., CANTRILL, T. C., DIXON, E. E. L. & THOMAS, H. H. 1909. The geology of the South Wales Coalfield. X. The country around Carmarthen. *Mem. geol. Surv. U.K.* viii + 177 pp.

STRAHAN, A., CANTRILL, T. C., DIXON, E. E. L., THOMAS, H. H. & JONES, O. T. 1909. The geology of the South Wales Coalfield. X1. The country around Haverfordwest. *Mem. geol. Surv. U.K.* viii + 262 pp.

Note added in proof.

Since this paper was submitted, further discoveries in the Llangynog area necessitate revision of the following:

Fig. 2. It is now clear from new exposures that the Tremadoc Clyn-côch Shales lie above the Cwm Crymlyn Shales.

Locality 11 is now known to be of early Tremadoc age (though in typical Festiniog Beds facies).

15
ORDOVICIAN AND SILURIAN SECTIONS IN THE LLANGADOG-LLANDILO AREA

by MICHAEL G. BASSETT

Maps *Topographical:* 1 : 50 000 Sheets 146 Lampeter and Llandovery, 159 Swansea and The Gower, 160 Brecon Beacons
1 : 25 000 Sheets SN61, SN62, SN72

Geological: 1 : 50 000 Sheet 230 Ammanford

THE area to the S of the river Tywi [Towy] between Llandilo [Llandeilo] and Llangadog [Llangadock] in eastern Dyfed (Fig. 1) exposes a complex of Ordovician and Silurian sediments and volcanic rocks ranging in age from the lower Llanvirn to the Downton Series. Structurally, the area forms part of the SE flank of the Tywi anticline, whose axis runs more or less along the river valley and which is one of the most prominent Lower Palaeozoic features in Wales. Detailed mapping by Williams (1953) has demonstrated that pulsatory movements along the anticline throughout upper Ordovician and Silurian times produced a number of phases of Lower Palaeozoic faulting and folding, which led to marked lateral and vertical changes in facies. There were also major changes in facies across the core of the anticline, which appears to have controlled the position of the southern edge of the Welsh basin to some extent, separating deeper water and basinal shales to the NW from the shallower shelf deposits to the SE; none of the localities in this excursion are to the NW of the anticlinal axis.

Based on the work of Williams (1953), the Ordovician succession in the area can be summarised as follows:

CARADOC SERIES

'Dicranograptus shales', only thinly developed on the SE flank of the anticline, but thickening on the NW limb to over 180 m; dark grey to black calcareous and graptolitic shales with a poor shelly fauna.

LLANDEILO SERIES

Over 850 m of flaggy to massive bedded limestones, sandstones,

[pp. 271-287 *In* BASSETT, M. G. (ed.). 1982. Geological excursions in Dyfed, south-west Wales.]

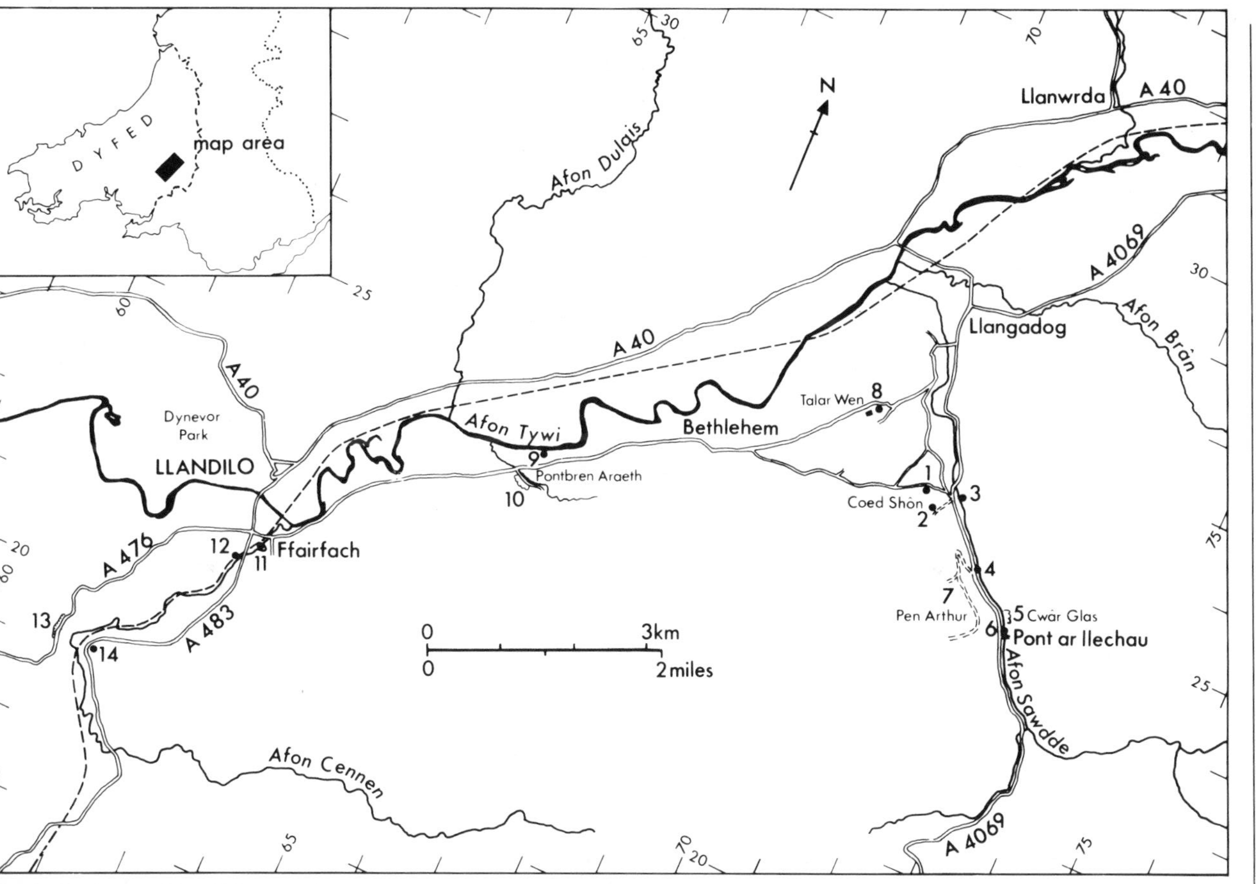

Fig. 1. Position of localities 1-14 between Llangadog and Llandilo.

siltstones and shales, mostly containing a rich shelly fauna; the type area is around Ffairfach and Dynevor Park near Llandilo (Fig. 1). Divisible into lower, middle, and upper units partly on faunal grounds and partly on the relative proportions of the different rock types. Basal sands rest unconformably on the underlying Llanvirn.

LLANVIRN SERIES

Represented by two major divisions, the lower 'Didymograptus bifidus shales' (at least 195 m), and the upper Ffairfach Group (about 120 m). The bifidus shales are blue-black to grey and brown, with bands of rhyolitic tuff in the basal 90 m and uper 45 m; graptolites are common throughout, with less common shelly fossils. The Ffairfach Group comprises a complex facies array of grits, conglomerates, sandstones, flags, limestones, and rhyolitic lavas and tuffs; these beds both thicken and become coarser from Llandilo north-eastwards, suggesting derivation from a land area or volcanic island chain to the NE, possibly around the Builth-Llandrindod inlier where the thick volcanic rocks could have formed the major sediment source.

Throughout the area the Ordovician rocks are succeeded with gross unconformity by Silurian strata. Nowhere are beds of uppermost Ordovician (upper Caradoc and Ashgill) known in this segment of the SE flank of the Tywi anticline, and in addition repeated movements along the fold led to persistent overlap and overstep of virtually all divisions of the Silurian from NE to SW. Although beds of Llandovery age are present near Llangadog, they are very thin compared to the full sequence in the type Llandovery area only a short distance to the NE, and before Llandilo they are overlapped by Wenlock strata which then rest on various members of the Ordovician. Because of the limited development of Llandovery rocks in the area described here, beds of this age are best studied around the type area by reference to the excursion described by Cocks (1971).

Both the Wenlock and Ludlow Series in the area are developed mainly in shallow shelf to near-shore marine and deltaic regressive facies, derived from a land source no great distance to the S and mostly containing fairly rich shelly faunas. In general the beds shallow upwards into Old Red Sandstone continental facies, which were introduced across the area in late Ludlow and Downton times; minor marine reincursions interrupt this general pattern in places. Increasing intensity of overlap and overstep to the SW in the Wenlock, Ludlow, and Downton has resulted in fairly considerable differences in the vertical succession across the area, so that no one general Silurian sequence can be summarised; instead the relevant successions at the NE and SW ends of the area described here are given at the appropriate points in the itinerary.

ITINERARY

Although described as starting at Llangadog (Fig. 1), the itinerary is arranged essentially as two separate traverses from N to S, running up through the succession in each case; the first covers localities 1 to 7, and the second localities 11 to 14. For a detailed study and comparison between the successions at opposite ends of the area, at least a full day should be devoted to each traverse; in a more general excursion within one day, localities 8 to 10 can be visited between the two traverses. All the roads used in the excursion are passable in vehicles up to the size of a small coach though some roads are quite narrow and cars should be used if possible.

1. Coed Duon. From Llangadog (Fig. 1) follow the A4069 road SE alongside the Afon Sawdde to Bont Fawr (SN 7142 2602), then after 200 m turn back to the NW on the minor road at SN 7149 2585. Keep left at the next fork and stop after a further 250 m, where there is an **old quarry** and cromlech just to the S of the road (SN 7110 2580, Fig. 2); the quarry is sometimes known locally as 'Colonel Jones' Quarry'. The low ground between the road and the quarry is mostly in the unexposed lower Llanvirn bifidus shales. The quarry itself exposes unfossiliferous basal grits of the upper Llanvirn Ffairfach Group, dipping at about 15° to the ENE. The grits are massive, medium grained, blue-grey to yellow or grey, with pebbles of quartz and tuffaceous intercalations.

The **crags above the top of the quarry** expose lithic and crystal rhyolitic tuffs higher up in the Ffairfach Group, in faulted contact with the grits below (see Williams 1953, fig. 2). In turn these are succeeded **higher in the slope** by nodular and vesicular albite-rhyolite flows, which can be followed along the hummocky ground forming the **crest of Coed Duon** for about 400 m to the SW (SN 7112 2568 to SN 7085 2536). The SE face of Coed Duon is in lower Llandeilo Flags following unconformably above the rhyolite flows (to be examined at locality 2).

Descend from Coed Duon down its NW slope, which traverses back down through the sequence, but now in the **middle of the slope** (SN 7085 2552) crossing through fossiliferous flags and tuffaceous sandstones intercalated between the tuffs and basal grits. The brachiopods *Dalmanella parva, Macrocoelia llandeiloensis,* and *Sowerbyella antiqua* are very common. From here take the lane S of Bryn-têg back to the road at SN 7069 2566.

2. Coed-Shôn quarry (SN 7125 2562). Return towards the A4069 road, but just before the road junction (SN 7145 2585) there is a track to the SW leading to an **old quarry** in the lower Llandeilo Flags (Fig. 2). The beds comprise dark blue-grey, flaggy bedded, muddy siltstones and fine sandstones with thin shale partings, dipping to the ENE at 15 - 20°. The sequence is a little way above the more sandy basal beds of the local Llandeilo, which form the slope of Coed Duon to the NW. The siltstones in the quarry are well laminated and frequently bioturbated, and contain a restricted, shallow water fauna including the lingulid brachiopod *Palaeoglossa attenuata* and the trilobites *Ogygiocarella debuchii* and *Lloydolithus lloydi*. Coed-Shôn quarry is the type locality for the latter species, whose common occurrence at this level throughout the area has led to the beds being named the Lloydolithus lloydi Flags.

3. Between Coed-Shôn quarry and Bont Fawr, the small stream known as Ffrwd y Felin joins the Afon Sawdde at SN 7148 2595 (Fig. 2). **Permission** should be obtained from Rhydsaint Farm (SN 7150 2590) to visit this locality, which is unsuitable for large parties. On the **NW side of the confluence** between the two streams the unconformable junction is exposed between the lower Llandeilo Flags and Silurian siltstones and mudstones of upper Llandovery (Telychian) age. The Llandeilo beds contain rare trilobites *(O. debuchii)*, and the overlying Llandovery mudstones contain the brachiopod *Clorinda globosa* which is suggestive of relatively offshore environments. Beds close to the junction are both faulted and cleaved, but there is a change of dip (from about 50° to 40°) across the boundary that appears to be independent of tectonics. This exposure is important in being one of the few that demonstrates the relationship between the Ordovician and Silurian in the area, and indicates the extent to which lower, middle, and basal upper Llandovery beds have been cut out by overlap and overstep within a very short distance from the Llandovery district to the NE.

4. Sawdde Gorge (Fig. 2). Between locality 3 and Pont ar llechau (SN 7282 2446), the narrow gorge of the Afon Sawdde exposes an almost continuous section from the upper Llandovery through Wenlock and Ludlow rocks in a generally shallowing upward sequence. Although the gorge is accessible with care along most of its length, it is steep and unsuitable for large parties making only a general study, particularly since representatives of most divisions can be examined at localities 5 - 7. However, because of the extensive exposure the gorge is the main reference section for the various formations of the Silurian in this area, and its study is essential for understanding the detailed relationships between them; as such the succession is summarised below (based mainly on Potter & Price 1965 and Hurst *et al.* 1978); throughout the section the beds dip steeply to the SE at up to 70°:

DOWNTON SERIES

Old Red Sandstone facies with marls, sandstones, quartzites and some pebbly to conglomeratic horizons. Silurian thickness unknown.

Long Quarry Formation (20 m)
The 'Tilestones' of earlier accounts; green to grey-green, highly micaceous, flaggy bedded sandstones; base exposed in the river 5.5 m below the bridge at Pont ar llechau (see also locality 6);

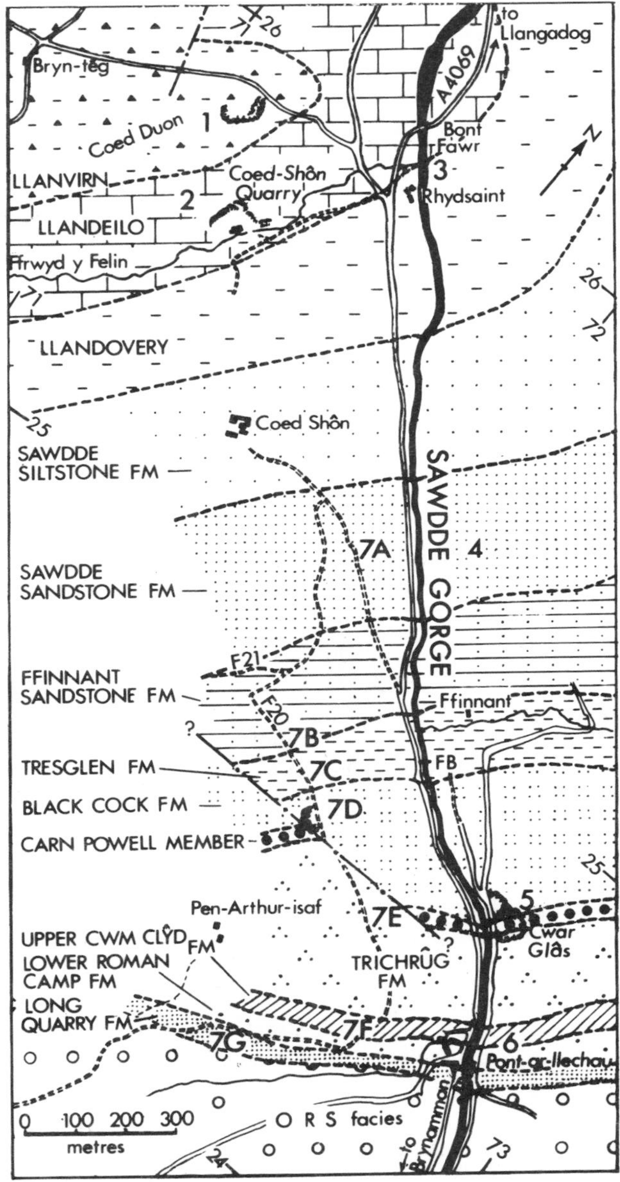

Fig. 2. Sketch map of the geology along and adjacent to the Sawdde gorge between Bont Fawr and Pont-ar-llechau (localities 1 - 7).

unconformable on older beds but there is no angular discordance, the break being attributed to regional overstep from the NE to SW across the Ludlow; succeeded conformably by ORS marls and sandstones.

unconformity

LUDLOW SERIES

Lower Roman Camp Formation (54 m)
Grey to greenish-grey, hard mudstones with interbedded siltstones; for details of the base see locality 6; the unconformity at the top of this formation cuts out the Upper Roman Camp Formation as developed in sections farther to the NE.

Upper Cwm Clŷd Formation (33 m)
Hard green to greenish-grey laminated and flaggy mudstones and siltstones with thick shell lenticles; some sandstone units have sharply erosive bases; conglomeratic sandstones near base (see locality 6); this formation represents a marine reincursion over the underlying beds.

Trichrûg Formation (185 m)
Thick bedded, predominantly red sandstones, pebbly sandstones, conglomerates, and coarse siltstones; classified in some early accounts within the Old Red Sandstone; base defined at locality 5; mainly represent deltaic to fluviatile facies with a variety of cross bedding structures; some thin grey beds indicate marine or estuarine incursions over the delta; fauna restricted to sparse *Lingula* and *Orbiculoidea,* with some bands of gastropods (*Bucanopsis* and *Loxonema)* in the marginal marine facies near the top.

Black Cock Formation (294 m)
Lower beds comprise dark grey to black calcareous fossiliferous shales and siltstones with medium bedded buff and grey sandstones; base defined at SN 7239 2490, approximately 70 m upstream from the small footbridge over the Sawdde (Fig. 2); there is little lithological change from the underlying formation except that argillaceous beds are less common; the basal transition is marked by a disappearance of an assemblage dominated in the Tresglen Formation by *Dicoelosia biloba.* The uppermost 90 m comprise more massive arenaceous shales and mudstones, with siltstones and sandstones becoming increasingly common. The top 40 m are thick to flaggy bedded purple and grey sandstones with thin conglomerates and calcareous lenses and rottenstones; these highest beds form the *Carn Powell Member,* whose base is defined at locality 5.

Tresglen Formation (90 m +)
Mainly grey, laminated siltstones, shales, and mudstones with thin sandstones; base defined at the base of a 0.25 m reworked bed at SN 7225 2503.

WENLOCK SERIES

Ffinnant Sandstone Formation (215 m)
Grey to greenish-grey and buff, medium to coarse grained micaceous sandstones with interbedded siltstones and shales, and a 1 m thick ironstone oolite forming the top bed; base defined at SN 7213 2519; most units are cross bedded, showing abundant evidence of wave and current action.

Sawdde Sandstone Formation (295 m)
Parallel laminated and bedded sandstones, siltstones and shales, with no evidence of wave action; base defined at prominent parallel bedded unit at SN 7193 2541. Some sandstones are graded and have basal groove and scour marks.

Sawdde Siltstone Formation (325 m)
Mainly grey siltstones and shales with slumped horizons throughout; base defined at the base of a shale sequence at SN 7174 2566.

LLANDOVERY SERIES (180 m +)
Unnamed dark mudstones and siltstones resting unconformably on the Llandeilo Flags (see locality 3).

The highest Llandovery mudstones in the Sawdde section represent a relatively offshore environment and contain the brachiopod *Costistricklandia lirata lirata;* this species is also indicative of an uppermost Llandovery (C_6) age for these beds, above which there is conformable transition into the Wenlock Series (Bassett 1974; Hurst *et al.* 1978). Above this level Calef & Hancock (1974) have described a sequence of Wenlock and Ludlow communities that support the sedimentary evidence in an environmental interpretation. Slumped horizons and the presence of a *Dicoelosia biloba* community in the Sawdde Siltstone Formation indicate gradients in a more offshore position than the underlying Llandovery beds. Above this level the Wenlock beds shallow upwards fairly persistently to the top of the Ffinnant Sandstone Formation, with a *Salopina* and bivalve community at the top in flaser bedded and herring-bone cross bedded units indicative of very shallow water. Deeper water facies at the base of the Tresglen Formation are accompanied by a return to an offshore *Dicoelosia* community, above which there is a steady regression upwards into *Salopina* and bivalve/gastropod assemblages at the top of the Black Cock Formation; this sequence can be interpreted as a regression before an advancing delta, which finally covered the area as the Trichrûg Formation and eventually passed up (with only minor marine reincursions) into the fluviatile Old Red Sandstone facies of the Long Quarry Formation and younger beds.

5. Cwar Glâs (SN 7268 2478). Follow the A4069 along the W side of the Sawdde gorge to Pont-ar-llechau, and then turn over the bridge and back to the NW for 300 m to the large Cwar Glâs quarries (Fig. 2). The **northernmost**

of the two quarries (SN 7263 2480) is entirely in the upper part of the main member of the Black Cock Formation. Steeply dipping, medium to thick bedded micaceous sandstones and siltstones exhibit a wide variety of ripple mark structures on extensive bedding planes. Both interference and regular symmetrical ripples are common, with crests aligned in a variety of directions. Calcareous coquinas and rottenstones contain a dominantly bivalve/gastropod fauna, including *Grammysia, Modiolopsis,* and *Loxonema,* but brachiopods also occur, including *Microsphaeridiorhynchus* cf. *nucula, Howellella elegans* and *Isorthis orbicularis.*

These beds continue up into the **NW face of the southern quarry,** which again displays a variety of magnificently preserved ripple structures. A few metres above the NW face, in the **E side of the quarry,** the incoming of coarse thick purple sandstones defines the base of the Carn Powell Member. The fauna in calcareous lenses is similar to that in the underlying beds. High in the **SE corner of the quarry** the Carn Powell Member is succeeded by the basal red sandstones of the Trichrûg Formation (Fig. 2).

The fauna of the Black Cock Formation is correlated by Potter & Price (1965) with that of the Middle Elton to low Upper Bringewood formations of the type Ludlow in the Welsh Borderland.

6. Pont-ar-llechau. The Trichrûg, Upper Cwm Clŷd, and Lower Roman Camp formations can be examined in the **bed of the Sawdde** immediately N of the bridge at Pont-ar-llechau (SN 7275 2460 to 7280 2450); there is easy access down to the river bed on the N side of the confluence of the Sawdde with the small stream (Afon Meilwch) entering from the W. About 30 - 40 m downstream from the confluence, thick red pebbly sandstones of the uppermost Trichrûg Formation are prominent in the **bed and banks of the river.** The base of the overlying Upper Cwm Clŷd Formation is defined sharply by the abrupt change from coarse red sandstones to greenish coloured flaggy to tabular bedded fine siltstones and sandstones; close to the base there are a number of coarse quartz conglomeratic sandstones among the siltstones. Shelly lenticles in the upper part of the sequence contain a restricted marine fauna of brachiopods and gastropods, including *M. nucula, I. orbicularis, Protochonetes* sp., *Sphaerirhynchia* sp., and *Loxonema.* On the basis of more extensive faunas in sections to the NE, Potter & Price (1965) correlate these beds with the Lower Leintwardine Formation of the Welsh Borderland, while the Trichrûg Formation is equated with the upper part of the Upper Bringewood Formation.

In the N bank of the Afon Meilwch, **immediately below the small bridge** over the confluence with the Sawdde (SN 7278 2452), is the base of the Lower Roman Camp Formation. The change from the underlying beds is gradational into slightly thicker bedded and darker grey coloured units, accompanied by an incoming of an ostracode fauna containing *Neobeyrichia* *lauensis,* which suggests a correlation with the Upper Leintwardine Formation of the Welsh Borderland. Shelly lenses contain a fauna similar to that of the underlying formation, with the notable addition of *Salopina lunata.* **Before the main bridge** over the Sawdde the base of the Long Quarry Formation is marked in the river bed by a sharp upward change to very micaceous sandstones; these latter beds are best examined back at road level in the **small quarry behind the Three Horseshoes Inn,** directly facing the bridge (SN 7279 2446). S of this point the A4069 road climbs through the full sequence of Old Red Sandstone facies and Carboniferous rocks of the Black Mountains, and an excursion along the route has been described by Simpson (1971).

7. Pen Arthur. From Pont-ar-llechau return NW along the A4069 for about 1 km to where a forestry track leads off to the NW (SN 7217 2502) into the plantation known as Pen Arthur. In recent years new forestry tracks through this area have provided excellent supplementary sections to those in the Sawdde gorge, though as yet they have not been mapped in detail; a sketch map of the geology along the main track is incorporated in Fig. 2.

Exposure is poor at the bottom of the track near the entrance to the section, but the beds here belong to the Ffinnant Sandstone Formation. Within **200 m up the track** the sequence descends to the Sawdde Sandstone Formation, which is well exposed up to and around the hairpin bend from where a subsidiary track leads to Coed Shôn farm (SN 7180 2525). About 100 m before the bend there is a **small waterfall** (locality **7A,** SN 7190 2522) over the section, about which the beds are continuously exposed. The olive to buff and grey, slightly micaceous fine siltstones and sandstones contain a rich shelly fauna dominated by brachiopods, of which *Atrypa reticularis, Strophonella euglypha gentilis* (type locality), *Cyrtia exporrecta, Isorthis* sp. and *Resserella* sp. are particularly common. There are also bivalves, gastropods, crinoid columnals, tentaculitids, and abundant carbonaceous debris, and rare graptolites belonging to *Monograptus flemingii* have been collected at the waterfall itself (Bassett 1974). Around the hairpin bend the track continues to climb, but now running back up the sequence of the Sawdde Sandstone; some horizons around the bend have yielded abundant specimens of the brachiopod *Meristina obtusa.*

Continue climbing the slope to the point where the forestry tracks diverge (SN 7196 2492), and take the left hand fork (F20). After rounding the sharp left hand bend the track begins to descend the slope, and after about 150 m there are exposures in the Ffinnant Sandstone Formation, with a poor shelly fauna (locality **7B**). Just before the **dip at the bottom of the slope** there is a transition up into thinner bedded dark grey to green micaceous siltstones and shales of the Tresglen Formation, and within the dip at the **lowest point in the track** (locality **7C**) the shaly beds become dominant. Beyond this point sandstone units appear again, forming a transition into the basal beds of the

Black Cock Formation which are well exposed in a **quarry cut in the W side of the track** (SN 7225 2469, locality **7D**).

The lower half of the quarry comprises blue-grey siltstones and shales with grey to buff sandstones, which then become thicker upwards and are dominant in the higher beds. Rottenstone bands contain a rich brachiopod/bivalve assemblage, in which *Leptostrophia filosa, A. reticularis* and *Grammysia* are particularly common. The beds are frequently bioturbated. The fauna conforms closely to that of the lower part of the Black Cock Formation elsewhere in the area, and appears to confirm a mid Ludlow age. High in the **S corner of the quarry** there is evidence of a fault, bringing in reddened beds against the normal Black Cock facies; these higher beds are reddish to buff sandstones, some slabs of which are crowded with large specimens of *Grammysia,* and which appear to represent the Carn Powell Member as seen at Cwar Glâs. Normal facies of the Black Cock Formation continue around the **bluff at the S entrance** to the quarry, and then some disturbed ground marks the possible line of the fault, above which there are red sandstones, coarse siltstones, and pebbly sandstones apparently belonging to the Trichrûg Formation and extending along the track for over 300 m. Although the full nature and direction of the faulting has not yet been established by detailed mapping, its existence can be confirmed by walking for about **170 to 200 m along the track** from the quarry. At this point the exposures are in coarse red sandstones, but directly across the valley and directly along the line of strike are the Cwar Glâs quarries in the upper Black Cock and Carn Powell members, which must therefore be displaced before reaching the forestry track section at locality **7E.** From 7E the distinctive hummocky ridge formed by the Trichrûg Formation in the hillside immediately SE of Cwar Glâs is clearly visible.

From locality 7E the track swings round to the W, and on the **crown of the bend** (SN 7262 2445) there are good exposures of coarse pebbly sandstones and grits in the Trichrûg Formation. From here the track climbs and runs obliquely across the strike through the Upper Cwm Clŷd and Lower Roman Camp formations, which can be traced around locality **7F,** and eventually across excellent exposures in the Long Quarry Formation at **7G** (approximately SN 7232 2418) which pass transitionally up into Old Red Sandstone marls and sandstones.

8. Talar Wen, near Bethlehem. From Pen Arthur return via the A4069 across Bont Fawr towards Llangadog, and turn to the SW 500 m before the village at SN 7069 2776, across the Sawdde towards Felindre and Bethlehem. On the **S side of the road** at SN 7010 2660, about 250 m before the house and nurseries named Talar Wen, is a **small old quarry** in the Llandeilo Flags. Most of the face is now covered by earth and scree, but there is abundant loose rock on the quarry floor. Buff to grey decalcified sandy limestones yield abundant specimens of the trilobites *O. debuchii* and *L. lloydi,* together with less common lingulid brachiopods *(?Palaeoglossa)*.

9 and 10. Pontbren Araeth. From Talar Wen continue to the SW via Bethlehem along the SE side of the Tywi valley. From Bethlehem the road runs continuously across the Llandeilo Flags. At a point where the Tywi swings to within 200 m of the road, stop at the entrance to a small electricity substation (SN 6590 2385) and walk for about 200 m to the NE to where a **small stream enters the Tywi flood plain** (SN 6602 2408). The low wooded cliff running along the river here forms a narrow outcrop of 'Dicranograptus shales' of lower Caradoc age, following conformably above the Llandeilo Flags. This is one of the few localities on the S flank of the Tywi axis that exposes strata of this age. The section comprises a few metres of dark blue-grey to brown calcareous shales that yield graptolites, including species of *Dicellograptus* and *Leptograptus*, and the trilobite *Talaeomarrolithus radiatus*.

On the main road continue to the SW for approximately 250 m to Pontbren Araeth, and on the SW side of the bridge turn back immediately along a narrow lane to the SE (this lane is not suitable for large vehicles). On the **S side of the lane** at SN 6589 2369 is an **old quarry** in the Llandeilo Flags dipping at about 60° to the NNW and comprising well bedded to lenticular limestones and calcareous siltstones with dark shale partings. Fossils are not common but include *O. debuchii, Marolithoides anomalis, Basilicus* sp., and *Dalmanella* sp.

11. Afon Cennen, Ffairfach. From Pontbren Araeth continue SW for 4 km to meet the A483 road at Ffairfach, 1 km S of Llandilo. About 200 m S of the road junction vehicles can be parked in the vicinity of the railway level crossing adjacent to Ffairfach Station (SN 629 213). In the E bank of the Afon Cennen about 200 m NE of the level crossing (SN 6310 2135) there are exposures of soft, blue-black, finely laminated graptolitic shales belonging to the middle part of the bifidus shales of the lower Llanvirn. The beds dip steeply to the S and contain *Didymograptus artus, D. bifidus, Glyptograptus* sp., and the trilobite *Protolloydolithus ramsayi*.

12. Ffairfach railway cutting (SN 6282 2117, Fig. 3). The black shales of locality 11 pass up into grey, tuffaceous, irregularly bedded shales of the upper part of the lower Llanvirn, the topmost beds of which are exposed at the NE end of Ffairfach railway cutting immediately adjacent to the level crossing on the W side of the road. **Permission to examine the section** in the railway cutting should be obtained from the signal box on the NE side of the level crossing. The tuffaceous shales are irregularly bioturbated and contain fragments of quartz, feldspar, and chlorite; fossils are rare but the brachiopod *Tissintia prototypa* has been obtained here.

Succeeding the shales in the cutting are the basal grits of the upper Llanvirn Ffairfach Group, for which this is the type section; in detail the

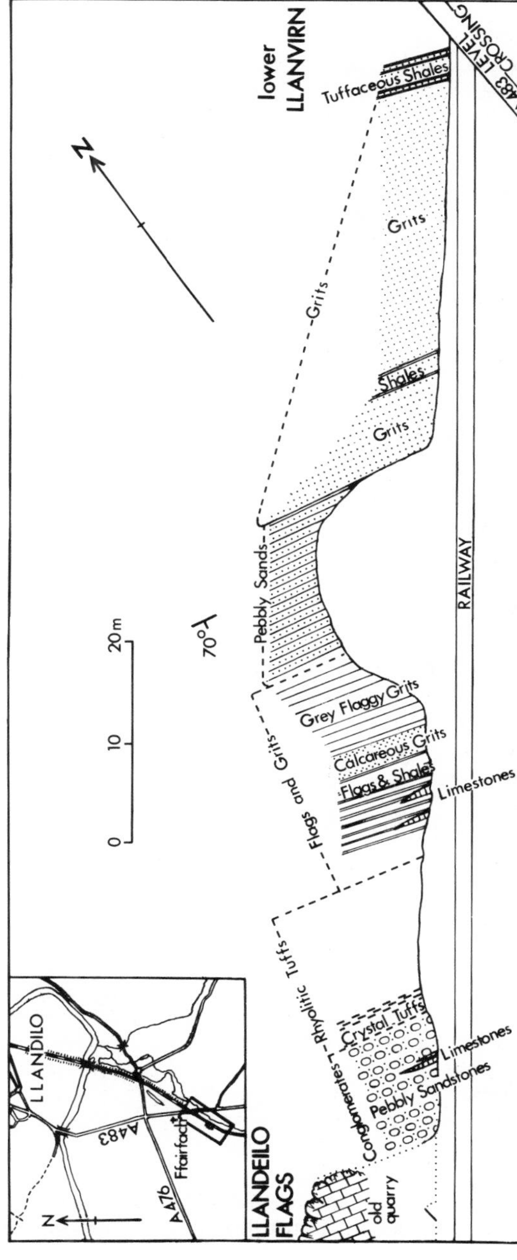

Fig. 3. Plan of the geology of the Ffairfach Group along the railway at Ffairfach (locality 12); re-drawn after Williams 1953, fig. 4.

transition into the grits is gradational, with intercalations of gritty bands in the shales increasing upwards in number and thickness until the finer material becomes negligible. The complete sequence through the Ffairfach Group has been described by Williams (1953) and can be followed by reference to Fig. 3.

The basal grits are approximately 33 m thick and comprise massive, medium grained, blue-grey to whitish-grey quartzitic beds with subordinate volcanically derived grains and clasts. The succeeding pebbly sands member includes 17 m of coarse, grey, current bedded, friable grits of deltaic origin, overlain by brown sandstones containing conglomeratic bands, pale volcanic clays and coarse, light grey to yellowish-brown pebbly grits. These beds reflect a maximum extent of emergence of a source area to the NE. Shale partings throughout this part of the sequence contain worm burrows, and in the clastic beds broken brachiopods and trilobites can be collected. The flags and grits above the pebbly sands are about 22 m thick and include thin nodular limestone lenses at a number of horizons; the grits are finer grained than in the underlying beds, grey to yellowish brown, and contain more shaly bands, especially towards the top. Fossils include the brachiopods *Sowerbyella* and *Dalmanella,* and the trilobites *Basilicus* and *Marrolithus,* though collecting is not easy. Some 12 to 15 m of rhyolitic tuffs succeed the flags and grits, though their lower part is poorly exposed (Fig. 3); elsewhere in the area there is a suggestion of a break between the two units. The tuffs are probably a direct lateral equivalent of those seen above the quarry at locality 1, but here at Ffairfach they are better bedded and finer grained, consisting mostly of pale, whitish crystal tuffs with chloritic bands. The highest member of the Ffairfach Group in the cutting consists of 11 m of rhyolitic conglomerates, yellow pebbly and tuffaceous sandstones, and some interbedded limestones.

The top of the conglomerates is not exposed at this locality, but within a few metres they are overlain by the lowest beds of the Llandeilo Flags, which are exposed in an **old quarry set back from the railway** at the SW end of the cutting (Fig. 3). Flaggy bedded, brown weathering sandstones and fine calcareous siltstones contain a fairly rich fauna. Although parts of the low quarry faces are covered by slipped earth and scree, well preserved fossils can be obtained from loose blocks, including *O. debuchii, Basilicus tyrranus, Marrolithus inflatus,* and the brachiopods *Dalmanella parva, Lingulella* sp., and *Schizocrania salopiensis.*

13. Llandilo-Cross Hands road section. To the S of Ffairfach the Ordovician is overlain unconformably by upper Wenlock strata, though the junction is rarely exposed. The succeeding Tresglen Formation is also poorly represented, but most of the remainder of the Ludlow succession is very well exposed in fairly new **cuttings along the A476 road** running along the W side of the Cennen valley around SN 609 193. The succession in this cutting and adjacent areas has been described and illustrated in detail by Squirrell & White (1978), whose work forms the basis of this account. The stratigraphical nomenclature of these authors differs in detail from that of Potter & Price (1965), who have also described the Ludlow succession in the Cennen valley.

Vehicles can be parked in the lay-by at the N end of the cuttings (SN 610 195). All the beds are almost vertical or slightly overturned, but young consistently to the S. The succession from immediately S of the lay-by is given below (youngest beds listed at top):

DOWNTON SERIES

Raglan Marl Group (ORS facies)
Green beds at base comprise the Capel Berach Beds of Potter & Price, 64 m thick in this section; green to greenish grey and olive siltstones and micaceous sandstones, passing up into up to 800 m of red mudstones, siltstones and sandstones. Base conformable on 'Tilestones' at SN 6102 1897.

Long Quarry Formation or *'Tilestones'* (40.4 m)
Base unconformable on underlying beds, exposed directly opposite small road leading SE off the A476 to Cwm (SN 6103 1902); typical highly micaceous brown to greenish flaggy sandstones with some conglomeratic bands and rare *Lingula.*

LUDLOW SERIES

Cennen Formation (3.55 m)
Base unconformable on older beds, marked by a distinctive undulating surface that can be seen by standing back from the section (see Squirrell & White 1978, plate 2b); mainly mudstones and siltstones with micaceous sandstones; fossils include shallow water brachiopods and molluscs. Incorporates the Upper Cwm Clŷd and Lower Roman Camp formations of Potter & Price. The junction with the overlying beds is drawn at the top of a 15 cm unit of greenish grey silty mudstones, along a slightly uneven contact.

Trichrûg Formation (exposed for 61 m in uppermost part)
Massive to thick bedded grey to greenish-grey, medium to coarse grained and conglomeratic sandstones, with subordinate silty mudstones.

'Grammysia Beds'
Only exposed intermittently along the road section (SN 6100 1913) below the Trichrûg Formation; equivalent to the Carn Powell Member to the NE. Flaggy to thick bedded siltstones and fine to medium grained sandstones, grey to purplish in colour. Fauna includes species of *Grammysia* together with the brachiopods *Salopina, Hyattidina,* and *Microsphaeridiorhynchus.*

Coed Wenallt Formation (exposed for 54.0 m in lower part)
Equivalent to the Black Cock Formation of Potter & Price; the upper part of this formation is not exposed in the road section,

occupying the tree-filled depression between the two main parts of the cutting. Interbedded sandstones, siltstones and silty mudstones, ranging from brown to grey and greenish-grey in colour. Lower beds generally unfossiliferous, but higher beds contain rottenstones with brachiopods and bivalves.

Lletty Formation
Equivalent to the basal part of the Black Cock Formation to the NE, these beds form the lowest 18 m of the road cutting immediately S of the lay-by; they comprise thickly bedded to massive grey and greenish-grey coarse sandstones, with silty mudstones at the top overlain conformably by the Coed Wenallt Formation. Fossils are mainly brachiopods.

As in the Sawdde valley sections, the Ludlow sequence in the Cennen valley is interpreted as being mainly a product of near-shore marine to deltaic environments; the additional breaks in the sequence and the general thinning of all units reflects the degree of overstep and overlap of all units along the flanks of the Tywi axis.

14. All the divisions exposed in the A476 road cutting extend along strike E across the Cennen valley, where the full succession can be traced along the A483 Llandilo-Ammanford road (see Potter & Price 1965, fig. 6, and Squirrell & White 1978, plate 7 for details). Although the degree of exposure is not so good as on the A476, one outcrop in the Long Quarry Formation justifies examination; this is a **small quarry above the road** on the E side of the sharp bend 3 km SW of Ffairfach station (SN 6145 1915). Here the typical micaceous sandstones of the 'Tilestones' lithology weather to a rusty-brown colour, and contain a fairly rich fauna of brachiopods dominated by *Microsphaeridiorhynchus nucula* and *Hyattidina* cf. *canalis*, together with bivalves, gastropods, and ostracodes.

REFERENCES

BASSETT, M.G. 1974. Review of the stratigraphy of the Wenlock Series in the Welsh Borderland and South Wales. *Palaeontology*, **17**, 745-777.

CALEF, C.E. & HANCOCK, N. J. 1974. Wenlock and Ludlow marine communities in Wales and the Welsh Borderland. *Palaeontology*, **17**, 779-810.

COCKS, L. R. M. 1971. The Llandovery district. pp. 155-161 *In* BASSETT, D.A. & BASSETT, M. G. (eds.), *Geological excursions in South Wales and the Forest of Dean*. 267 pp., Geologists' Association, South Wales Group, Cardiff.

HURST, J. H., HANCOCK, N. J. & McKERROW, W. S. 1978. Wenlock stratigraphy and palaeogeography of Wales and the Welsh Borderland. *Proc. Geol. Ass.* **89,** 197-226.

POTTER, J. F. & PRICE, J. H. 1965. Comparative sections through rocks of Ludlovian-Downtonian age in the Llandovery and Llandeilo districts. *Proc. Geol. Ass.* **76,** 379-402.

SIMPSON, B. 1971. The Palaeozoic succession in the Black Mountains between Pontardawe and Llandilo. pp. 143-154 *In* BASSETT, D. A. & BASSETT, M. G. (eds.),

Geological excursions in South Wales and the Forest of Dean. 267 pp., Geologists' Association, South Wales Group, Cardiff.

SQUIRRELL, H. C. & WHITE, D. E. 1978. Stratigraphy of the Silurian and Old Red Sandstone of the Cennen Valley and adjacent areas, south-east Dyfed, Wales. *Rep. Inst. geol. Sci.* **78/6,** ii + 1-45.

WILLIAMS, A. 1953. The geology of the Llandeilo district, Carmarthenshire. *Q. Jl geol. Soc. Lond.* **108,** 177-208.

16
PLEISTOCENE DEPOSITS AND FLUVIOGLACIAL LANDFORMS OF NORTH PRESELI

by D. Q. BOWEN

Maps *Topographical:* 1 : 50 000 Sheets 145 Cardigan, 157 St David's and Haverfordwest

1 : 25 000 Sheets SM83, SM93, SN03, SN14, SN24

IN THE coastal area of north Preseli, between Mathry and the Teifi estuary (Fig. 1), the Pleistocene sequence is particularly well exposed, with only incomplete exposures occurring inland. The general Pleistocene litho-stratigraphical succession and its chrono-stratigraphical classification is:

5	Upper Head ('rubble drift')	
4	Fluvioglacial sand and gravel	Late Devensian
3	Irish Sea till	
2	Lower Head	Early and Middle Devensian
1	Raised Beach	Last Interglacial

Note. Unit 1 is correlated with Oxygen Isotope Stage 5e of the deep-sea stratigraphical record, but could, however, represent stage 5c.

Unit 1 is well exposed at Poppit (SN 150 489 to SN 144 493) on the Teifi estuary and is described elsewhere in this volume (excursion 19, locality 1). Scattered erratics lie within the Raised Beach and Lower Head and it is thought that they have been derived from an earlier glaciation, discrete deposits of which, now highly dissected, occur S of this area beyond the Treffgarne-Preseli upland. In terms of existing notions on the classification of glacial deposits Jehu (1904) recognised : a lower boulder clay (unit 3), middle sands and gravels (unit 4), and an upper boulder clay (unit 5). Thus two glaciations separated by deglaciation, when unit 4 was deposited, were postulated. Contemporary opinion, however, would group the till and fluvioglacial deposits together to recognise one glaciation only, for the 'rubble drift' (unit 5) of Jehu is clearly a periglacial deposit. Direct

[pp. 289-295 *In* BASSETT, M. G. (ed.). 1982. Geological excursions in Dyfed, south-west Wales.]

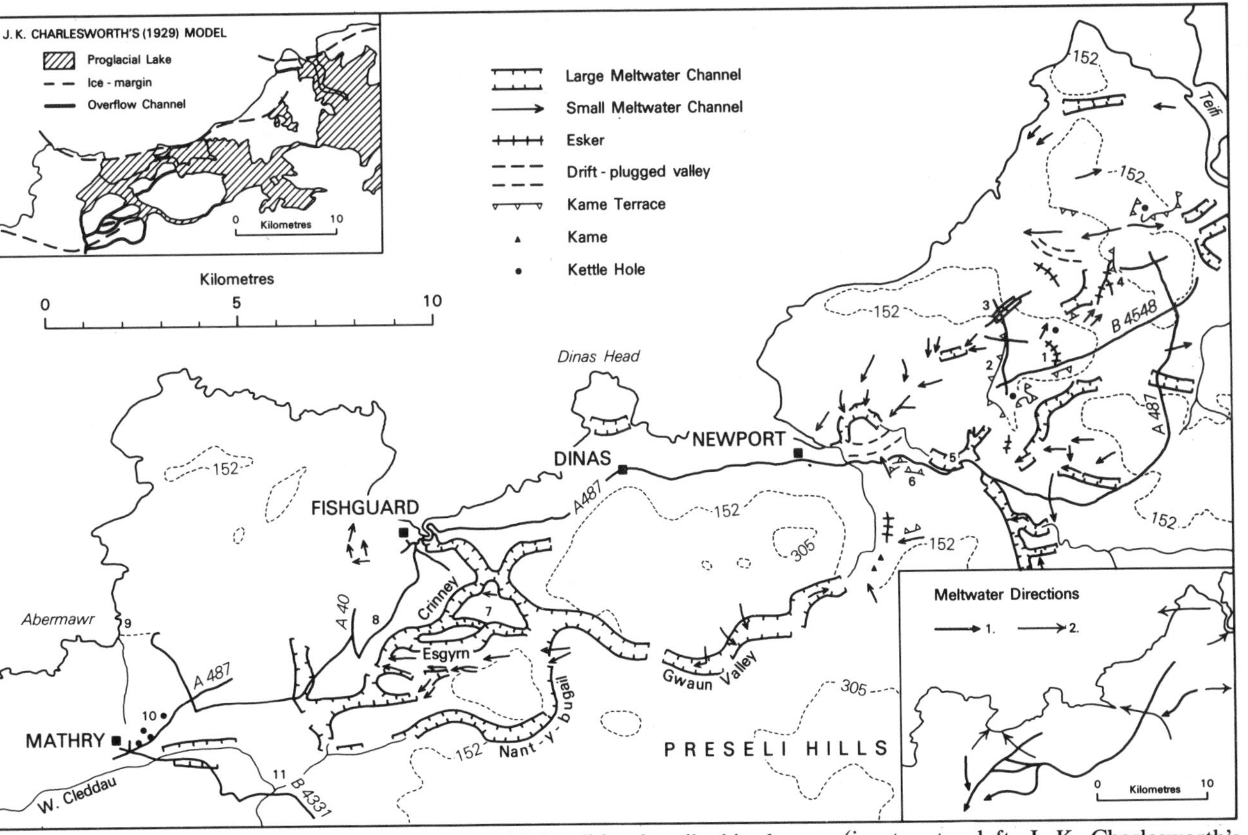

Fig. 1. Deglaciation landforms of North Preseli, with localities described in the text (insets : top-left, J. K. Charlesworth's model; bottom right, two stages in meltwater drainage direction).

stratigraphical evidence, therefore, shows only one glaciation, although the inference drawn from erratics in both raised beach and lower head deposits allows recognition of an earlier one also (Bowen 1973*a*).

Charlesworth (1929), in outlining the extent of the 'Newer Drift' (Last) Glaciation by means of his 'South Wales End-moraine' identified ice-marginal overflow channels in the Fishguard district, and morainic deposits on the upland between Newport and Cardigan. In so doing he relied on a model of deglaciation which involved ice-marginal retreat, the formation of proglacial lakes between the retreating ice-margin and the emergent topography, and the fashioning of overflows as lake water spilled over from one lake into another (Fig. 1, inset). From S to N successive overflow channels indicate the former position of the retreating ice margin. Subsequent work has compelled a re-evaluation of both his data and conclusions. For the Teifi valley Charlesworth's ideas have been vindicated largely by the discovery of evidence unknown to him at the time (see this volume, excursion 19). But in the area covered here radical revision is necessary. This arises because the overflow channels of the Fishguard area, and elsewhere, have been shown to be subglacial in origin (Bowen & Gregory 1965). Also, Charlesworth's 'morainic deposits' between Newport and Cardigan have been shown to be fluvioglacial (Gregory & Bowen 1966). This re-evaluation necessitates a somewhat greater cover of ice than envisaged by Charlesworth, which is, however, fully substantiated by stratigraphical evidence over a wider area (Bowen 1973*b*, 1974).

Deglaciation took place by ice thinning (and not by active ice margin retreat and proglacial lake formation) although minor and temporary bodies of standing water may have existed in the Newport and Fishguard Bay areas at a late stage in this process. The fluvioglacial landforms on the Newport-Cardigan upland show that, initially, meltwater converged on the entrance to the Gwaun Valley along which it flowed to feed the Fishguard subglacial channels. These also received meltwater from the Dinas area by way of the Cwm-Onnen channel (Fig. 1) (see below, locality 5). Later, when ice thinning had occurred sufficiently to allow meltwater to flow N and W into Cardigan Bay, the Gwaun Valley was abandoned (Fig. 1, inset). Stages in the development of the Fishguard channels were established by Bowen & Gregory (1965) (locality 5), but in the NE four stages in deglaciation occurred (Fig. 2) :

> (i) downwasting ice surface at no great elevation above present topography when subglacial stream erosion and esker formation occurred; (ii) coincidence of summit areas with the ice-surface and deposition of sand and gravel on the former; (iii) ice-surface just below summit areas — kame terrace deposition; (iv) ice confined to valley bottoms — subglacial stream erosion producing deeply incised valley reaches.

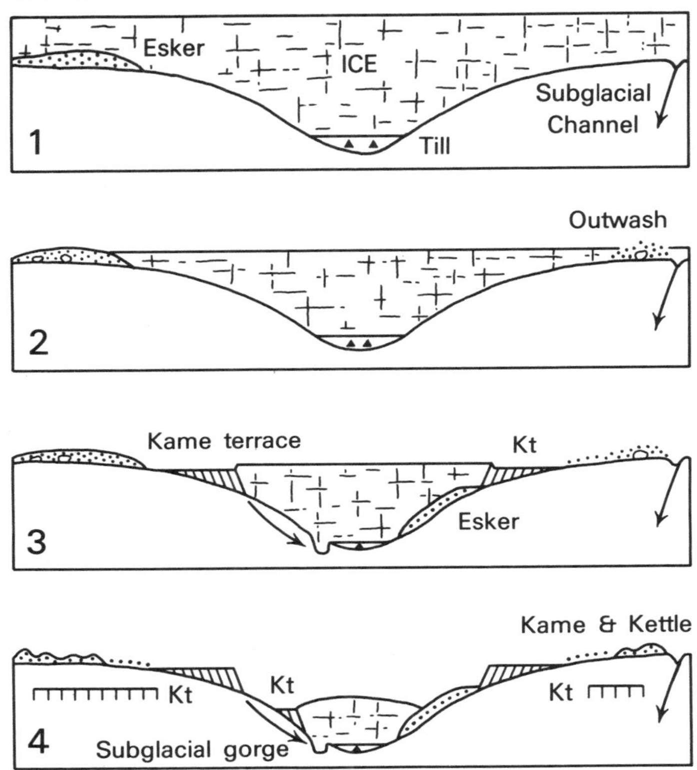

Fig. 2. Stages in the deglaciation of the Newport-Cardigan upland.

Attempts have been made to date the glaciation by radiocarbon determinations on wood fragments and shells derived from the sea floor and incorporated into the glacial deposits (John 1970). But the unknown provenance of the samples and effects of contamination are such as to render this approach valueless (e.g. Shotton 1967).

ITINERARY

1. Extensive fluvioglacial deposits cover the upland between Newport and Cardigan where the excursion commences near a National Park viewing point (SN 126 415). The esker ridge, of which the **hummock bearing the trigonometrical point** (SN 126 416) forms a part, runs NW, and indicates the earliest stage (stage i) recognised in deglaciation. Immediately **below the B4582 road** at the lay-by, lies a small kame terrace containing a small gravel pit (SN 126 414). This formed during stage (iii) when the downwasting ice-surface lay below the highest points. This locality also provides fine views of 1, the Preseli Hills, along which the dolerite tors of the 'bluestones' stand conspicuously; 2, the entrance to the Gwaun Valley; and 3, the meltwater channel of Cwm-yr-eglwys (SN 010 400), which all but separates Dinas Head from the mainland. Recent boreholes have shown a thick sequence of Holocene deposits on the channel floor (pers. comm. J. A. Taylor). It should be noted in passing that no geological evidence exists to support the notion that ice transported the Preseli dolerites to Stonehenge (Bowen 1980).

2 and 3. The third stage in deglaciation is shown by the long kame terrace along which the road runs from SN 112 420 to SN 109 410, the steep ice-contact slope coinciding with the 152 m (500 ft) contour line. A large coach may be reversed at **the cross roads** (locality **3,** SN 110 428) where a subglacial meltwater channel (with hump profile indicating that water flowed uphill under hydrostatic pressure) related to stage (i) occurs.

4. Also related to stage (ii) is the **Monington esker** (SN 138 439), best approached from Cross Way (SN 157 430) on the A487. The esker runs from N to just W of S (shown by the contour lines on the O.S. map) and at its proximal end passes into a kame terrace. It seems clear that the meltwater stream which deposited the terrace suddenly turned into the ice at this point, the sinuous course of the esker reflecting the course of what then became a subglacial stream, and its steep sides an approximation to the ice-contact of the subglacial tunnel. Its internal structure may be inspected in **the gravel quarry** where it is sometimes possible to see ice-wedge pseudomorphs in the upper workings. The pebbles are a typical Irish Sea assemblage from the N, together with Lower Palaeozoic clasts of Welsh origin.

5 and **6.** Proceed to Fishguard via Cross Way (SN 157 430) and the A487 (because the B4582 may be negotiated at Nefern bridge only with a small vehicle). En route note: (a) channelled valley sides at **Velindre** (SN 101 391, locality **5**) and elsewhere; (b) kame terraces low on the valley sides around **Temple Bar** (SN 086 388, locality **6**) and (SN 086 391), where road widening operations in recent years have exposed widespread sand deposits; (c) just **E of Newport** the Afon Nefern follows a deep gorge; this subglacial meltwater channel fashioned on the side of the valley appropriated the post-glacial drainage leaving the earlier, 'preglacial', course, drift-plugged (SN 085 395 to SN 073 394); it may readily be seen from the A487 at SN 075 395; (d) **between Newport and Fishguard** views of several tors (e.g. Garn Fawr SN 007 369) may be obtained; remnants of a distinct coastal platform at *c.* 76 m occur around **Dinas;** (e) passing **across the bridge** at Fishguard Lower Town, note the entrace to the lower end of the Gwaun Valley today.

7. The subglacial origin of the Fishguard channels (Bowen & Gregory 1965) may be partially demonstrated at **Llanwern** (SM 976 349), reached by way of Trebover (SM 969 358) and Llaneast (SM 969 351), along Criney Brook from the B4313 road. Criney Brook carried meltwater from Cwm

Onnen (SM 982 364) at one stage, drainage across the Gwaun valley being accomplished englacially, to which the bench at Criney Farm (SM 974 358) probably relates. The Onnen-Criney glacial drainage line only ceased to function when the meltwater was appropriated to the NW by the Gwaun valley due to ice thinning. The Llaneast-Llanwern channel is characterised by a reversed or hump profile, a feature common to subglacial drainage channels in which meltwater has been forced to flow a short distance uphill under hydrostatic pressure. Many such channels occur in the district as a whole. The upper part of Esgyrn Bottom is aligned with the Llaneast-Llanwern channel (the bench at Cronllyn SM 987 348 relates to this stage also), but this route was subsequently abandoned in favour of Esgyrn Bottom, which is demonstrably younger than the Llanwern-Llaneast channel as it is incised below the level of the latter.

8. Proceed along the minor road to SM 947 346, where a panoramic view of the Fishguard meltwater channels may be obtained, notably of Criney Brook and Esgyrn Bottom (Fig. 1).

9. Where it joins the A487 take the minor road (SM 901 331), signposted to Tregwynt Woollen Mill, for Abermawr. At the **N end of Abermawr** (SM 884 347) is a good exposure of the Pleistocene succession dipping S off the partially concealed Pleistocene cliff (Bowen 1977). Younger units are best inspected where they approach beach level from N to S. At the base is some 11m of head. In detail several lithofacies occur, ranging from large angular blocks of Cambrian quartzite and small fragments of shale, to discontinuous lenses of small gravels (mostly <1 cm), and which could indicate fluviatile action under conditions of climatic amelioration. More rounded erratic pebbles occur throughout the head. It is overlain by up to 3m of typical Irish Sea till — a purple-blue-black calcareous clay containing small shell fragments, and with erratics from North Wales and Scotland. This is followed by 5m of sand and gravel, which correlates with the similar deposits inland of which the fluvioglacial depositional landforms are composed. The upper head, which contains redistributed glacial materials, represents cold conditions after deglaciation, probably when ice-wedges formed elsewhere in the area.

10. Near Mathry, kettle-holed fluvioglacial drift (SM 887 321, 889 322 and 894 327) plugs the former course of the Western Cleddau which, prior to glaciation, entered the sea at Abermawr. The postglacial drainage was appropriated eastwards along a meltwater channel (Fig. 1).

11. Passing the **Mathry Road Quarry** (SM 923 310) note the position of the fluvioglacial sands and gravels filling the valley bottom. **It is not recommended** that a visit be made to this now dangerous, water-filled quarry.

CONCLUSION

The deposits and landforms of Preseli relate predominantly to the deglaciation of the Late Devensian ice sheet (*c.* 18 000 to 15 000 years ago). From N to S, along the route of this excursion, changing erosional and depositional activities of this period may be demonstrated. Initially, on the Newport-Cardigan high ground, deposition occurred, but was replaced by erosion as the meltwater flowed through the Gwaun Valley to feed the Fishguard channels. Farther S, downstream of the Treffgarne gorge, and beyond the ice-margin, deposition again occurred, this time as an outwash plain complex which has been subsequently terraced. An extensive example of this outwash plain, with exposures in road cuts, occurs around (SM 955 215) at 46m O.D.

Note. **Permission** is required to visit the Monington gravel quarry (locality 4), and must also be obtained from Llaneast and Llanwern farms to visit locality 5.

REFERENCES

BOWEN, D. Q. 1973*a*. The Pleistocene history of Wales and the borderland. *Geol. J.* **8,** 207-224.

BOWEN, D. Q. 1973*b*. The Pleistocene succession of the Irish Sea. *Proc. Geol. Ass.* **84,** 249-272.

BOWEN, D. Q. 1974. The Quaternary of Wales. pp 373-426 *In* OWEN T. R. (ed.), *The Upper Palaeozoic and post-Palaeozoic rocks of Wales.* viii + 426 pp. Univ. Wales Press, Cardiff.

BOWEN, D. Q. 1977. The Coast of Wales. *In* KIDSON, C. & TOOLEY, M. J. (eds.), The Quaternary history of the Irish Sea. *Geol. J.* Special Issue No. 7, 223-256.

BOWEN, D. Q. 1980. Pleistocene scenario for Palaeolithic Wales. *In* TAYLOR, J. A. (ed.), Culture and Environment in Prehistoric Wales. *Brit. Archaeol. Rep.* **76,** 1-14.

BOWEN, D. Q. & GREGORY, K. J. 1965. A glacial drainage system near Fishguard, Pembrokeshire. *Proc. Geol. Ass.* **74,** 275-282.

CHARLESWORTH, J. K. 1929. The South Wales end-moraine. *Q. Jl geol. Soc. Lond.* **85,** 335-358.

GREGORY, K. J. & BOWEN, D. Q. 1966. Fluvioglacial deposits between Newport, Pembs. and Cardigan. *In* PRICE, R. J. (ed.). Deglaciation. *Occ. Publs Br. geomorph. Res. Grp.* **2,** 25-28.

JEHU, T. J. 1904. The glacial deposits of northern Pembrokeshire. *Trans. R. Soc. Edinb.* **41,** 53-87.

JOHN, B. S. 1970. Pembrokeshire. pp. 229-265 *In* LEWIS, C. A. (ed.), *The glaciations of Wales and adjoining regions.* xvi + 378 pp. Longman, London.

SHOTTON, F. W. 1967. Problems and contributions of absolute dating within the Pleistocene Period. *Q. Jl geol. Soc. Lond.* **122,** 357-383.

17
THE QUATERNARY GEOLOGY OF THE LOWER TEIFI VALLEY

by D. Q. BOWEN *and* D. L. LEAR

Maps *Topographical:* 1 : 50 000 Sheet 145 Cardigan
1 : 25 000 Sheets SN14, SN24, SN34

THE TEIFI valley (Fig. 1) is a celebrated area among Pleistocene investigations in the British Isles because of the work of J. K. Charlesworth (1929), later developed by O. T. Jones (1965). Both postulated the existence of a large proglacial lake impounded by a barrier of Irish Sea Ice across the estuary of the Teifi NW of Cardigan. Charlesworth's (1929) reconstruction was based partly on his identification of the 'South Wales End-moraine' along the immediate coastal hinterland, but also on sands and gravels interpreted as deltas, and on dry valleys deemed to be overflow channels. Whereas Charlesworth's identification of proglacial lakes in the country immediately to the S, around Newport and Fishguard, has not withstood detailed re-examination (see this volume, excursion 18), proglacial Lake Teifi has certainly been confirmed. This has been one of the results of a long term research project mapping the Quaternary geology of the valley from Tregaron to the sea. Based on detailed six-inch mapping, assisted by an extensive drilling programme, it is near completion.

The Quaternary succession and classification in the area are given below:

Blown sand and alluvium	Holocene
River Terrace Gravels	Late-glacial and Holocene
Head	
Sand and Gravel	
The Llechryd Clay (lacustrine)	Late Devensian
Sand and Gravel	
Till	
Head	Early and Middle Devensian
Raised beach sediments	Last Interglacial

Note. 'Last Interglacial' is used in the sense that it correlates with Oxygen Isotope Stage 5e of the deep-sea stratigraphical framework.

Most of the Pleistocene surface geology relates to the deglaciation of an ice sheet which covered the entire area. Outcrops of till are rare, but substantial thicknesses (up to 50m) have been inferred from geophysical investigations

[pp. 297-302 *In* BASSETT, M. G. (ed.). 1982. Geological excursions in Dyfed, south-west Wales.]

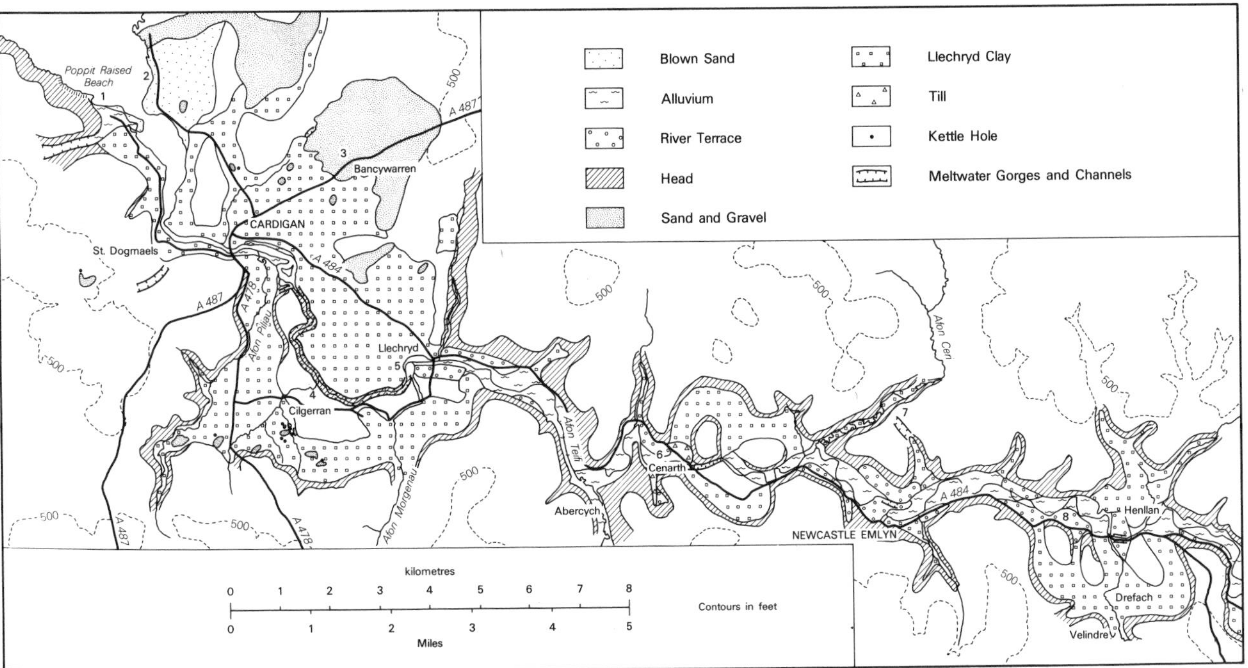

Fig. 1. The Quaternary geology of the Lower Teifi Valley between Poppit and Drefach-Pentrecwrt, showing localities described in the text.

of the drift-plugged abandoned former reaches of the Teifi at Cilgerran and Cenarth. Except for the area downstream of Llechryd, outcrops of fluvioglacial sands and gravels are also rare, but upstream from Drefach and Henllan (Fig. 1), considerable thicknesses occur. Much of the area forming the Teifi Valley floor and its adjacent slopes is covered by the Llechryd Clay, a lacustrine deposit which formed in proglacial Lake Teifi. This is both underlain and overlain by fluvioglacial sands and gravels. Lying at the base of most slopes is a variable thickness of head whose boundaries feather out upslope.

The sequence of events following the raised beach interglacial appears to have been: (1) cold climate conditions with head formation; (2) complete glaciation by an Irish Sea ice sheet (its relationship to the coeval Welsh ice sheet has yet to be established precisely); (3) deglaciation, (a) erosion of subglacial stream channels to fashion the Lower Teifi gorges as at Cilgerran, Cenarth, Newcastle Emlyn and Henllan, (b) at a later stage, the impounding of proglacial Lake Teifi by an ice barrier downstream of Cardigan, (c) catastrophic drainage of Lake Teifi, for no evidence exists to demonstrate stages in its development; (4) cold climate with head and stratified scree formation; some river terrace gravel aggradation; (5) postglacial alluviation and dissection of terrace gravels, accumulation of blown sand downstream, and hillslope colluvium elsewhere.

ITINERARY

1. The **Poppit raised beach** (Fig. 1) is exposed for about 1 km between Trwyn Caregddu (SN 150 489) and Trwyn-yr-Olchfa (SN 144 493) on the W side of the Teifi estuary. It lies on a raised shore platform, which is spectacularly bevelled across tightly folded Lower Palaeozoic rocks. Exposed to greatest advantage at SN 146 489, it there consists of a cemented cobble beach overlain by stratified sands and gravels. Iron and manganese staining is much in evidence. Other than for scarce shell fragments it contains no readily recognisable fauna. Overlying the beach unit is an indifferently exposed head deposit of angular and subangular local rock fragments. This is succeeded by Irish Sea till, sometimes exposed in slump features, but always detected at shallow depths using a hand augur. It is a typical calcareous Irish Sea till, dark blue in colour, clay rich with few stones, and containing shell fragments.

Near **Trwyn Caregddu** (at SN 148 489), some 50 cm of laminated clay is interbedded with angular and rounded boulders of the raised beach. The clay contains a foraminiferal assemblage including *Ammonia batavus, Cibicides lobotudes, Elphidium clavatum, Elphidium crispum, Protelphidium anglicum,* and *Protelphidium orbiculare*. Of some importance is the presence of *E. crispum,* which also occurs in a sand and gravel unit lying between two tills in cores from the central part of Cardigan Bay. It is not present in the modern fauna of the bay, and thus is of some use in correlation, for the upper till of Cardigan Bay is ascribed to the Late Devensian (Garrard & Dobson 1974).

2. Unlike Poppit, Irish Sea till is well exposed on the opposite side of the estuary near **Gwbert-on-Sea** (SN 162 492). It overlies a well developed rock platform (Jones 1965), and is overlain by a unit of outwash sands and gravels, in turn covered by a head, some loess, and postglacial blown sand. The till is dangerous to walk upon in wet conditions.

3. The conspicuous mounds of sand and gravel at **Banc-y-warren** (SN 205 478) have long excited interest and comment on their origin. In general a sand unit is overlain by gravels, both of which contain shell fragments and a variable amount of organic debris. Over-optimistic attempts to obtain radiocarbon age determinations on these have generally been criticised on methodological and technical grounds (e.g. Boulton 1968). Orginally mapped by Williams in 1927, the extent of the sands and gravels is now known to be very much greater (Fig. 1).

Charlesworth (1929) thought that the Banc-y-warren mounds were part of the 'South Wales end-moraine', but Jones (1965) believed them to be deltaic in origin, a conclusion supported by detailed sedimentological analysis and work on sedimentary structures by Helm & Roberts (1975). They concluded that Banc-y-Warren consists of three delta lobes, related to different lake levels, the complex having advanced into a deepening proglacial lake.

Permission to visit the working quarries in the Banc-y-warren mounds must be obtained from the site office. Although the faces change constantly, the basal sands, with fault lines cemented by calcium carbonate, overlain by upper gravels very occasionally displaying ice-wedge casts in the upper layers, are all clearly visible.

4. The **dry valley** (SN 185 425) **and gorge** (SN 194 433) **at Cilgerran** (SN 195 430) are typical of similar situations along the lower and middle Teifi valley. The Teifi presently occupies the gorge, but previously followed the wide, flat-floored valley which lies immediately S of the gorge. This abandoned valley is plugged by drift, which geophysical investigations (Allen 1960) found to be up to 50 m thick. The drift consists of 25m of till, overlain by 25m of lacustrine clay (Nunn & Boztas 1977). The gorge, seen to advantage from the ruined Norman Castle of Cilgerran, is up to 60m deep in places along its length of 5 km. O. T. Jones (1965) estimated that some 28 million cubic metres of rock were removed during its fashioning. The quarrying of cleaved mudstones of Ordovician age has added to this in more recent times. Jones (1965) believed that catastrophic meltwater flows from a decaying Irish Sea ice sheet in Cardigan Bay entered the upper Teifi valley and flowed downstream to fashion the gorge. But no erratics of Irish Sea type are known from the middle and upper Teifi, and in an alternative view Bowen (1967) argued that the gorges had been cut sub-glacially. This occurred early in deglaciation through the superimposition of englacial and subglacial streams across rockhead spurs, most of which lay across the principal valley axis, and thus along the main direction of glacial drainage. It is a well known fact that subglacial meltwater tends to flow towards depressions in the overall subglacial rockhead morphology.

5. The best and most persistent exposure of the Llechryd Clay occurs close to the village of **Llechryd** in a **disused gravel pit** (SN 211 436). Despite being greatly overgrown, the Llechryd clay is clearly seen to be laminated when faces have been weathered to some degree and to overlie current bedded outwash gravels.

6A. At **Glan Nawmor** (SN 265 417) an exposure shows 0.6m of till overlain by 1.5m of coarse gravel and 1.1m of alluvium. The till is dark greyish brown (Munsell 10YR 3/2) and calcareous (5.3% Ca CO3). 92% of its matrix is finer than 7 ∅. Most of the clasts are local but with the addition of Irish Sea erratics. Their preferred orientation is from due N.

6B. The association of meltwater gorge and abandoned Teifi course at **Cenarth** is similar to that at Cilgerran except for two such dry valleys north and south of the Cenarth gorge (Jones 1965). The sequence of events leading to the formation of the two dry valleys is unknown, but the origin of the gorge is attributed to subglacial stream erosion (Bowen 1967).

7. An **old gravel pit at Old Cilgwyn** (SN 420 315) contains an excellent exposure of stratified scree (a lithofacies of the youngest head unit in the area). Scree fragments are exclusively local and are penetrated by thin ice-wedge casts.

8. Discontinuous river terraces along the Teifi rarely reveal exposures, but at **Dolhaidd,** where the Bargod stream joins the Teifi (SN 350 405), is a good section through the lower of the two Dolhaidd Terraces. The gravels show clear imbrication and in this case are Holocene (postglacial) in age.

Acknowledgements. Dr. J. R. Haynes kindly identified the foraminifera from the Poppit raised beach and discussed their correlation with the Cardigan Bay borehole sediments. R. J. Whittington kindly discussed the geophysical evidence.

REFERENCES

ALLEN, A. 1960. Seismic refraction investigations of the preglacial valley of the River Teifi near Cardigan. *Geol. Mag.* **9,** 276-282

BOULTON, G. S. 1968. A middle Würm Interstadial in South West Wales. *Geol. Mag.* **195,** 190-191.

BOWEN, D. Q. 1967. On the supposed ice-dammed lakes of South Wales. *Trans. Cardiff Nat. Soc.* **93** [for 1964-1966], 4-17.

CHARLESWORTH, J. K. 1929. The South Wales End-Moraine. *Q. Jl geol. Soc. Lond.* **85,** 335-358.

GARRARD, R. A. & DOBSON, M. R. 1974. The nature and maximum extent of glacial sediments off the west coast of Wales. *Mar. Geol.* **16,** 31-44.

HELM, D. G. & ROBERTS, B. 1975. A re-interpretation of the origins of sands and gravels around Banc-y-warren, near Cardigan. *Geol. J.* **10,** 131-146.

JONES, O. T. 1965. The glacial and post-glacial history of the lower Teifi valley. *Q. Jl geol. Soc. Lond.* **121,** 247-281.

NUNN, K. R. & BOZTAS, M. 1977. Shallow seismic reflection profiling on land using a controlled source. *Geoexploration,* **15,** 87-97.

WILLIAMS, K. E. 1927. The glacial drifts of western Cardiganshire. *Geol. Mag.* **64,** 205-227.

18
REMAINS OF PINGOS IN THE CLEDLYN VALLEY NEAR LAMPETER

by EDWARD WATSON

Maps *Topographical:* 1 : 50 000 Sheet 146 Lampeter and Llandovery
1 : 25 000 Sheet SN44

A PINGO is an ice-cored mound formed within permafrost. Borings and natural exposures suggest that the cores are often of clear ice, but sometimes they consist of stratified ice and sediments. In its growth the ice forms a mound, which splits open at the summit as it grows larger, to expose the ice core. This core then melts in summer to form a crater lake. The heat of the water causes the lake to sink deeper into the core and to get wider as it thaws the ice on its shore, undercutting the crater walls and causing continued slumping of material down their inner face. These processes result in the surface of the crater lake being steadily lowered and its area increased until only the lowest part of the mineral skin of the pingo remains, forming a rampart surrounding the lake (Fig. 1).

Contemporary pingos are usually classified in the two types proposed by Müller (1959), as closed system and open system, though Mackay (1979, p. 53) prefers the terms hydrostatic system and hydraulic system. The former type occurs on flat plains and results from the freezing of a pocket of unfrozen sediments beneath a lake in continuous permafrost, the excess water being expelled into the surface zone where it freezes to form a pingo. This is a 'non-repetitive' process which tends to produce a 'solitary hill' (Müller 1959, p. 101). Open system pingos form at the foot of valley sides where subpermafrost or intrapermafrost water is under hydraulic pressure (Fig. 2). Where this water rises into the surface zone it may freeze to form pingos. Unlike the closed system type, open system pingos continue to grow and decay in a favourable area so long as these hydrological conditions persist, so that 'clusters of mutually interfering pingos of different ages' are produced (Holmes *et al.* 1968 p. 15).

In siting and distribution the rampart forms of northern Dyfed closely resemble the contemporary pingos of Central Alaska and Yukon Territory; they are typically sited on the lower valley slopes and occur in clusters, often

[pp. 303-312 *In* BASSETT, M. G. (ed.). 1982. Geological excursions in Dyfed, south-west Wales.]

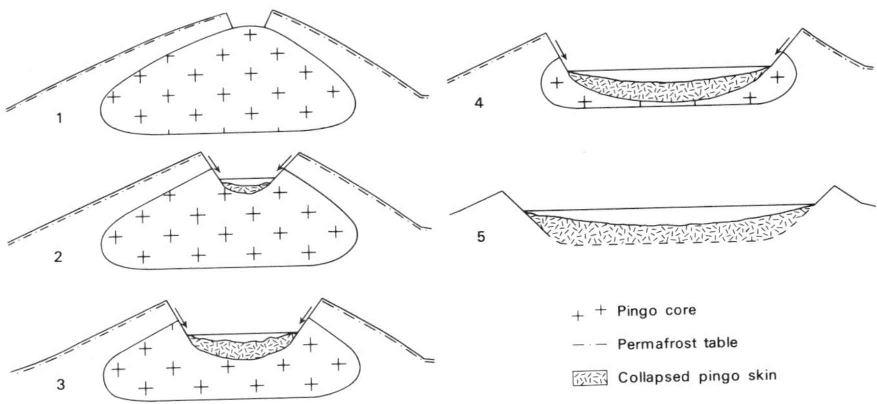

Fig. 1. The collapse of a pingo; from Watson 1977, fig. 1.

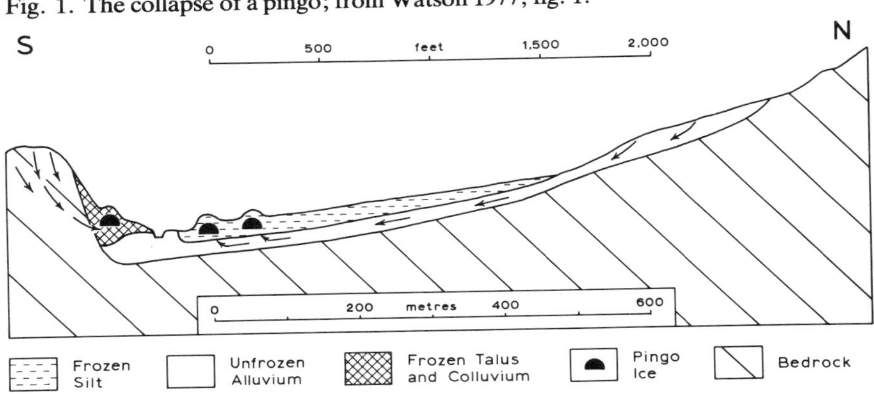

Fig. 2. Typical location of open system pingos in central Alaska. Arrows show ground water movement. Vertical scale is twice the horizontal. After Holmes *et al.* 1968 p. 29.

cutting across one another. The majority of the ramparts do not enclose the pingo basin, but have a wide gap on the upslope side, as in contemporary examples in Alaska (Holmes *et al.* 1968 p. 27) and in Yukon (Watson, unpublished).

ITINERARY

The upper Cledlyn valley is located west of Cwrt Newydd, which is on the B4338 road from New Quay to Llanybyther. The unclassified road (not signposted) to the pingo remains leaves the B4338 at the centre of Cwrt Newydd (SN 4895 4789), heading west-north-west. The exit, which is between two houses, is not obvious and is identifiable only by the white 'stop' line. The road is suitable only for minibuses and small coaches (less than 30 seats); limited roadside parking is available just north of the Cledlyn bridge (at SN 4726 4817). The general location is shown in Fig. 3. The fields containing pingos T and U belong to Bedw-lwyn Farm, R and S to Rhydnis, V, W and X to Coedlannau-fawr, and N, M and L to Clyncoch.

1. 30m south-west of Bryn-hyfryd (SN 4757 4852) is the best general viewpoint (see Watson 1971, plate 34*b*). To the south of the Cledlyn the rampart of pingo L is conspicuous, and those of P, M and N can be distinguished (see Fig. 3).

2. The road has been widened on both sides just north of the bridge over the Cledlyn (SN 4726 4817). This forms one of the few possible parking points. From here return up the road to the first field gate on the left, **opposite Ael-y-bryn** (SN 4721 4828). This gives access to the crest of rampart T. Follow the rampart to **locality 3** (SN 4714 4815) where profile LM (Fig. 4) crosses the crest of rampart U. This is the steepest and most imposing rampart in Dyfed. Its level crest should be noted, like that of T and, across the Cledlyn, rampart R; this regularity is a distinguishing feature of pingo ramparts. Rampart U, like T, has an open, horse shoe plan; the hill slope here is about 4° (computed from levelled profile LM; Fig. 4). A vertical profile through the basin deposits at 68m on LM (10m from the inner foot of the rampart) shows organic deposits to 2.54m and grey clay to 11.77m (base not reached). This is about 8m below the level of the stream bed at L. In the grey clay, 40-50% of the fine fraction (i.e. smaller than 2mm) is smaller than 0.002mm, and the coarse silt fraction increases only slowly with depth. Thus at 65m on LM (7m from the rampart foot), and at a depth of 3.30m, 98% is smaller than 0.02mm; at 5.05m the figure is 91%, and at 6.30m it is 89%. At greater distances from the rampart this figure decreases still more slowly; e.g. 10m from the rampart foot and at a depth 8.75m it is 95%. For futher details on the sediments see Watson and Watson (1972, table 1, p. 220).

The soluble humate in two parts of a sample from the base of the organic deposits at 68m on LM gave radio-carbon dates of 10,080 and 10,060 yrs. (Shotton *et al.* 1975 p. 257-8).

Return to the road and parking point, beyond which the first field gate on the right (about 50m south of the bridge) gives access to the site of pingo R, whose basin has been partly filled in.

4. (SN 4716 4810). This locality is near the centre of the rampart on the downslope side of basin R. Pingo R (Fig. 5) was elongated perpendicular to the slope, as is sometimes the case with contemporary open system pingos. The length of the basin was 160m and its maximum width about 45m (at the centre), though for much of its length it was only 20-25m wide. The external dimensions appear to have been about 250m by 100m. Since the plan on Fig. 5 was made, in 1970, the eastern half of the basin has been filled in.

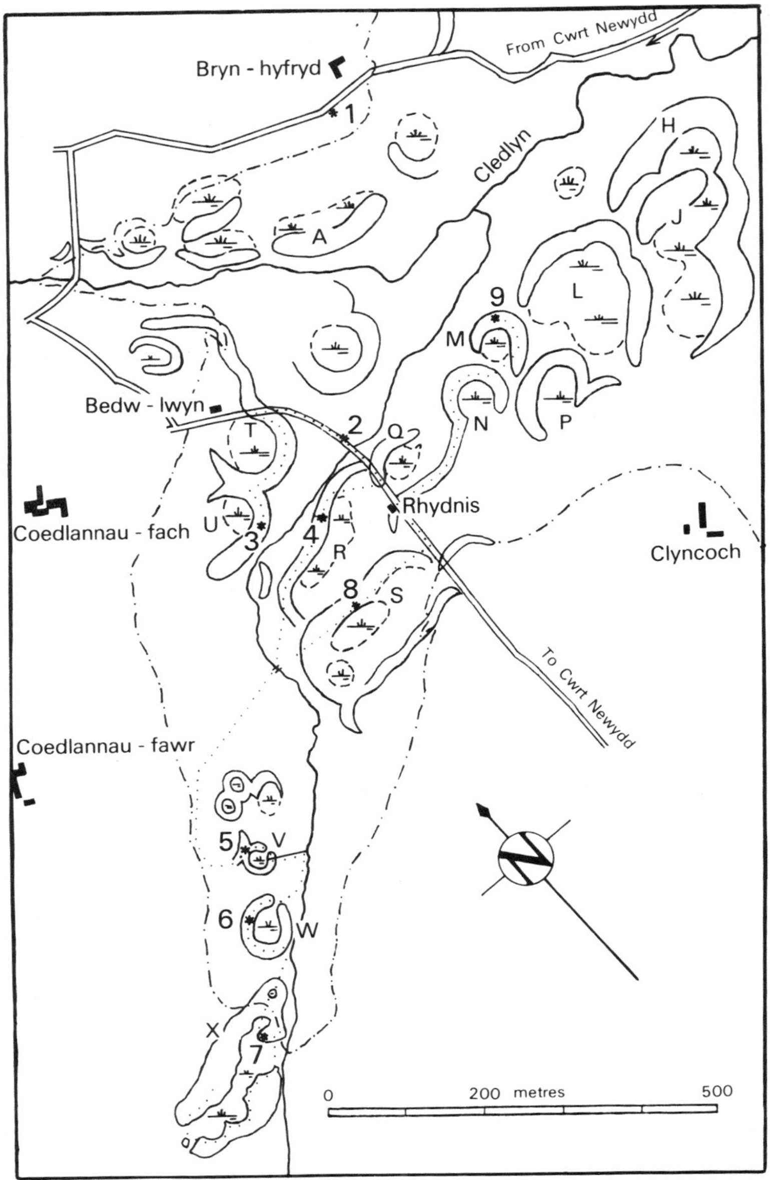

Fig. 3. Pingo remains in the Cledlyn basin. Localities numbered as in text. Contour line at 213m or 700 feet.

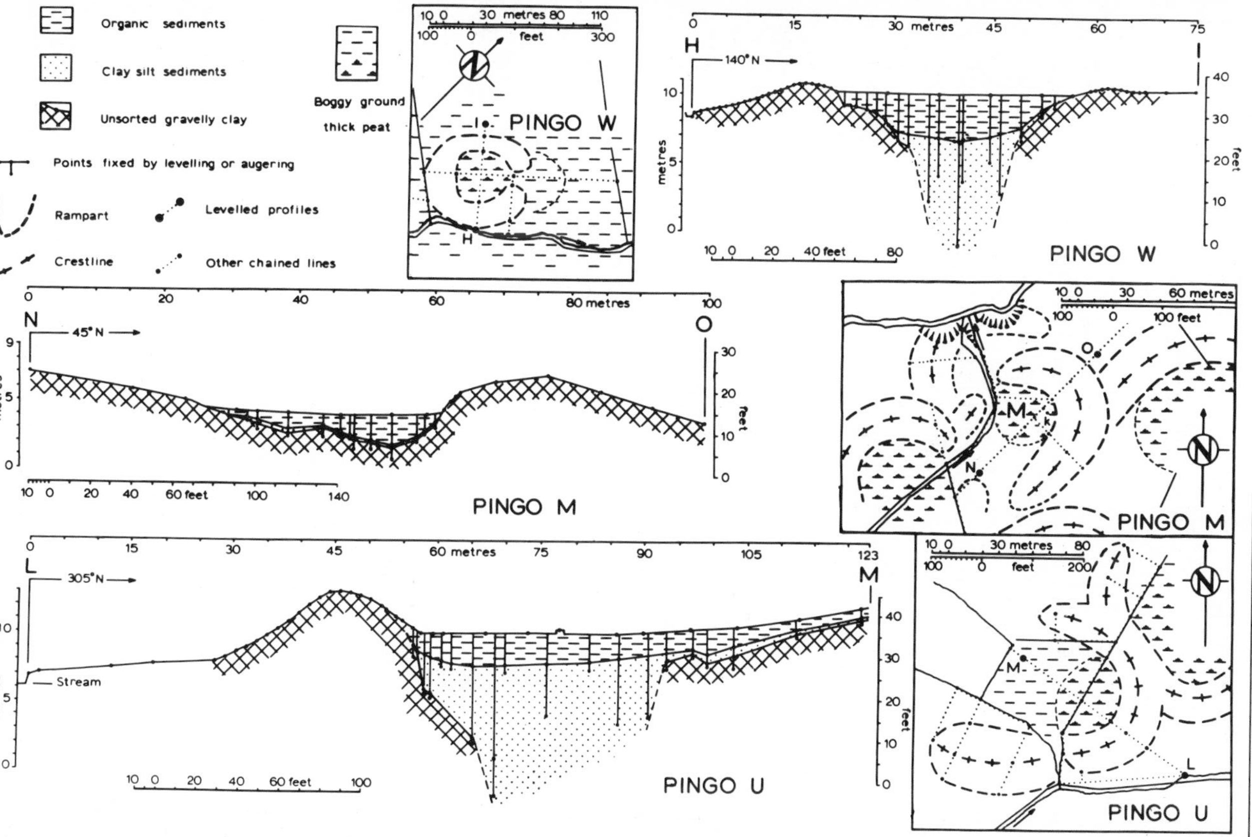

Fig. 4. Plans and profiles of pingos W, M and U. After Watson & Watson 1972, figs. 2 and 4.

As profiles PQR and UV show (Fig. 5), the pingo basin had a deep central area, at locality **4,** which exceeds 7m in depth, but outside this it is quite shallow. This variation in depth was not related to rampart form, which was regular in height and slopes (c. 11°) as is still seen in the surviving part. It is suggested that the deep part of the basin housed a central body of ice which passed into ice lensed with sediments on both sides, along the pingo axis, as described from contemporary pingos by Shumskii (1964 pp. 226, 227).

Continue along the rampart through the gate, past the end of the basin to the second gate at the bridge over the Cledlyn, following the old track towards Coedlannau-fawr. Do not enter the lane to the farm but keep along the field boundary to the old bank leading to pingo V, as much of the ground here is very wet.

5. (SN 4682 4782). Locality 5 is on the **upslope sector of the rampart** which surrounds the basin of V. Like W it is on a flat site, which seems to be necessary for the survival of a closed rampart. The rampart of V forms only a very low dry ring, but the basin it encloses is steep sided and deep (like the cross profile of W; Fig. 4), exceeding 7.32m at the centre. Many ramparts have a shallow col on the downslope side where excess water spilled from the basin after the collapse of the pingo, as is seen on the east side of V. The ground between V and W is very wet so it is advisable to follow the drainage ditch from V to the Cledlyn and then the river bank to W.

6. (SN 4676 4776). This is on the **upslope rampart** where it is crossed by profile HI (Fig. 4). This rampart is also low and has an overflow col on the north-east side. The basin is deep; a vertical profile at 40m on HI showed organic deposits to a depth of 3.35m sitting on grey clay to 10.13m (base not reached). This is 8.5m below the level of the stream bed at H. The grey clay is similar to that in U, the vertical profile at 40m on HI showing 98% of the fine fraction to be smaller than 0.02mm at 4.00m depth; 98% at 5.25m; 97% at 6.05m; 97% at 8.60m; and 96% at 9.95m. The bottom 5 cm of the organic deposits gave a ^{14}C date of 9360 years (Shotton & Williams 1973 p. 461).

Pingo X, approached from the north-east (as on Fig. 3), suggests a very low mound enclosing a small peat basin. The mound, however, extends to the south-west, widens, and embraces a second peat basin but does not fully enclose it. **Locality 7** (SN 4668 4764) is sited on this **second threshold.** Beyond it, a very boggy, elongated basin extends to B and with a slight change of direction continues along the profile line to A (Fig. 6). The features here represent a chain of close-set basins, probably representing a line of cores which together formed an 'esker-like' pingo, 255m long. The thawing of these cores produced a central linear depression from which water spilled over the downslope rampart, breaching it between D and F (Fig. 6). The flow of water through this breach was augmented by run-off coming down the slope from the west and entering the axial depression near A, as it does

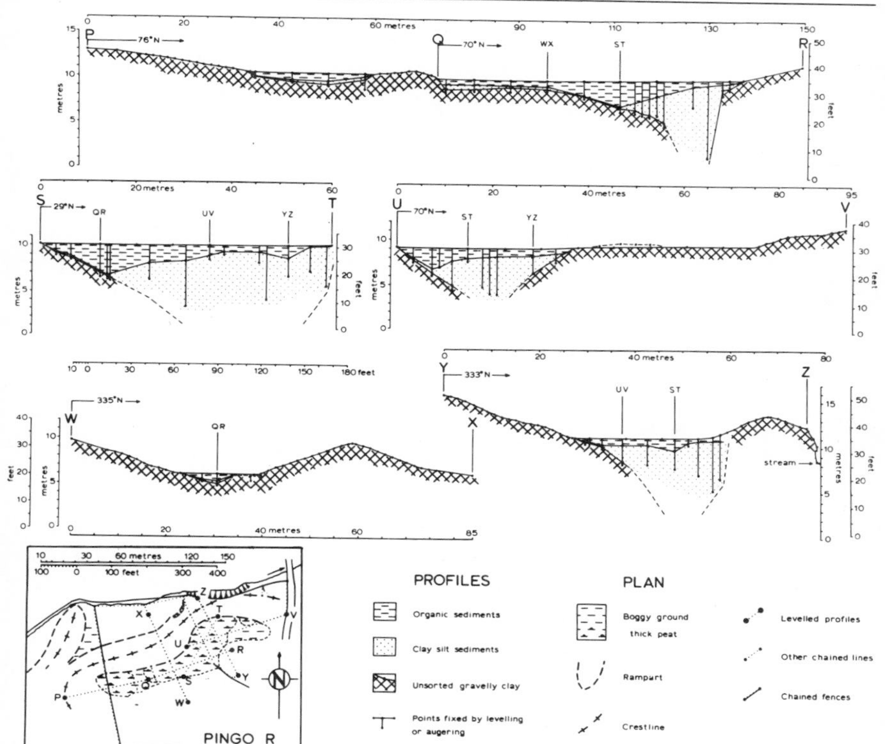

Fig. 5. Plan and profiles of pingo R. After Watson & Watson 1972, figs. 4 and 5.

today.

In the main basin (120 to 170m on AC) the maximum depth recorded was 2.48m of organic deposits on 2.60m of grey clay. The basins further up the profile (AB) are shallower though not so shallow as the profile line suggests. The individual basins resemble those impounded by horse shoe ramparts, in being deepest close to the inner rampart foot (*cf.* profile DE, Fig. 6).

The return journey may be made along the broad low rampart on the northern (upslope) side. After recrossing the footbridge over the Cledlyn, the road may be reached at Rhydnis by following the track along the downslope rampart of S.

8. (SN 4714 4798). This locality is on the north edge of the basin of pingo S (see Fig. 3). The location of an elongated pingo, S, on the slope above R shows that the hydrological conditions which produced a pingo elongated perpendicular to the slope at R persisted during the growth of S. A boring through the basin 12.5m south of locality 8 showed 1.40m of organic deposits

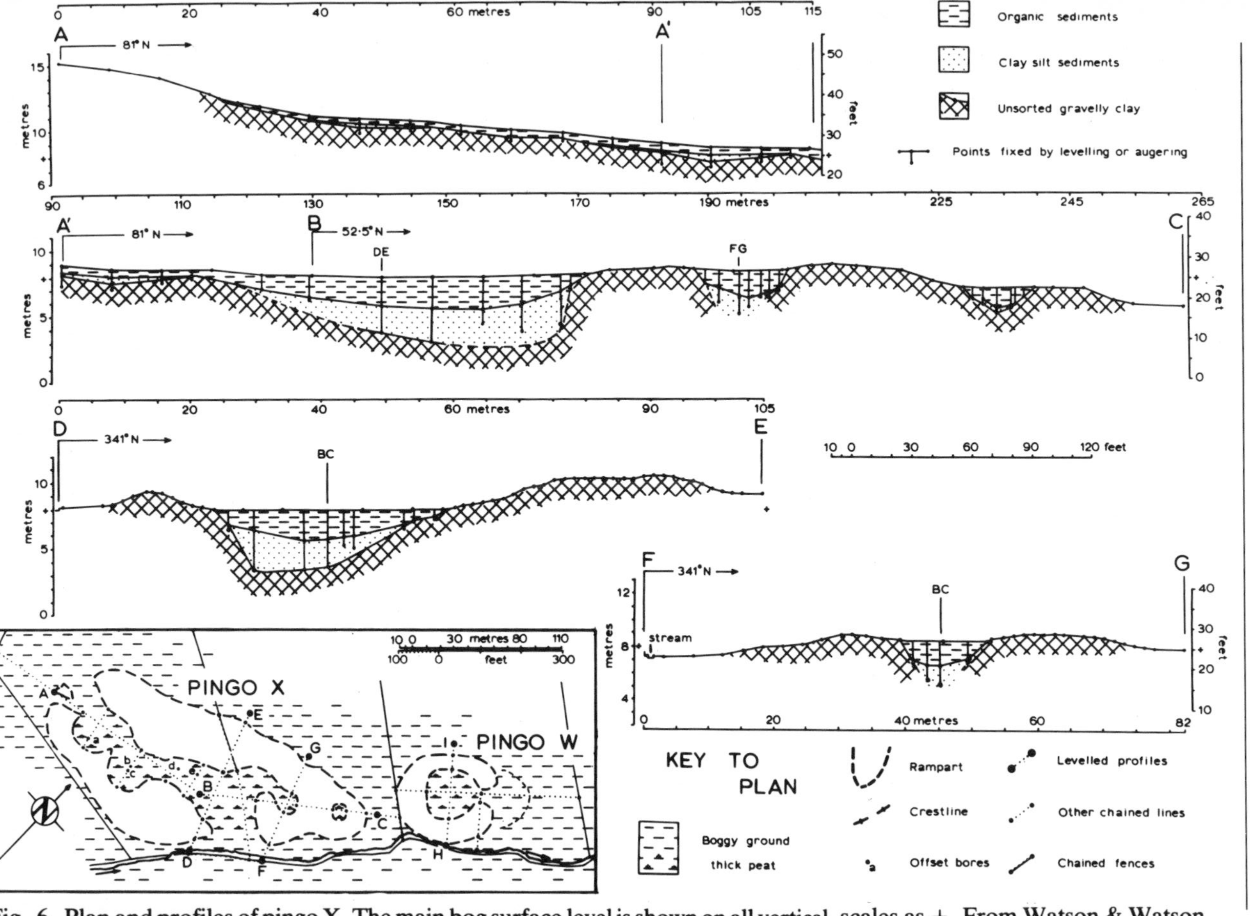

Fig. 6. Plan and profiles of pingo X. The main bog surface level is shown on all vertical scales as +. From Watson & Watson 1972, figs. 2 and 3.

on 3.28m of grey clay.

The group of ramparts viewed from locality 1 may be reached through the **gate opposite Rhydnis.** Follow the rampart by pingo N to **locality 9** (SN 4751 4815) where profile NO crossed the rampart crest of pingo M (Fig. 4). M has a round basin enclosed by a horse-shoe rampart, open on the upslope side. The general slope here is about 3°. The basin is shallow (Fig. 4), with the greatest depth of 2.5m being only 7.5m from the foot of the lower rampart, where a vertical profile showed 2.35m of organic deposits on 0.17m of grey clay which rested on gravelly sandy clay (augered to a depth of 0.80m). A sample from the base of the organic deposit gave a radio carbon date of 9550 years (Shotton *et al.* 1975, p. 257).

Pingo L, immediately to the east of M, is the largest in the Cledlyn valley. Its width, including ramparts measured perpendicular to the slope, is 210m, and the basin width is 140m. Its plan suggests several cores fused together in one mound. In spite of its size the basin is shallow like M, the grey clay being less than 5cm thick at three points 10m from the lower rampart foot.

DATING

The pingos described above represent successive growth over a period. The survival of the rampart of M on the site of L shows that L must have wholly collapsed before M formed. A slope such as that below Clyn-coch would support only one or two growing pingos at any one time. At no time would this slope be studded with mounds.

The collapse of a pingo does not represent a deterioration in climate. Pingo growth leads 'to its own destruction by the dilation cracking of the material capping the ice core' (Washburn 1979, p. 187). Pingos are growing and collapsing today under the same climatic conditions. In the Cledlyn basin, the pingos did not all grow at once in response to a climatic deterioration, say in the Younger Dryas, and then all collapse in response to an amelioration of climate at the beginning of the Flandrian. They grew and collapsed as a result of hydrological conditions associated with a period of discontinuous permafrost; they stopped growing when those hydrological conditions ceased due to the disappearance of permafrost.

The basin deposits consist of grey silty clay which has been sampled by augering to a depth of nearly 12m below the bog surface in U, and over 10m in W. Overlying this are organic deposits whose pollen indicates that their deposition began 'prior to the invasion of trees and before the initial expansion of juniper at the opening of the Flandrian', (Handa & Moore 1976, p. 205). Radio-carbon dates confirm this. At this time the pingos were completely collapsed and ground ice thawed since the base of the organic muds has not been disturbed by subsidence. The pingos represent a period of discontinuous permafrost which ended about 10 000 years ago. This period would have begun when continuous permafrost was degraded to discontinuous permafrost probably around 13 500 years ago (Watson 1977, p. 191).

REFERENCES

HANDA, S. & MOORE, P. D. 1976. Studies in the vegetational history of mid Wales IV. Pollen analysis of some pingo basins. *New Phytol.* **77**, 205-225.

HOLMES, G. W., HOPKINS, D. M. & FOSTER, H. L. 1968. Pingos in central Alaska. *Bull. U.S. Geol. Surv.* 1241-H, 40 pp.

MACKAY, J. R. 1979. Pingos of the Tuktoyaktuk Peninsula area, Northwest Territories. *Geogr. phys. Quat.* **33**, 3-61.

MÜLLER, F. 1959. Beobachtungen über Pingos. *Meddr Grønland,* **153**, no. 3, 127 pp.

SHOTTON, F. W. & WILLIAMS, R. E. G. 1973. Birmingham University Radio-carbon Dates VII. *Radiocarbon,* **15**, 460, 461.

SHOTTON, F. W., WILLIAMS, R. E. G. & JOHNSON, A. S. 1975. Birmingham University Radiocarbon Dates IX. *Radiocarbon,* **17**, 257, 258.

SHUMSKIY, P. A. 1964. *Principles of structural glaciology.* 497 pp. Dover, New York.

WASHBURN, A. L. 1979. *Geochronology.* 406 pp. Arnold, London.

WATSON, E. 1971. Remains of pingos in Wales and the Isle of Man. *Geol. J.* **7**, 381-392.

WATSON, E. 1977. The periglacial environment of Great Britain during the Devensian. *Phil. Trans. R. Soc.* B, **280**, 183-198.

WATSON, E. & WATSON, S. 1972. Investigations of some pingo basins near Aberystwyth, Wales. *Rep. 24th Int. Geol. Congr.* (Montreal), Section 12, 212-233.

19
PERIGLACIAL SLOPE DEPOSITS AT MORFA-BYCHAN, NEAR ABERYSTWYTH

by EDWARD WATSON

Maps *Topographical:* 1 : 50 000 Sheet 135 Aberystwyth
1 : 25 000 Sheet SN57

THE cliffs that extend for about 1.5 km S of Morfa-bychan form one of the most spectacular drift exposures in Cardigan Bay. Keeping (1882), who first described these drifts, regarded them as glacial. Both he (1882, p. 252) and Reade (1897, pp. 418, 9), pointed out they are composed entirely of local rock debris. Williams (1927, p. 215) agreed and subdivided them into: 1, a basal scree; 2, the lower boulder clay; 3, the sands and gravels; and 4, the upper boulder clay. Wood (1959, p. 275; 1962) interpreted the drifts as 'solifluction distributed boulder clay (Head)'.

At first sight the topography might suggest a bench or platform composed of drift at the foot of a steep seaward slope (Fig. 1), but as Reade (1897) pointed out, the bench is fronted by rock cliffs over considerable distances (e.g. Fig. 2, profiles 1, 2, 6, 7); between these rock sections, the drifts dip off the buried rock with a 'sloping stratification.... as if tipped over the cliff' (Reade 1897, p. 418). Watson & Watson (1967) stressed that the deposits have the structure of slope deposits (Fig. 3). They have a consistent dip towards the sea; individual beds are concave, with the dip of any one bed decreasing downslope, and the dips of a series of beds decreasing upwards in any one vertical profile. In strike the beds are horizontal to very gently dipping, with the outcrop rising as the modern cliff line approaches that of the buried cliff and falling as they diverge from each other. On the view that materials laid down by slope processes are slope deposits (head) even if earlier superficial deposits are incorporated (as often occurs), Williams' (1927) four divisions of the drifts have been renamed: 1, Yellow Head; 2, Blue Head; 3, Gravels; and 4, Brown Head (Watson & Watson 1967 p. 420).

The Yellow and Brown Head are widely accepted as typical head, but views on the Blue Head differ. It is true that 'its preferred stone orientation

[pp. 313-325 *In* BASSETT, M. G. (ed.). 1982. Geological excursions in Dyfed, south-west Wales.]

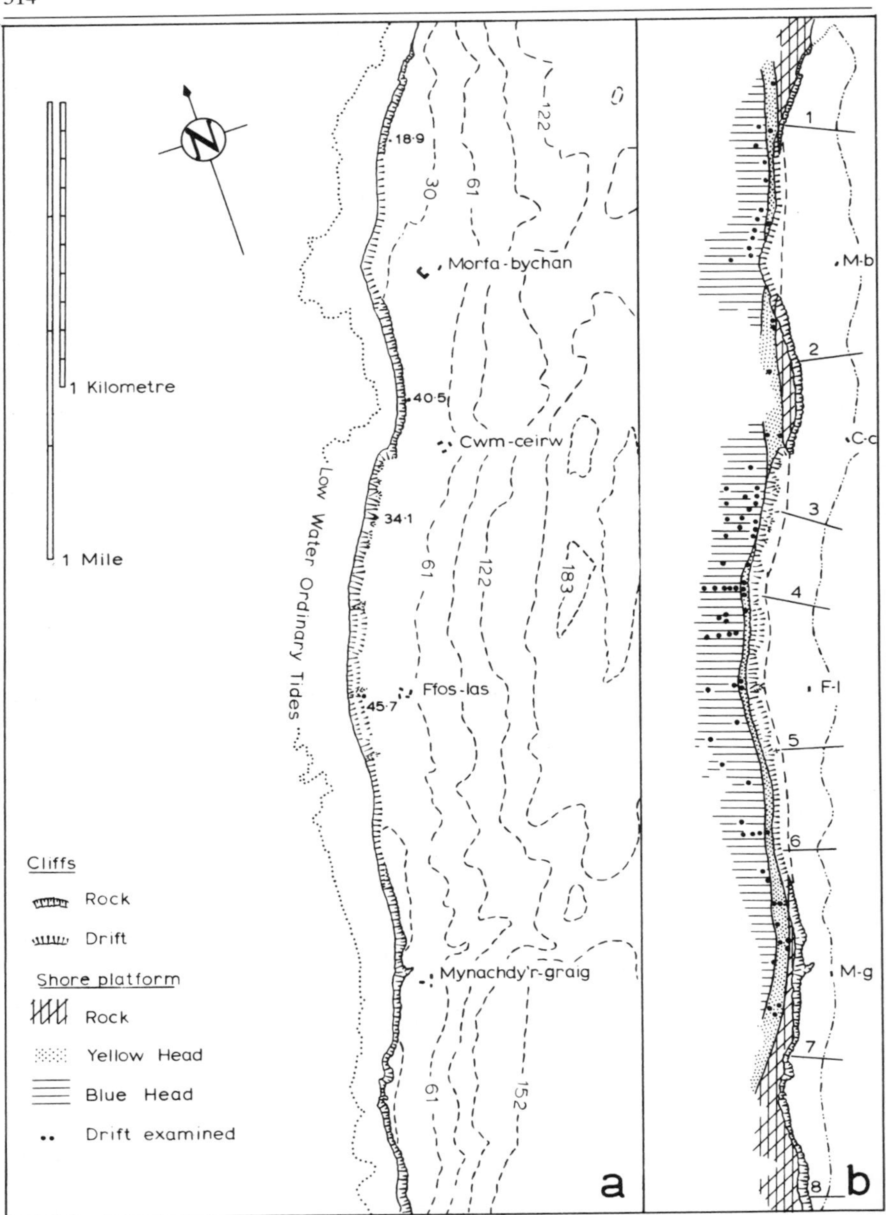

Fig. 1. Relief of the Morfa-bychan platform (a), and deposits on shore platform (b). Lines 1 to 8 on b refer to profiles on Fig. 2, and the broken line shows position of buried cliff edge, estimated from width of Yellow Head outcrop on shore platform. From Watson & Watson 1967, fig. 2.

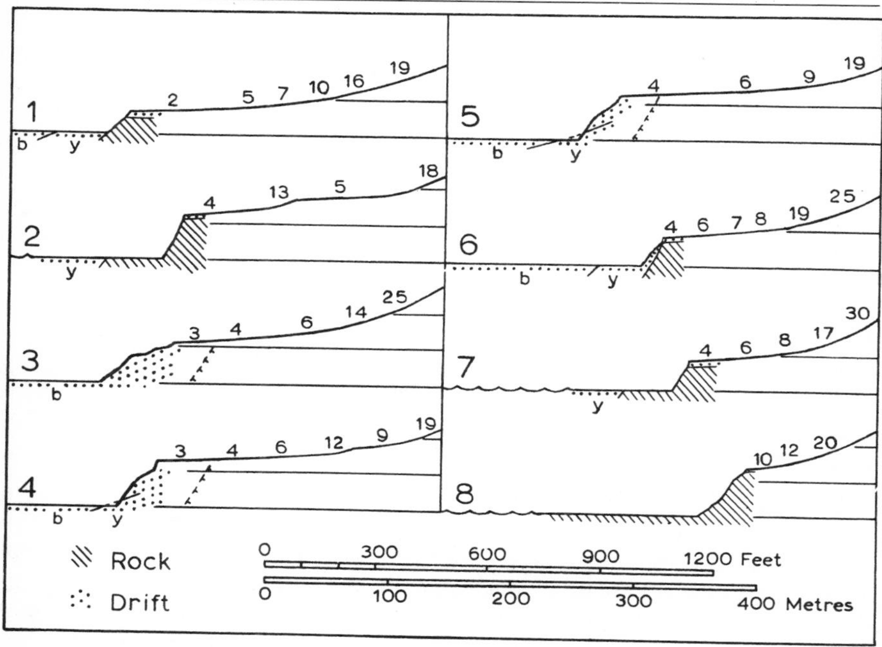

Fig. 2. Profiles across the Morfa-bychan platform as located on Fig. 1. Yellow Head — y, and Blue Head — b. Vertical scale equals horizontal. From Watson & Watson 1967, fig. 3.

often resembles that found in till' (Bowen 1977, p. 244), when azimuths only are recorded. With three-dimensional data, the concentration of dip values within narrow limits (Watson & Watson 1967, fig. 8, p. 431) is atypical of tills. It is probable that the basal 2-3m of the Blue Head contains material derived from earlier deposits on the bench (see below, locality 14). Vincent (1976) found that sand grains in the upper part of the Blue Head and from a lens of washed sand near the base, have a surface texture 'attributable to glacial abrasion'. As a lens of undoubted Irish Sea Till occurs in the overlying Gravels (locality 9), the inclusion of some glacial influence is not improbable. But the angularity of the larger blocks in the mass of the Blue Head argues against its acceptance simply as 'recycled Welsh till'.

THE DEPOSITS

Yellow Head. A typical head derived entirely from the bedrock, this consists of very angular clasts in a yellowish (Munsell 2.5Y 6/4, moist), clay-silt matrix (*c.* 60% of the fine fraction is <20 μm — Watson 1976, table 1, p. 91), and frequently shows some sorting in which the coarser beds may be open work. In places the basal part contains large bedded blocks of the Silurian

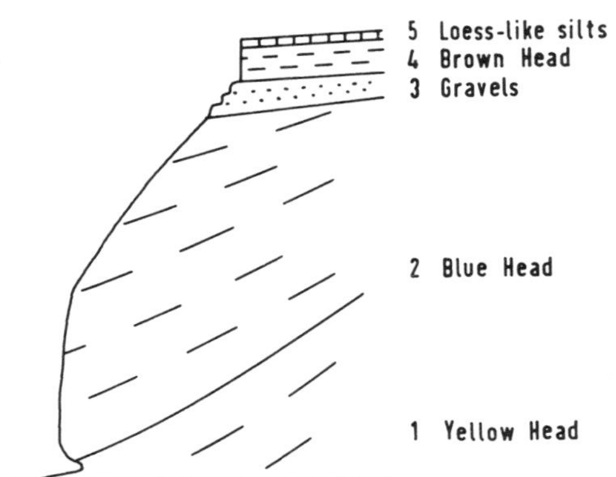

Fig. 3. The Morfa-bychan sequence. Dips and relative thicknesses about average for Ffos-las area. From Watson & Watson 1967, fig. 11.

Aberystwyth Grits, sometimes 7-8m long, suggesting that deposition began with the collapse of large blocks from the upper cliff.

Blue Head. The matrix is dark grey (Munsell 5Y 4/1, moist; 'dark gray') suggesting that it is derived from chemically unweathered rock. The volume of matrix is greater than in the Yellow Head but the particle size distribution in the fine fraction is very similar (Watson 1976, table 1, p. 91). Above the basal 3m the clasts are angular, and this is especially striking in the larger blocks, up to 1m long, which have the sharp edges of fresh joint blocks. Any striae are shallow, (as Reade 1897, p. 418 wrote, 'lightly striated') and seem mainly confined to small mudstone clasts as is common with solifluction deposits. In the basal 2-3m, clasts are often discoloured and brittle, and a variable proportion of worn and even rounded pebbles occur, suggesting that glacial or fluvio-glacial material had been incorporated. Any drift deposits lying on the platform above the 'fossil' cliff when the cycle of slope processes that laid down the Blue Head began, would be the first material to be moved and would be incorporated in the basal layers (Watson and Watson 1967, p. 436). At close hand, the Blue Head generally has a massive structure, but from a distance a persistent layering which dips seaward is observed. To some degree this reflects boulder concentrations, and the effect is reinforced by lenticular beds of washed sand and fine gravel. These washed beds begin imperceptibly and gradually thicken downslope; they may be compared with similar beds produced by slopewash on poorly vegetated solifluction slopes by summer rain (Watson & Watson 1967, p. 434). The impression of a rough bedding is also partly due to the fabric. In dip section the dominantly tabular and platy clasts have their a/b planes approximately parallel to the dip and to the strike, respectively. In horizontal exposures such as the shore platform, the elongated clasts which characterise the deposits have their long axes

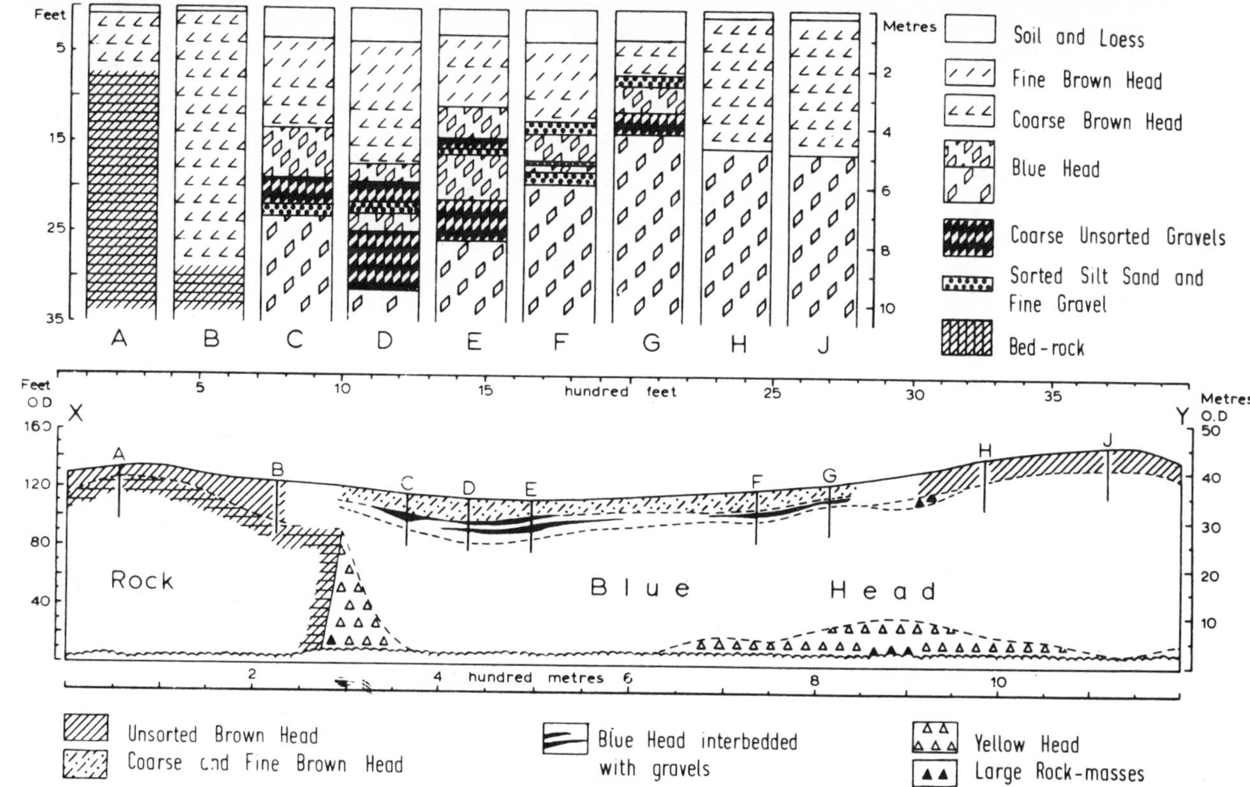

Fig. 4. Cliff exposure between locality 1 (A) and locality 8 (J). Vertical scale is five times horizontal. From Watson & Watson 1967, fig. 4.

aligned perpendicular to the cliff face. These visual impressions have been confirmed by widespread fabric studies of the deposits (Watson & Watson 1967, pp. 428-433). Dip exposures suggest that the Blue Head rests conformably on the Yellow Head, but that there has been some incorporation of Yellow Head material into its basal zone.

Gravels. This series consists largely of coarse, edge-rounded to angular gravel, poorly washed and sorted, associated with lenses of washed small gravel and sand, and thin beds of silt. Interbedded with these are beds of dark grey stony clay similar to the Blue Head. The series as a whole appears to thicken downslope. It rests unconformably on the Blue Head which dips seaward more steeply than the overlying Gravels. In strike section (Fig. 4), the Gravels are seen to occupy a shallow basin between the high rock area at A (locality 1) and the highest level of the Blue Head at J (locality 8). Their nature and siting suggest an interval when slopewash was dominant.

Brown Head. This consists of angular rock debris in a muddy brown matrix, (Munsell 2.5Y 5/2 (moist), grayish brown). About 35-40% of the fine fraction is $<20\mu m$ (Watson 1976, table 1, p. 91). It is the most widespread of all the deposits.

Loess-like silts. Over a large area, the Brown Head is capped by 0.3 to 1.0m of silty material, about 70% of which consists of fine sand and silt (0.2 to 0.002mm). It is unbedded and has a rough vertical cleavage. Though it lacks sand and small gravel, it does, like loess in hilly areas, contain flat angular stones, sometimes in layers. It has, however, a clay content of 20-25% and is non-calcareous (like all the Morfa-bychan deposits), yet it is difficult to interpret this as a primary slope deposit in view of its coarse sand content of 2-4% compared with 15-25% in the underlying Brown Head. No ice-wedge casts have been seen in the Morfa-bychan deposits, but fresh exposures of Brown Head show a polygonal pattern of narrow cracks filled with the loess-like silt. Particle size analysis of the fill shows a paucity of coarse sand (in one crack 4%, where the adjoining Brown Head has 15%). These cracks are interpreted as dessication fissures filled with the loess-like silt.

ITINERARY

Going S from Aberystwyth towards Cardigan, leave the A487 by the unclassified road to the right, signposted Morfa-bychan, at the T-junction (SN 5920 7890) S of Rhydyfelin. Then at the T-junction 200m beyond a sharp ascending bend to the left, leave by the unclassified road to the right signposted Morfa-bychan (SN 5837 7845). After 2km, turn right at Ty'n-y-fron Farm to follow the minor road signposted Morfa-bychan Caravan Park, to Morfa-bychan. For **permission to park** there, telephone Aberystwyth 617254. The road from Rhydyfelin is narrow and unsuitable for coaches, as is the road from the S leaving the A487 at SN 5710 7502. In planning this excursion it should also be borne in mind that for a considerable period

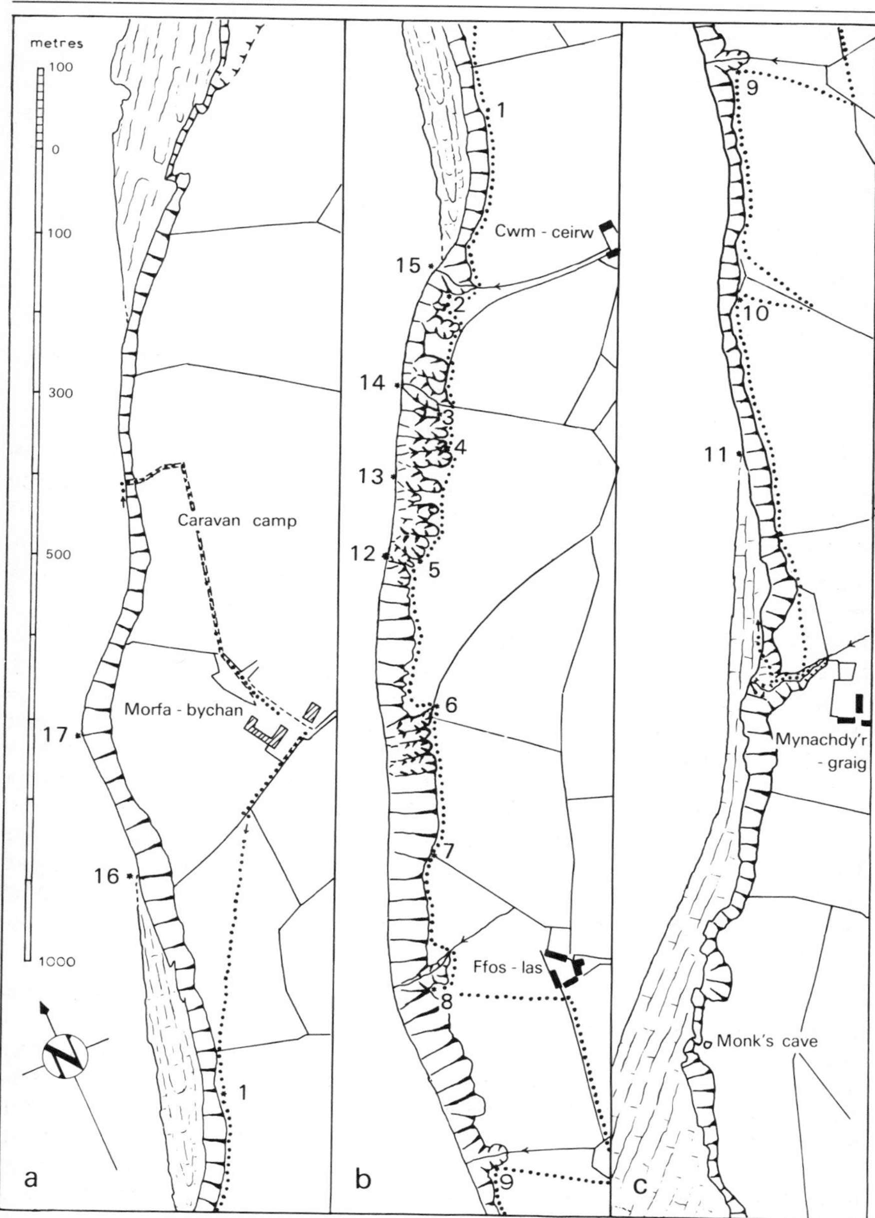

Fig. 5. Itinerary showing localities numbered as in text.

before and after High Water, the sea reaches the cliff foot SW of Morfa-bychan (just S of locality 16) and at the headland NW of Mynachdy'r-graig (200m S of locality 11 — Fig. 5). The most favourable tide conditions will be obtained by starting from Morfa-bychan at 9 to 10 a.m. when High Water at Aberystwyth is at 9 to 10 a.m.; days with High Water in the afternoon are unsuitable. With other H.W. times in the morning, the starting time will need to be adjusted. The following table may be helpful:

High Water at Aberystwth	6h	7h	8h	9h	10h	11h	12h
Coast at Morfa-bychan,							
clear at	9	10	11	12	13	14	15
until	15	16	17	18	19	20	21

The distance from Morfa-bychan to Mynachdy'r-graig is about 2 miles (3.25km). Safety helmets are advisable.

1. Leave Morfa-bychan by the continuation of the approach road (Fig. 5a), following the coastal bench to point A on Fig. 4 (SN 5636 7672). This is the **highest point on the cliff edge** between Morfa-bychan and Ffos-las; the profile parallel to the cliff face is shown in Fig. 4. The view southwards is typical of coastal head terraces, with a steep hill slope (20-30°) at the rear flattening towards the cliff top in a concave curve. At this point the bench is largely composed of solid rock with only 2.3m of head. 130m S of locality 1 at an angle in the cliff edge, the cliff face showing the head resting on the Aberystwyth Grits can be seen.

2. (SN 5622 7655) This locality is on the **first promontory S of the gully** of the stream from Cwm-ceirw. The N side of the gully is formed by the stripped 'fossil' cliff, while the S side shows the slope deposits banked against it. The bedrock can be seen passing behind the Blue Head, which is overlain by Brown Head and the loess-like silts. Both of the latter may be examined on the S face of the gully head back at the stream crossing. When the tide is out the buried rock cliff may be seen to be continued by the almost straight edge of the rock shore platform and to disappear behind the Yellow Head at locality 16, with the tilted blocks of bedded Aberystwyth Grits which form the base of the Yellow Head on its outer edge.

Between localities 2 and three the route passes along the heads of a series of spectacular gullies developed in the drift. These show a metre of loess-like silt, on 3-4m of Brown Head, on interbedded blue head and gravels, on the main Blue Head. The interbedded blue head and gravels thicken southwards (cf. Fig. 4 profiles C and D). Profile D is that seen across the gully from locality 3 (SN 5615 7642), which was the viewpoint for Plate 21C in Watson & Watson 1967. The sequence may be examined closely by entering the gully head 25m N of the bank and fence beside locality 3. This is the most accessible exposure of the beds overlying the Blue Head; it is not so difficult of access as might appear at first sight.

4. (SN 5616 7636) Locality 4 is on the **NE edge of an open gully** which can be seen to be fairly well graded down to the beach. Between 1958 and 1978 this provided the easiest descent to the beach (if one wished to shorten the itinerary). Recently the head of the gully has steepened so that it is better to enter it from the N side at locality 4, where incidently the loess-like silts are most accessible. The gully whose head is 500m to the S (and whose foot is locality 13) currently provides a better route to the beach (again the cross-profile is fairly open and the route can be seen through to the beach). These gullies are fairly steep and in wet weather trampling by a party can start off a muddy debris flow. This might make the ascent arduous for any party cut off on the beach by the tide.

5. Between localities 4 and 5 several dip sections show the unconformity at the top of the Blue Head. At present the most striking view is from locality 5 (SN 5608 7626) on the **S side of a large gully head.** The 'bedding' of the Blue Head is clear and near the top is a lenticular bed of sand and sandy small gravel. The steeper dip in the Blue Head is sharply truncated by the base of the more gently dipping gravels (Fig. 3).

6. (SN 5601 7609) Locality 6 is at the **head of a long gully** which also shows the bedding of the Blue Head dipping seaward. At the top is a thin series of sorted sand and gravel beds at the base of the Brown Head, (cf. Fig. 4, between profiles F and G).

7. (SN 5595 7595). **At the fence end** there is a good view back along the platform.

8. (SN 5589 7578). This is the **highest point** on the cliff edge (J on Fig. 4). On the opposite side of the gully the Blue Head shows the development of lenticular beds of washed sand and fine gravel.

9. (SN 5587 7557). The exposure **at the gully head shows:**

4.	Soil and 'loess'	0.91m
3.	Fine Brown Head	2.44
2.	Muddy gravel containing a contorted lens of red-brown clay (max. thickness 0.45m)	1.37
1.	Blue Head.	

The red-brown clay is of interest in that it alone, of these deposits, contains heavy and clay minerals not present in the Aberystwyth Grits but present in the Irish Sea Till.

10. (SN 5581 7531). This locality is on the **S side of a low knoll** truncated by the sea cliff. Wood (1959, p. 278) thought that this might be an 'old sea stack', but though it consists of Aberystwyth Grits it is clearly not *in situ*. The profile at locality 10 consisted (1964) of

5.	Shattered Aberstwyth Grits	11.58m
4.	Blue Head	1.00
3.	Muddy Gravels on	1.80
2.	Blue Head (largely vegetated), on	
1.	Yellow Head containing blocks to 6m long	

The thicker 'grits' keep their alignment in considerable part and indicate the former rock structure. The rock rests on the interbedded blue head of the Gravels series; it must represent a rock slide which reached its present position before the formation of the Brown Head. Fragments of the broken rock merge with the head and have contributed to it causing a local thickening and the concave slopes of the knoll. There is no obvious slip scar to the rear, but this may have been obliterated by the denudation involved in producing the Brown Head.

The smooth surface of the bench continues S to the Mynachdy'r-graig stream, which is sunk in the bedrock. The entrance to the path leading to the beach is through the fence just W of the point where this fence reaches the shoulder of the stream gully (SN 5575 7486). In the gully the path turns upstream and then near stream level turns downstream, leaving the stream through the gap in the arête on the N side of the gully. Note that the sea reaches the cliff foot here for about 3 hours before and after high tide.

11. At Mynachdy'r-graig and further S, the cliff is cut in rock, with a rock shore platform, seaward of which is a band of tumbled blocks. Pockets of finer Yellow Head may be excavated between the blocks. The edge of the *in situ* rock platform meets the modern cliff **(locality 11,** approximately SN 5575 7515) at a very acute angle so that the belt of blocks is seen in the cliff for some 470m to the N.

From the beach below locality 10, the succession at the truncated knoll may be further examined. It can also be seen how the loess-like silts feather out on its sides and the Brown Head thickens as it approaches the broken rock core. For 180m N of the knoll, large bedded blocks in the head show that the 'fossil' cliff is still close to the surface, but in the vicinity of locality 9 it has receded far enough for the present cliff to consist of the finer overlying Yellow Head. Good exposures occur here around the mouth of the gully, showing the typical elongated blade-shaped clasts oriented perpendicular to the cliff face. At times (e.g. during the 1960's) the sides of the gully provided a good dip exposure (cf. Watson & Watson 1967, pl. 20B and Watson 1976, pl 3) but during the 1970's it has been obscured by falls. The top of the Yellow Head falls northwards until it reaches beach level by the mouth of Ffos-las gully (below locality 8), and typical basal Blue Head is exposed around the gully mouth. N of this, the top of the Yellow Head rises again and between localities 7 and 6 large shattered blocks in the cliff foot show that the buried cliff line is approaching the surface. That these are crushed or shattered blocks is shown by the more competent beds which keep their alignment. Long axis orientations within these shattered masses may differ greatly from those of the clasts in the head; good exposures of this have been available (1976-9) in the headland W of locality 6. From out on the shore platform W of locality 6 good views of the bedding in strike section can be obtained at low water.

12. (SN 5604 7627). The point where the top of the Yellow Head descends to **beach level** again marks the beginning of the main exposure of Blue Head at beach level. Just to the N, below locality 5 is a good strike exposure of lenticular sand beds in the Blue Head (Watson 1976, pl. 2).

13. (SN 5608 7637). Locality 13 is at the **mouth of the gully** already recommended as offering the best route to the beach in the vicinity. From it to locality 14 (SN 5613 7646) the main characteristics of the Blue Head may be examined. Note the large very angular joint blocks, showing little sign of abrasion, some with flow casts freshly preserved, the regular parallel dip of the a/b planes of the frequent slab-like blocks projecting like angular teeth in succession up the cliff face above the basal 2-3m. Twenty years search by the author (aided by students and visitors) for smooth, worn boulders with deep striations, and for 'rare foreign erratic pebbles', (Bowen 1974 p. 402), has yielded no convincing examples.

14. At the **mouth of the gully** (SN 5613 7646) the Yellow Head appears for a short distance above the beach, and at one point has been rolled up into the base of the Blue Head. The Blue Head, like the Yellow Head, appears to have been occasionally affected by local rotational slips as it accumulated, so that the regular seaward dip of the a/b planes is replaced by areas of parallel inland dips. This occurred in the Blue Head just N of locality 14 but the slipped mass has been largely eroded away. The basal layers of the Blue Head which form the lower 2-3m of the cliff here and for some 30m N of locality 14, are very gravelly and contain many worn pebbles. These are interpreted as having been derived from older glacial or fluvio-glacial deposits on the bench above. 70m N of locality 14 the base of the Yellow Head rises quickly above beach level, and between this and locality 15 are some of its best exposures.

15. (SN 5622 7660). This locality is at the **mouth of the gully** which separates the Yellow Head from the fossil cliff. The exhumed cliff face forms the N side of the gully and its reduced slope angle may be compared with the steep modern cliff beyond the gully to the N. The buried cliff line is continued by the outer edge of the rock shore platform and if one excavates just outside the rock limit, the Yellow Head is found forming the continuation of the shore platform. Thus the foot of the fossil cliff and any associated beach is below the present high water mark. The rock shore platform cuts across the top of an anticline here so that the Aberystwyth Grits are almost horizontal, but the tension has produced joint blocks which are long and narrow in relation to the thickness of the beds. If these are prized off, they show a striking similarity to the long narrow clasts projecting from the Blue Head at localities 13 and 14.

16. The edge of this rock platform strikes the cliff again at SN 5637 7702, where there is a fine exposure of the contact between the 'fossil' cliff and the Yellow Head. The former is unusually steep and the latter contains few of the large bedded blocks. To the N, the head shows a truncation of the bedding where a slide during its accumulation has cut away parts of the beds and the trough has been filled with debris of a different calibre.

17. Before **Morfa-bychan headland** (SN 5636 7720) is reached the base of the Blue Head has reached the beach, and just N of the headland an area shows steep inland dips of the a/b planes, suggesting disturbance by rotational slipping. The Yellow Head soon reappears in the cliff face, and 140m N of locality 17 larger rock masses are being uncovered. Around the ramp leading up to Morfa-bychan camp site, large bedded blocks are common in the cliff and upper beach platform. On rare occasions when the beach gravel has been moved the great extent of these blocks suggests a massive cliff collapse and flow. The 'fossil' cliff re-emerges 150m N of the ramp. The contrast between the basal Yellow Head here and that at localities 15 and 16, where large blocks are few, invites comment. The explanation may lie in differences in the dip of the Aberystwyth Grits. Between localities 15 and 16 this is nearly horizontal and the weathered rock relatively stable. N of the ramp to the camp, where rock reappears in the shore platform, the bedding dips seaward. Further N towards Aberystwyth, a seaward dip is associated with massive slips and debris slides at the present day.

REFERENCES

BOWEN, D. Q. 1974. The Quaternary of Wales. pp. 373-426. *In* OWEN, T. R. (ed.), *The Upper Palaeozoic and Post-Palaeozoic Rocks of Wales.* viii + 426 pp. Univ. Wales Press, Cardiff.

BOWEN, D. Q. 1977. The coast of Wales. *In* KIDSON, C. & TOOLEY, M. J. (eds.), The Quaternary History of the Irish Sea. *Geol. J.* Special Issue No. 7, 223-256.

KEEPING, W. 1882. The glacial geology of central Wales. *Geol. Mag.* **19,** 251-257.

READE, T. M. 1897. Note on the drift of the Mid-Wales coast. *Proc. Lpool geol. Soc.* **7,** 410-419.

VINCENT, P. J. 1976. Some periglacial deposits near Aberystwyth, Wales, as seen with a scanning electron microscope. *Biul. peryglac.* **25,** 59-64.

WATSON, E. 1976. Report on field excursions held during the symposium at Aberystwyth, 1-10 July, 1975, by the I.G.U. Working Group on Periglacial Research. *Biul. peryglac.* **26,** 79-112.

WATSON, E. & WATSON, S. 1967. The periglacial origin of the drifts at Morfa-bychan, near Aberystwyth. *Geol. J.* **5,** 419-440.

WILLIAMS, K. E. 1927. The glacial drifts of western Cardiganshire. *Geol. Mag.* **64,** 205-227.

WOOD, A. 1959. The erosional history of the cliffs around Aberystwyth. *Lpool Manchr geol. J.* **2,** 271-287.

WOOD, A. 1962. Coastal cliffs: Report of a symposium. *Geogr. J.* **128,** 303-320.

LIST OF CONTRIBUTORS

Professor J. R. L. ALLEN, Department of Geology, The University, Whiteknights, Reading, RG6 2AB

Dr. J. W. BAKER, Department of Geology, University College, Cardiff, CF1 1XL

Dr. M. G. BASSETT, Department of Geology, National Museum of Wales, Cathays Park, Cardiff, CF1 3NP

Dr. D. E. B. BATES, Department of Geology, University College of Wales, Llandinam Building, Penglais, Aberystwyth, Dyfed, SY23 3DB

Dr. R. E. BEVINS, Department of Geology, National Museum of Wales, Cathays Park, Cardiff, CF1 3NP

Dr. D. Q. BOWEN, Department of Geography, University College of Wales, Llandinam Building, Penglais, Aberystwyth, Dyfed, SY23 3DB

Dr. J. C. W. COPE, Department of Geology, University College, Singleton Park, Swansea, SA2 8PP

Dr. W. M. DUNNE, Department of Geology and Geography, West Virginia University, Morgantown, West Virginia 26506, U.S.A

Dr. R. A. FORTEY, Department of Palaeontology, British Museum (Natural History), Cromwell Road, London, SW7 5BD

Dr. G. T. GEORGE, Department of Geology, City of London Polytechnic, Walburgh House, Bigland Street, London, E1 2NG

Dr. P. L. HANCOCK, Department of Geology, Queen's Buildings, University Walk, Bristol, BS8 1TR

Dr. C. P. HUGHES, Department of Geology, Sedgwick Museum, Downing Street, Cambridge, CB2 3EQ

Dr. C. J. JENKINS, Department of Geology, Australian National University, P.O. Box 4, Canberra, A.C.T. Australia

Professor G. KELLING, Department of Geology, The University, Keele, Staffs, ST5 5BG

Mr. D. L. LEAR, Department of Geography, University College of Wales, Llandinam Building, Penglais, Aberystwyth, Dyfed, SY23 3DB

Dr. J. D. MARSHALL, Koninklijke/Shell Exploratie en Porduktie Laboratium, Volmerlaan 6, Rijswijk (ZH), The Netherlands.

Dr. R. M. OWENS, Department of Geology, National Museum of Wales, Cathays Park, Cardiff, CF1 3NP

Dr. R. B. RICKARDS, Department of Geology, Sedgwick Museum, Downing Street, Cambridge, CB2 3EQ

Dr. R. A ROACH, Department of Geology, The University, Keele, Staffs. ST5 5BG

Dr. J. T. G. STEAD, 31 Cartersford Place, West Cross, Swansea

Dr. R. G. THOMAS, Department of Geology, Oklahoma State University, Stillwater, Oklahoma 74074, U.S.A.

Dr. M. TRINGHAM, Esso Exploration and Production U.K., Block 5, The Centre, Walton-on-Thames, Surrey, KT12 1QN

Dr. E. WATSON, Department of Geography, University College of Wales, Llandinam Building, Penglais, Aberystwyth, Dyfed, SY23 3DB

Dr. B. P. J. WILLIAMS, Department of Geology, Queen's Building, University Walk, Bristol, BS8 1TR